THE EAGLE AND THE SERPENT

Martín Luis Guzmán, the author of *The Eagle and the Serpent,* is one of the few survivors of the Mexican Revolution of 1910 which he has described so well in this work. First published in Madrid in 1928, it has gone through fourteen editions in Spanish, and has been translated into English, French, German, Dutch, and Czech.

This revolution was the first of the many that took place in different parts of the world during the twentieth century, and came about independently of all of them. Its origins were Mexican, and although it employed certain terms of European political thought, its guiding principle was the affirmation of the Mexican people, of the national character at all social levels, symbolized in the eagle and serpent of its flag. Its leaders who emerged from both the upper classes and the popular ranks triumphed momentarily and locally, and in the end they all became one in the profound unity of failure and death. Under their various standards the whole country took up arms, and all Mexico participated in the Revolution.

Guzmán himself is an outstanding example of this process. He was born in Chihuahua in 1887 of a good family, and was twenty-three years old when the Revolution broke out. His father, a colonel in the Mexican army, took no part in the Revolution as he died that same year of 1910. He had always opposed his son's following his own profession and on his deathbed made him swear that he would never make arms his career, a promise which Guzmán kept. He received his early education in the various cities where his father was stationed, and in Mexico City he completed his secondary studies and began to study law. But his real bent was for literature; he began to write for several papers started by young people, and from 1908 was one of the editors of *El Imparcial* of Mexico City.

It is unnecessary to go into his political activities and his participation in the Revolution. They make up the substance of this book. Suffice it to say that like so many other young liberals he faithfully supported the Revolution of Francisco I. Madero. After the latter's assassination Guzmán went to northern Mexico to join the enemies of Victoriano Huerta, the perpetrator of the crime, and to take part in the new Revolution developing there under various leaders, among whom Pancho Villa, the illiterate outlaw, was to become the most outstanding. *The Eagle and the Serpent*, however, is not an autobiography, but a search and probing into the soul of Mexico. Neither is it a historical novel, a *roman a clèf*, like *La Sombra del Caudillo*, published in 1929, nor a history of the Revolution which Guzmán might have written. In the *Foreword* to this English translation he has given a résumé of the Revolution to orient the reader in the background, the episodes, and the men dealt with in the subjective and poetic narrations which comprise the work.

Guzmán was seeking out what was happening in the souls of the participants in this moment of history and discovering the national characteristics of all the Mexicans, beneath the European veneer of the upper classes, and their clear and free expression in the folk. The figure which most attracted the young writer was that of Pancho Villa, who come to represent for him the most salient and significant actor of the Revolution. This, which is already apparent in *The Eagle and the Serpent*, is developed at length in the work he wrote after the Revolution, the *Memorias de Pancho Villa*, in which the life, the soul, and the style of this great popular leader are portrayed.

Guzmán saw all that Mexico is compounded of, and his works deal with his personal experiences and the men he knew at first hand. The circumstances of these experiences not only brought him into touch with the various regions of Mexico, but on several occasions led to his expatriation, first—from 1915–20–in New York, and later–1924–34–in Madrid. During his eleven years in Madrid he became completely incorporated into the literary life there, and published the works which deal with his memories of Mexico seen in the perspective of time and space.

Guzmán represents in literature the Mexican Renaissance brought about by the Revolution, not only in the political and social fields, but in art as well. It was marked by the discovery of the Mexican folk, and as a result a new literature, painting, and music came into being which are world famous.

Federico de Onís
University of Puerto Rico

THE EAGLE AND THE SERPENT

Martín Luis Guzmán

Translated from the Spanish
by Harriet de Onís

With an Introduction by Federico de Onís

Dolphin Books
Doubleday & Company, Inc., Garden City, New York

The Eagle and the Serpent was originally published in Spanish by Companía General de Ediciones, S.A. in 1928, under the title *El Águila y la serpiente*. An abridged version of the book, in English, was published by Alfred A. Knopf, Inc., in 1930. The Dolphin Books edition is published by arrangement with Alfred A. Knopf, and includes the complete text of the Spanish version.

Dolphin Books edition: 1965

Library of Congress Catalog Card Number 65–13087
Copyright © 1965 by Doubleday & Company, Inc.
Copyright 1930 by Alfred A. Knopf, Inc.
Printed in the United States of America

Contents

Foreword

In order that readers not familiar with the origin and nature of the Mexican Revolution may better understand the spirit of this book, it has seemed advisable to give a brief résumé of the political events that took place in Mexico from 1910 to 1915.

In 1910 Porfirio Díaz's dictatorship was still supreme—a liberal, progressive dictatorship. That same year, as the time for presidential elections approached—a periodical farce by which the letter of the Constitution was observed—the nation began to give evident signs that it wanted to regain possession of its civic will, which had been lost since 1880. In opposition to the invariable candidacy of Díaz, which satisfied only the groups in power, the nation put forward another, that of Francisco I. Madero. The dictator, however, paid no attention to these premonitory indications; he and his supporters attempted to continue in power, whereupon Madero, at the head of a rising which was not merely political, but revolutionary in character, overthrew Porfirio Díaz and took over the presidency after new elections held in 1911.

Madero was a reformer of gentle, apostolic character. He preached ideals of justice and a faith in the triumph of the right. As head of the government he attempted to divert the revolutionary tendencies he headed into legal channels. He also decided, in order to preserve the material well-being of the country, not to destroy the administrative machinery or the political instruments created by the dictatorship. He maintained the existing army; he respected the courts and the legislative bodies and made no changes in the personnel of the government departments. And in this way he lost the sympathy and support of his friends and delivered himself into the hands of his enemies, with results that were soon to prove fatal. A part of the army, headed by two ambitious generals, Bernardo Reyes and Felix Díaz, rose in February, 1913; another division, under the command of Victoriano Huerta, revolted a few days later, after solemnly swearing its loyalty. And then, all joining forces, Huerta had the revolutionary President assassinated a few hours after usurping his office.

The indignation and anger of the populace were so great that the day after Madero's death the real revolution broke out; the ideals of justice and agrarian reform the "martyr President" had advocated seemed too conservative; a vehement desire to regenerate everything asserted itself, an impulse to transform the whole social fabric of Mexico in its diverse aspects; and before the end of February the conflict had been kindled again. Venustiano Carranza, the governor of Coahuila, a civilian, was named First Chief of the revolutionary army; the political purposes of the new uprising were outlined in the Plan of Guadalupe, drawn up on March 27, 1913.

This new phase of the Revolution was much more widespread than the first. From the beginning there were four principal centers of revolutionary action, three in the north: Sonora, Chihuahua, and Coahuila; and one in the south: Morelos. The military leaders in the various sections of the north were respectively, Alvaro Obregón, Francisco Villa, and Pablo González; the leader in the south was Emiliano Zapata.

The advance of the four revolutionary armies, which was very slow at first, finally became irresistible, especially after the big battles won by Villa and Felipe Angeles in Torreón and Zacatecas. In the northwest, through the states of Sonora, Sinaloa, Nayarit and Jalisco, Obregón marched from victory to victory, all the way from the American border to the heart of Mexico. After Villa had broken through the main division of Huerta's army, Pablo González could move forward from the states of the northeast—that is to say, Tamaulipas, Nuevo León, and San Luis. And as Zapata was becoming more and more of a menace from the south—his activities had spread through the states of Morelos, Mexico, and Puebla, surrounding the capital—Huerta fled from the country seventeen months after his crime. After wiping out a part of Porfirio Díaz's former army and discharging from the service those who surrendered, the revolutionary troops marched into the city of Mexico in August 1914.

But the Revolution was already divided in its hour of triumph. Carranza, whose background and formation were those of the dictatorship, and who was devoid of sincere and deep revolutionary ideals and eager only for power, from the first moment did all he could to bar the advancement of all those revolutionists whose independence or whose faith in the just character of the Revolution might prove a stumbling block to the new leaders in the race of their personal ambitions. He was supported in this by Obregón and by the groups of Sonora and Coahuila, and he even went so far as to put obstacles in the way of Villa's and Angeles's military operations. This lost him the support of many leaders and large sections of the country; and it brought about a wide breach, which was already evident in December 1913, and of a frankly hostile character by August 1914.

To put an end to these dissensions, which threatened to destroy the fruits of the Revolution's military victories, the leaders of the different groups decided to call an assembly which should have sovereign authority, to be composed of generals and governors. This was the Convention. It met in October 1914, first in Mexico City and then in Aguascalientes, and voted to remove both Carranza and Villa from their commands, as their quarrels were the principal cause of strife, and to name General Eulalio Gutiérrez president *pro tem.* of the Republic. The generals and governors in favor of Villa submitted to the terms laid down by the Convention; but as Carranza and his adherents demanded, as a preliminary to their obedience of orders, the fulfilment of certain conditions that could not be accepted, the new President had to temporize with Villa while waiting for the Carranza faction to recognize his authority. Finally, disowned by the one and at the mercy of the other, he left the power in December 1914 and took refuge with his soldiers.

By the beginning of 1915 the Revolution had degenerated into a veritable state of anarchy, into a simple struggle between rivals for power. This went on until 1916, when Obregón and Carranza, in great part with the help of the United States, managed to reduce Villa to a position in which he could do nothing, though without ever conquering him. As a guerrilla leader Villa was invincible. In May 1920 he was still lording it in the stronghold of the sierras. His energy and his daring were unrivaled. Even General Pershing's famous expedition—the ten thousand men that Wilson sent to Mexico, with Carranza's and Obregón's approval, "to get Villa dead or alive"—had to relinquish the undertaking.

                                                          M.L.G.

Part One

REVOLUTION'S HOPES

BOOK I

Revolution Bound

---

1 THE BEAUTIFUL SPY

As I alighted from the train in Veracruz, I remembered that Isidro Fabela's house—or, to be more exact, that of his parents —had already served as a temporary refuge for revolutionists fleeing by way of that port toward the battlefields of the north. These were experienced fighters, veterans of the Madero revolution, setting a still valid example to the novice rebels. So I, too, decided to take advantage of this shelter which had been so kindly offered me, and I hid out there for one whole day, enjoying its friendly and thoughtful hospitality.

When night was well advanced I emerged from my hiding place and set out for the docks. I had only one worry: would they let me come aboard so late? I walked quickly, in spite of the two suitcases which, while they dragged me down with their weight, seemed to lighten everything by their touch. For, to be carrying them like that was, I cannot quite explain why, like holding in my hands the confirmation of the trip I hoped to embark on the next day.

In the streets adjoining the Customs House the smell of bales, boxes, recently unloaded merchandise filled my nostrils; I inhaled it with delight. Farther on, the open space approaching the wharfs brought to me the sea air; in the background I could make out the blurred shapes of ships, some of them perforated by luminous dots; the sheen of the water rushed to meet me; the great machines of the port's activities were resting, their arms flung wide.

Memories set the pulse of my emotions throbbing faster. Through those very places which had been the site of my fondest childhood dreams I now slipped, under cover of darkness, bound for a ship and the unknown.

In my wallet I carried fifty dollars; in my soul, a deep indignation toward Victoriano Huerta.

The captain of the *Morro Castle* showed no surprise when I told him that I must embark immediately, in spite of rules and normal procedure. My statement that I was a revolutionist affiliated to the Constitutional party, and that I was in grave danger of arrest by the police of Veracruz made an impression on the old sailor. For several seconds he rested his frank, open, blue gaze on me. Then, as though turning the matter over in his mind, he looked at the pipe in his hand; and, finally, looking at me again, he said in a deep, pleasant voice, which gave a certain softness to the typical accent of the sailors of New England:

"Of course you can come aboard, but on one condition: you're not to leave your stateroom until the passengers take ship tomorrow. Otherwise we might run into trouble."

He led me to the purser's office to legalize, in some way, my presence on the ship. There I produced my ticket, my consular permit, and complied with several other trivial requirements.

"I'm going to take you to your stateroom," said the captain as I made ready to follow the steward, who had picked up my suitcases and was walking ahead of me.

And taking me by the arm he led me, chatting away, along corridors and stairs. When we reached the door of my stateroom he held out his hand to say good-bye, but went on talking for a few moments. He wanted to know what I thought about Madero's death; he talked, without mentioning names, about a group of revolutionists who had traveled on his ship, on its previous trip, to Havana. In a word, when we parted it was like old friends. With a pat on the shoulder, he left, saying:

"Good night, old chap."

Moments later, as I settled down in my bunk, I was in a frankly optimistic frame of mind. "What a piece of luck," I said to myself, "that, with occasional exceptions, the Yankees are people you can talk to straight from the shoulder. What a wonderful country theirs would be if the nation were like the individuals!"

The passengers began to come aboard about one the next afternoon; by five the *Morro Castle* was swarming with people, and by six, departure time, it was impossible to move about the deck or to find an empty spot anywhere.

Once we were beyond the breakwater and set on course, the more sentimental of us—and who isn't at such moments? —drifted to the stern to watch Veracruz fade away in the distance. It was a mysterious twilight scene. Almost at the water line the strings of port lights blended with the white and red harbor signals; overhead the bright beam of a beacon turned. And everything, the blood-hued twilight clouds, the gloomy shoreline, was swallowed up in the sunset as though they were all set in the same plane of the sky. . . . What we were leaving behind was a horizon relentlessly weighed down by the heavenly bodies.

The passengers of the *Morro Castle*, though numerous, were not especially attractive. For the most part they belonged to that gray, half-uprooted, half-cosmopolitan species who, with their self-assured bearing and facile stupidity, infest all the seas. At first glance I saw only a few who looked interesting: a group of four men—all of them Mexicans, none very well dressed, and all, to judge by a few phrases I overheard in passing, rough in their language—a beautiful North American woman, blonde, seductive, of a somewhat dubious air and age, and a Yankee who would have been about thirty years old—strong, smiling, simple, and energetic—who turned out to be my stateroom companion. To be sure, this first superficial impression could not be taken at its face value; the crowd of passengers that filled the lounge was not in a mood, during those early hours, to make friends with anybody; on deck everything was shrouded in darkness which, though conducive to rest and thought, was also completely insulating.

The next day I initiated my shipboard activities by approaching the group of the four Mexicans. I soon discovered that they were Constitutional revolutionaries. One of them, whom the others treated with great deference, even though the tone they used when talking to him was somewhat jocose, was a doctor called Dussart. His slight build contributed to the pleasant contrast between his gray hair and his youthful bearing; he was restless, alert, vociferous. He seemed the youngest of the group, in spite of the fact that there was only one old man among them: the rich member who, it seemed, was financing the trip. The other two were young, one of them dark, curly-haired, husky and talkative, and the other, a relative of the rich man or connected with him in some way, the youngest of all, well-bred and docile.

Some trifling pretext served us as an introduction. Then, as soon as they found out where I stood politically, an intimacy sprang up as though by magic. With one voice we blasted Victoriano Huerta; with one voice we praised the memory of Francisco I. Madero and glorified the feats of Cabral and Bracamontes. In this way the better part of the morning slipped by in political discussions and the building of castles in the air around the person of Venustiano Carranza, whose strength of character we felt guaranteed the success of the revolution.

It did not take Dr. Dussart long to strike up an acquaintance that very same day with many of the passengers, given his communicative nature for which obstacles did not exist. The beautiful North American, on whom he concentrated his fire, was one of the first to succumb, and apparently she was so receptive that two hours after their meeting Dr. Dussart had her in a flutter with his overwhelming Mexican gallantry, and was treating her with a familiarity that left the rest of us astounded. And the most amazing part of the whole affair was that she did not know a word of Spanish—or, at least, that was what we thought—nor did the doctor have more than four words of English at his command.

"Doctor," we asked him, "how do you manage to make the lady understand you?"

"It's very easy. The only international language (forget about Esperanto or Volapuk) is that of gestures, which never fails you."

"But even so," we persisted, "it's unusual; for, to judge from her appearance, she's a decent woman."

"Of course she's decent! If she weren't, I wouldn't have anything to do with her."

On the afternoon of our first day Dr. Dussart briefed us on our behavior toward his new friend. He had not stopped talking about the valuable connections she undoubtedly had in the United States, or how useful she could be for the aims of "the cause." What we had to do, he told us, was dance attention on her, win her over. And as he was possessed of the impulse to rapid, efficient action—a species of executive demon—he arranged things with the deck steward so that, without quite knowing how, our deck chairs were alongside that of the charmer. From that afternoon on, the group we formed around her was one of the most picturesque and typical features of the trip. When we were not all on hand, at least one was keeping her company.

But it was Dr. Dussart who had the inside track. He was her constant companion; the favorite, the indispensable. The night of the second day out he talked with her—a highly animated conversation, pointed up with gestures, laughter, exclamations—until nearly eleven. The rest of us, in the meantime, were playing chess in the smoking room.

The third day brought a number of new developments. When the passengers awoke, the ship was anchored off Progreso. As I was anxious to make the acquaintance, even at a distance, of Yucatán (the land of my forebears), I had been on deck since before daybreak. How simple an episode and, at the same time, full of evocations and mystery, watching the slow looming up of the low-lying coast of Yucatán against the mother-of-pearl horizon of a May dawn. A strange sheen gleamed on the waters, as in an eclipse of the sun; the sky broke up, and through layers of clouds came gleaming streaks that were harbingers of the torrent of light. And on a lower level in the distance there emerged, just above the water line, the faint profile of a green and vaporous land with the distant hues of its tropical vegetation, here sparse, and reminiscent of a battlement.

As we were to lie alongside for hours while the ship took on a cargo of hemp, the wait occasioned changes in shipboard life. The sportsmen gathered in the stern and, when the morning was well along, organized a shark-fishing match. The ferocious brutes were swarming around both sides of the vessel. At times they surfaced, cutting the waves with their sinister dorsal fins; at times the blazing rays of the Gulf sun revealed them deep in the water in all their blackness against the greenish liquid mass.

Many passengers had gathered to watch the maneuvers of the fishermen, among them Dr. Dussart, the handsome North American, my Yankee cabin mate, and I. The doctor was doing his best to describe to her, partly by signs, partly in Spanish, and partly in his weird English, the life and habits of the sharks. To bear out his theories he told her incidents such as that of the legendary Negro of Veracruz, who slept on the breakwater with his baited fishing line tied around his waist, waiting for the shark to bite. One night the Negro disappeared, and two days later his body was washed ashore in two pieces. The doctor described all this with such picturesque and vivid details that the other conversations around us died down and everybody was listening to him.

When he got around to the story of another Negro, the one who used to plunge into the water with his knife between his teeth, looking for sharks, I took my cabin mate by the arm and, moving away from the group, asked him, looking toward the beautiful North American:

"Do you know that lady?"

"No, I don't," he answered. "But I did happen to overhear something about her. A few hours before sailing time, she was lunching at the Hotel de Diligencias at a table near the one where I was sitting with a group of friends. Her looks intrigued us, we began to talk about her, and someone said she was a police agent—"

"Of the Mexican police?" I interrupted him.

"That I don't know. It did not occur to me to ask whether it was the Mexican police or some other."

This news did not please me in the least, and I was tempted to put my revolutionary friends on their guard at once. But then, not wanting to be overofficious, I decided merely to tell them in a general way to be careful.

Some hours later an unforeseen incident made me change my tactics. Shortly before the *Morro Castle* weighed anchor off Progreso, Dr. Dussart received a mysterious message. It was handed to him by a man who had come on the tug towing the lighters carrying hemp. After a few minutes aboard ship, he returned to land. When the messenger had left, the doctor herded us into the smoking room to tell us what had happened.

"I have just been informed," he said, "that there is a police agent on board watching us. We have to be on guard, for two things may happen: they may try to prevent us from disembarking in New York, or, afterwards, try to keep us from crossing the border at Sonora."

This piece of news was followed by a veritable torrent of speculations as to the identity of the presumptive spy, as well as the consequences, immediate and remote, of such spying. On the first count the suppositions were so many, and some of them so farfetched, that I felt it was my duty to reveal what I had heard.

"The worst of it is that if what I heard this morning is true," I said, "the spy may be none other than the doctor's beautiful friend and our acquaintance, the North American we've been with ever since the beginning of the trip."

"Are you serious?"

"Impossible!"

"I've told you what I was told—"

"Ridiculous!"

"Have it your own way," I continued. "I neither affirm nor deny it. I'm only telling you what I heard."

"Whom did you get it from?"

But at this point our conclave was interrupted. A horde of passengers was crowding into the smoking room, and some of them came over and sat down near us. It would have been unwise to talk.

Night had fallen. We were now making for Havana, and all that remained visible of the Yucatán coast was the blinking of a beacon.

2 A PLOT AT SEA

When we found ourselves alone again, none of my four companions displayed the same incredulity my words had previously aroused in them. Our conversation had been suspended for over an hour, and during that time, while people around us were telling each other their impressions of the layover off Progreso or making plans for the coming call at Havana, we had been thinking. The caviling had borne fruit for my friends: the information looked upon as utterly absurd a short time before now seemed not only plausible but even probable.

It was the doctor who brought up the topic: "A nice kettle of fish we've got ourselves into! But who in the devil would have thought that such a beautiful, ladylike Yankee was going to turn out a spy of Victoriano Huerta?"

With this our ideas began to flow unanimously and harmoniously. For, once we assumed that the lovely lady was a secret agent, many details which had seemed extremely strange began to fall into place. This explained her sudden affection for all of us; it also explained—at least in part—the enjoyment she had taken in the doctor's assiduous company (pure and above reproach, but, nevertheless, open to malicious interpretation). The most convincing proof of our suspicions seemed to us the unequivocal fact that in the three days since our departure from Veracruz our friendship with her, thanks to her contribution, had made amazing headway —amazing because she was such a respectable woman, or at least outwardly so.

"Do you know what I think?" said one of the doctor's companions. "I think she was fooling us even about not knowing Spanish. That's why she could understand the doctor even when he only made faces."

Naturally, the doctor had the last word. With that youthful vehemence which was in such amusing contrast to his years, he decided that the one important, essential, unique thing to do was to devise a plan and put it into practice without delay.

"Each of the five of us should think up something by himself," he said. "Then we'll compare the different plans and decide which is the best. As far as I am concerned, I'm beginning to think right now. When we meet this evening, I will tell you what I've come up with. I hope you will put your trust in me."

As a matter of fact, the thing did not warrant the importance we were attaching to it. But Dr. Dussart, with his restlessness and his revolutionary enthusiasm, had his own laws of dynamics; he was one of those who must always be imagining things. During our voyage, nothing upset him so much as the idea of not being able to get to Coahuila or Sonora. The mere possibility was enough to drive him out of his mind: he shouted, his usually pale face flushed; he twitched, and finally resorted to such modes of expression that the throbbing of the engines of the *Morro Castle* was drowned out by the doctor's fury.

At our second meeting that night he outlined his plan

with a profusion of imaginative and picturesque phrases. Reduced to its essentials, the plan was as follows: first, the doctor would make love to the beautiful spy—irresistible, high-voltage love, of lightning effect; second, once he had her in his toils, he would propose marriage; third, when she had accepted his proposal, he would convince her that instead of going on to New York, they should get off in Havana and be married by Cuban law; and finally, in Havana he would find a way to ditch our enemy just before the *Morro Castle* sailed, and rejoin us on board. Supplementary details: first, we would help with the carrying out of the plan by repeatedly alluding to the doctor's fabulous wealth—ranches, palaces, carriages, accounts in Mexico's biggest banks—in front of the lady; second, in her presence we would behave as though we knew nothing about the planned marriage, so we could never be called as witnesses at some later date.

"And do you think you can manage all this in the day and a half before we get to Havana?"

We all asked him this same question. He answered with supreme self-assurance:

"All of it. That's child's play for us."

The plan seemed to me so wildly out of keeping with reality, and so fantastic of accomplishment, that I felt as though I were dreaming as we discussed it. But evidently it was I who was mistaken, for in view of the aplomb of its author, the plan received majority approval; nearly all looked upon it as shrewd, feasible, heroic, magnificent, and, therefore, to be implemented at once.

That same night Dr. Dussart began his amorous siege of the lady. For our part, encouraged by the evident pleasure with which she listened, we spent the next morning singing the praises of the doctor's physical, intellectual, moral, and financial attributes—especially the latter. One spoke of the degrees, diplomas, university honors which had been conferred upon him; another, of his coffee and sugar plantations; another of his vast acres dotted with cattle, and of his bank accounts and bonds; and another, finally, of the loftiness of the soul hidden behind that small, smiling exterior, a soul which existed to make those near it happy.

Our joint efforts did not seem in vain. The evening before we were to arrive in Havana, the doctor informed us triumphantly that it was practically a sure thing; the lady had almost made up her mind about marrying him, and would decide that very evening, after dinner, whether she would interrupt her trip and stop over in Havana.

"But there's no danger of her turning it down," the doctor concluded. "Those cattle ranches and the bank accounts have gone to her head. . . . She'll accept, she'll accept. . . ."

And so she did.

Our thirty-six hours in Havana could hardly have been more pleasant, exciting, and entertaining.

The lady went ashore, but not as a visitor at a port of call, as we did, but with all her trunks, suitcases, hatboxes. We felt both horror and amusement at seeing how easily that beautiful woman had fallen into Dr. Dussart's snare. Perhaps, at bottom, he really was a great psychologist? At any rate, he had applied the instinctive code of those who really understand people: never count on others' intelligence; as a general rule they are stupid. And this explains the success of his plan.

All the time the *Morro Castle* was entering port, dropping anchor, and being visited by the Cuban officials, the doctor was completing his arrangements with the lady. The two of them went through Immigration and Health as though they were one, and, meanwhile, he kept repeating his advice about hotels and other minor details. The final arrangement was that, for the time being, she would stay at the Hotel Telégrafo, and he in some other; then, as soon as they were married, they would take an apartment at the Hotel Miramar, and spend their honeymoon there until they were ready to embark for the United States or Europe.

Dr. Dussart went about laying all these schemes with a

mischievousness that was both cynical and convincing. I don't know how he managed it, but he laid his plans to remain in Havana so astutely that the purser of the ship was completely taken in. Once ashore, he carried out with perfection the pretense of going through Customs with a great quantity of luggage; and when, finally, the lady came over to tell us good-bye, in a tone both affectionate and grateful, with a note of deep satisfaction in it, he, too, came over to hug us and take his leave with a great display of sentimental effusiveness. It was a pleasure to watch him.

"And now," he said to us in an aside, "watch your step. Wish me good luck. So far, so good. Let's see how it works out."

We didn't see him again until the next day, at the crucial hour. We knew, because he had told us beforehand, how he planned to carry out the undertaking. The procedure was as simple as all that had gone before: to lull our enemy into a sense of security with continuous distractions and dazzling and delightful promises until the moment came to rejoin the ship. They would take a car and visit all the gardens and show places of Havana. They would go to the cable office, and, with her looking on, he would send a code message to Mexico requesting substantial funds for the wedding, a superb wedding befitting the beauty of the bride, his great love, and his social position. They would spend one whole morning visiting jewelry shops so she could select the set of jewels he would give her as a wedding present. . . .

There was only one point which the doctor considered vulnerable and difficult: how to get away from the spy without arousing suspicion when the moment came to go aboard again. There lay the possibility of danger or scandal. To be sure, he was counting on the effectiveness of a noble subterfuge: at first he would pretend that he was delighted to be rid of his revolutionary comrades; then, feigning a sentimental nostalgia, he would hurry to the ship at the last minute for one final farewell—and stay there.

And that was what he did. Ten minutes before sailing time, we saw Dussart leap from a gasoline launch and clamber up the ship's ladder. He gave such a lunge as he leaped for the ladder that he almost fell into the water, but fortunately he only wet his feet. He came toward us brimming with gaiety and satisfaction; his step was elastic, he seemed younger than ever.

His three friends and I were waiting for him at the head of the stairs. "Embrace me, embrace me," he said, "for that she-devil is waiting for me at the end of the pier and is watching us through opera glasses. At the last minute she began to get suspicious, and on the excuse that she wanted to say good-bye to you again, even though from a distance, she brought them along. Look, look, how she doesn't take her eyes off us."

He was absolutely right. At the end of the pier we could make out a woman in a light dress standing as though focusing binoculars on us.

"And now, Doctor, how are you going to get out of this mess?" I asked him, knowing the view the United States took of such matters.

"Just leave it to me, leave it to me," he answered. "What an adventure! I don't mind telling you that a little more, and I would have been caught in my own trap. For you will agree that our enemy is quite a morsel, quite a morsel. Anyone else would have lost his head. What do you want to bet you would have? Why in the devil doesn't this ship start moving? What time is it?"

"We ought to be out at sea by now," one of us said. "It's five minutes past sailing time."

And, without leaving the head of the gangplank, we went on talking. But as time went by and the *Morro Castle* gave no signs of taking off, the doctor began to get uneasy, then nervous, and then indignant.

"What do you want to bet," he suddenly burst out, "that this damned ship is going to ruin the whole business?"

Fifteen minutes went by, and things began to look bad to

us. The doctor, more worked up than before, began to shout.

"The captain, let's go and talk to the captain. They said the boat would be leaving at five this afternoon, and here it is five-twenty and it's still here. We ought to be three miles offshore by now. Let's go and see the captain."

It was a job to quiet him down. We pointed out that he couldn't say such things to the captain, and besides, we'd do better to keep our mouths shut; we reminded him that we were on foreign territory. Finally he calmed down, and so the pretty North American would not get impatient, he embraced us all over again, while she stood watching at the end of the pier. Unfortunately, another quarter of an hour went by, there was a new series of embraces, but the *Morro Castle* gave no signs of leaving. And with implacable cruelty, still another fifteen minutes went by identical with those which had preceded them.

"Doctor, it's time for a new round of embraces; another quarter of an hour has gone by."

"No, no," he answered, worried and on edge. "She'll realize that we are making fun of her."

As he said this we all looked curiously toward the pier. The woman was no longer looking at us. She was talking to a man who was gesticulating violently. She, too, seemed to become excited and insistent. The man pointed to the city, then toward the wharf where the launches were tied up, then to our ship. She seemed to be saying no. He kept on in the affirmative. Finally they went off together, at first slowly, and then almost running. They came to one of the doors of the pier shed, and vanished.

At that moment the last rays of the sun gilded the figure of Mercury that tops the Exchange Building.

"Didn't I tell you?" Dr. Dussart broke out. "Didn't I tell you? This son-of-a-bitching ship is going to ruin our trip. In half an hour that gringa will be here with trunks and everything."

The handwriting on the wall was plain. In a little while the beautiful spy was back on the pier, accompanied by the man to whom she had been talking. Several porters were bringing her luggage. A boat pulled in to the wharf, and the lady jumped into it. The motor began to sputter—it sounded to us like the noise of a machine gun—and five minutes later she was coming up the gangplank of the *Morro Castle* with the dignity of a betrayed queen, the woman who until that moment had had for us the importance of a presumptive spy, but who now appeared before us in a new guise—that of a woman we had tried to trick.

Dr. Dussart fled to his stateroom. We, feigning complete detachment from all that had happened, stayed where we were, half hidden among the other passengers. Nevertheless, she made it perfectly clear that she was aware of everything. As she went by us, she swept us with a withering glance, and said loud enough to be heard, but as though she were talking to herself:

"My goodness me! Who could believe it! Such a crowd!"

3 THE DOCTOR'S BAG OF TRICKS

For about an hour we had been sailing north, and the image still remained in my eye of the willowy figure of the North American as she walked through the door of the lounge, which, in turn, riveted my thoughts on the doctor. I had a vision of him in the refuge of his stateroom, alone with the memory of his shattered plot; he was probably looking through the porthole of his cabin at the indigo blue of the sea of Havana and the pearly luster of the distant city, observing with tremors of rage how the *Morro Castle*, with the steady hum of its engines, was putting distance between us and that city where his stratagem to shake off our beautiful enemy had not worked out. And the beautiful enemy, more hostile now than ever, was right there on board. There still floated through the evening twilight those mordant phrases in which she had expressed her opinion of us, and each word grew, its echoes multiplied a thousandfold, as they reverber-

ated in the ears of the hundreds of passengers who filled the
ship. Fortunately, the doctor had not taken in the full meaning of her words, though he got the sense of them. But I had,
and I still blushed when I thought of them, as I had when
she swept by us.

Hours later I discovered that the "crowd" was not as bad,
in the opinion of Huerta's spy, as those phrases of hers had
implied, or, at any rate, if her opinion of us was deplorable,
at least her inclination to forgive us seemed good—if not to
completely forgive us, at least nearly so.

It happened at an unexpected conversation after dinner.
The ritual stroll of passengers around the deck had begun.
The doctor and his three friends were still hidden in the
bowels of the ship, trying to assess the consequences of what
had happened in Havana. I took two or three turns and then
went to stretch out in the isolated, shadowy corner where my
deck chair stood. The darkness around me was so pleasant
that I could observe, as in a cinema, the movement of the
passengers engaged in their peripatetic exercise. The figures
followed one another in a kind of counterpoint to the cadence
of the waves slapping against the prow. Swift and agile, the
Yankee who shared my stateroom went by; in keeping with
the pace of her three-year-old son, the handsome Spanish
wife of the Mexican consul in Galveston; the French couple,
perfumers of Puebla, brazenly erotic—she old, ugly, ridiculous; he ridiculous and stupid; groups of Yucatecans, unmistakable in their way of walking, talking, and dressing, and
even in their self-assurance of experienced travelers, which
goes to prove that, geography notwithstanding, Yucatán is
not a peninsula but an island.

The moonlight dappled the shadow in which I was sitting.
A white figure crossed in front of me and sat down in the
chair beside mine; I caught a whiff of perfume—that of our
spy. There came a creaking of the chair, an insistent clearing
of the throat, and then, like perfectly aimed shots in the blur

of my thoughts, these words with typically Knickerbocker accent and phrasing:

"I wonder if you would be good enough to help me put this rug around my feet."

Her English was like the chime of silver bells. I leaped up obediently and bent over the other chair to carry out, in silence, the beautiful spy's request.

She spoke again. And then I answered. And the upshot of the ensuing conversation was the conclusion—she arrived at it in her own fashion—that of the group of five revolutionists, the only one who was unpardonable was the knavish Dr. Dussart.

"I shall be merciless toward him."

I interceded on his behalf, but to no avail; her last words left no hope of clemency:

"No. No magnanimity."

In his first attacks of rage, Dr. Dussart thought up plans that were as cruel as they were absurd. He outlined them, with that feverish intensity of his, at the meetings we held in his stateroom, at which, more to put him on his guard than to encourage him, I reminded him of the provisions of North American jurisprudence for cases of breach of promise.

"We'll sink the ship," he said; "that way the gringa will drown and the ship's company will pay for the damages the delay of the Morro Castle in Havana occasioned us."

"But, Doctor!"

"Not another word. We'll soon be off Cape Hatteras. In a lifeboat, swimming, somehow we'll make land. As for the others, let them drown. Thousands of relatives will collect damages. Let the Ward Line foot the bill for our failure!"

After two days had gone by he began to simmer down, stopped prophesying disasters, and smiled. He was once more the same conspirator, optimistic and full of ideas, who while we lay off Progreso had thought up the scheme of deceiving the spy with the promise of marriage.

Gesturing and with a mysterious air, he stopped me one morning at the turn of a corridor—just as the pitching of the boat indicated that we were sailing by Cape Hatteras—and said to me:

"I've thought up a diabolical scheme. We won't sink the boat; we won't kill off the captain. We'll go ashore in New York as though nothing had happened, and we'll defy the laws of that stupid country which opposes sexual freedom. The gringa is going to pay for everything. . . . We'll talk about it. . . ."

From that morning he again appeared on deck. He appeared wearing his unbleached linen suit, his yellow shoes, his Panama hat with its light ribbon—all relics, to judge by their blatantly Cuban air, of the outfit he had bought in Havana for his wedding.

The first encounter between him and the lady had us on the edge of our seats. They had not seen one another since that scene on the pier. Now, face to face once more, the entire history of their acquaintance was concentrated in a single second. For a moment she seemed on the point of scratching out his eyes or exploding; he, of defending himself as best he could. But the next second it was as though a sponge had been wiped across their faces, leaving them expressionless. The doctor walked on without breaking stride. The spy let him pass, looking him over with indifference as though he were a complete stranger, and then, resting her hands gleaming with imitation diamonds and pearls on the rail, she kept her blue gaze fixed on the blue of the waves.

In three long-drawn-out sessions we could not get out of Dr. Dussart the details of his plan. The stateroom echoed with our arguments, but he kept mum. All we learned was that it was diabolical, and would not interfere with our trip through United States territory to our destination in Sonora or Coahuila, and that the spy would find herself in the role of accused, not accuser, and it would serve her right for being in the pay of Victoriano Huerta.

All this mystery in a person by nature so talkative alarmed us, and even contributed to the fact that on the last two days of the trip we felt our mounting concern grow in pace with the swell of the sea. For the doctor—what had happened in Havana left no room for doubt—was capable of the most incredible schemes if his fancy were left free rein.

With things in this state, caution suggested to me that it might be well to try to come to terms with our adversary.

The evening before we were due to dock in New York the lady and I ran into each other. On the spur of the moment I said to her:

"Why not make peace with the doctor? At heart he is a fine man and a friend such as one rarely finds."

"Make peace with him? Never!"

"Well then, let bygones be bygones."

"No. The doctor deceived me, made a laughingstock of me, and has caused me unspeakable mental anguish, and if he is as rich as you have told me he is, I don't see why I shouldn't collect several million from him in return for the suffering he has made me undergo."

"Millions!"

"Yes, millions. It's only fair."

Was she serious? The sharp edge of her covetous indignation—it seemed to me—was blunted by an accompanying smile. Notwithstanding, I decided to use one last argument:

"If that is how you feel," I said, "I am going to take the liberty of giving you a piece of advice. Dr. Dussart talks about defending himself, if he is attacked, in a manner which he himself describes as 'diabolical.' . . . And when he says the word, his eyes begin to glitter. Don't forget that you are dealing with a Mexican."

About the middle of the morning the excitement of a number of the passengers revealed the proximity of the coast of New Jersey and of Long Island. The horizon became dotted with puffs of smoke—ships going or coming. One felt the presence of the Hudson and the East River.

Shortly afterward the shoreline became visible to starboard; then to prow, then to larboard. The launch of the harbor pilot approached, and the cadence of the waves splashing against the moving boat died away. After a brief pause this was resumed.

A huge ocean liner crossed the bow of the *Morro Castle*, sending us its forward wash and the white reflection of its name: *Rotterdam*. To our left and right came the melodic toll of the bell buoys, prolonged and sad. We were sailing between red buoys which ended in little posts that swayed like inverted pendulums. Those beacons, gleaming under the noonday sun, formed a long marine alley. Far off, enormous and diminutive, the figure of a woman stood out, one arm on high, with vestments that seemed drenched by the waves of the sea from which she had emerged; and still farther off, and smaller, arose a mass of buildings, tightly aligned between two glitters of water.

It was the moment when all the ship's passengers, ready to disembark, crowd the deck and favor each other with the smiles, phrases, and greetings of old acquaintances; the moment when those who have not exchanged a word on the whole trip treat one another with familiarity.

The doctor's three friends and I exchanged impressions. The Yankee spy, even more beautiful than in Havana, had her blue eyes fixed on an invisible spot landward, and every once in a while she turned to us with an ironical, searching look. She was, undoubtedly, impatient to pit her forces against those of Dr. Dussart at that vital moment. But the latter, probably with malice aforethought, was nowhere to be seen. Was that the opening gambit in his diabolical scheme?

We were now within sight of the Department of Health. Launches flying a yellow pennant were tying up alongside the *Morro Castle*, and officials in blue or khaki uniform were coming up the ladder. The mail boat was standing off for the mailbags.

The spy moved over beside me and asked, half warily, half indifferently:

"Where's your friend?"

"Which friend?"

"The doctor. Who did you think?"

"Oh, him. I don't know. I haven't seen him since last night."

Which was the truth.

When we were all in the lounge—each passenger with a thermometer in his mouth, like a glass cigarette—Dr. Dussart made his appearance. His entrance gave rise to laughter that could hardly be restrained. There was the sound of breaking thermometers; some bit through them as though they were caramels; from the lips of others dripped threads of microscopic beads of liquid silver. And all because the doctor had turned up—he probably knew why—dressed in the most formal attire: frock coat, silk hat, patent-leather shoes, black spats, black gloves, and a gold-handled ebony cane.

The doctor paused for a second or two at the door, and then came in, without taking off his hat, to where his three friends and I were seated. He sat down on my left. He took off his hat. And resting both hands on the handle of his cane, vertically fixed between his knees, he looked calmly over the gathering, including his enemy. Calmly, but with a faintly sinister air.

His small body, in that extravagant outfit, had the air of an organ-grinder's monkey: one look at him and the cracking of the thermometers started up again. The health officials removed powdered glass from the passengers' mouths; the immigration officials, on the point of laughter themselves, looked at Dussart with an inscrutable expression.

He leaned over to whisper to me, "Quite an effect, don't you think?"

"Too good. Have you lost your mind?"

"The one who's going to lose hers is the gringa. If she moves a finger I'll squash her. She's going to find out who I am."

The health and immigration formalities concluded with the complete breakdown of established norms; the law abdicated to laughter. And when we went back on deck, the doctor's popularity overflowed the ship. He, indifferent to all this glory, remained silent and aloof.

The *Morro Castle* now moved forward through dirty, greenish water, above which rose the gigantic hum of thousands and thousands of whistles and sirens. Dark ferries were crossing the bay in every direction. The curtain of the skyscrapers, like a vast mountain randomly slashed by man's straight lines, covered part of the horizon with its folds.

The spy came to disturb my observations.

"What is the doctor up to, dressing himself at this time of day in that ridiculous fashion? Anybody would think he was going to a funeral."

A funeral! The word gave me my cue. Without turning an eyelash, I said, "That's where the trouble lies, in this business of the funeral."

"The business of the funeral?"

"Exactly. But as you won't listen to me, it's a waste of time to tell you anything."

"Oh, no. Go on, go on."

"Will you listen to me?"

"Of course."

My story was convincing and charitable. I don't regret it.

"Well, I want you to know," I said, "that Dr. Dussart—he told me so himself—had a friend who had a great influence on him. That man, who had the most charming manners, but the most terrible passions, was involved in fearful tragedies, and whenever he told about things that had taken place in his life, he always advised his friends to follow his example. 'Getting rid of a woman is not a criminal act if one shows a decent regard for appearances. Then God's forgiveness is preceded by human forgiveness. The fair-minded and skillful killer of women should approach his victim with the same solemn air with which he would attend a funeral. . . .'"

She turned pale and asked me nervously:

"Are you talking seriously?"

"Neither seriously nor in jest. But you listen to me as seriously as you know how. If I were you I'd let the doctor alone."

Under the broad shed of the pier the passengers lined up in alphabetical order. Huge capital letters hung from the roof. From the "G" group, where I was standing, I could see the small, restless figure of Dr. Dussart under the "D"s. Under the "W" there was not a sign of the beautiful North American.

BOOK II

En Route for Sonora

---

1 THE SECOND SORTIE

The rumor was going around among the turbulent Madero supporters of Mexico City that I was already in the north acting as secretary to Carranza. I think a statement to this effect even appeared in a newspaper. But the truth was that my revolutionary fortunes did not soar so high. In New York my plans for going to Coahuila failed to work out; my notions about the purchasing power of the dollar proved erroneous on its home terrain, and six days after my first bedazzled view of Manhattan's skyscrapers I set out for home in circumstances which I would rather not recall.

In Mexico City, Alberto J. Pani and I, on our own initiative, acted as the advance guard of the Revolution—an advance guard, it should be pointed out, without arms but not without pen or, above all, typewriter. Any subversive document that fell into our hands was assured a wide circulation. We made copies, sometimes in the office of the engineer Calderón, sometimes in our own homes, and distributed such propaganda by methods as primitive as they were bold. We would set out, and when we saw a passer-by who seemed a likely prospect, say to him in peremptory tone: "Take this; read it and pass it on to your friends." In the post and telegraph offices we would leave the avenging sheets lying about on the tables. We did the same thing in streetcars, banks, and the large stores. But our favorite ploy—which was a little more subtle—was to utilize the government offices themselves. The public employee, partly because of the sluggish rhythm of his official duties, partly because of the need for something exciting to break the monotony of his bureaucratic boredom, has always been a good medium for the spreading of political news. Pani and I knew this from firsthand experience, and we took advantage of it. In this way there were certain revolutionary documents which came to the notice of more readers than *El Imparcial*, among others the famous letter of Roberto V. Pesqueira to Jesús Flores Magón.

We were so successful that the secret agents of Pancho Chaves—I don't remember how we found out—were beginning to close in on us. Faced by the threat of Huerta's secret police, Pani and I held a council of war. I was of the opinion that our place was in the north. Pani agreed. And so the two of us, without much planning and on the q.t., took the night train at Villa de Guadalupe, and went to Veracruz to take ship.

As I was already familiar with the route, on this second trip toward our dreams of Revolution I had the post of honor reserved for guides. Pani, with the docility of the friendship that existed between us at the time, followed me unprotesting, or seemed to.

The revolutionists of Havana came to meet us in the person of Pedro González Blanco; we did not know whether he was welcoming us in his own name, or on behalf of Juan Zubarán, the official representative of our Revolution in the republic of Cuba. A suspicious-minded person might have suspected some hotel deal in González Blanco's greeting; we, probably a little naïve, preferred to think that Zubarán, even though friendly and enthusiastic, was too important a personage to handle the duties of protocol of the Constitutionalist movement. In any case, the presence of González Blanco pleased us greatly, and spared us the harassment of a hundred hotel agents.

We were being deafened by shouts of "Hotel Inglaterra," "Hotel Oriente," "Hotel Telégrafo," "Hotel Continental." During a moment's pause, we heard the familiar, dull voice of González Blanco:

"Hello! So you're here."

After this came pats on the shoulder and a gesture which routed the hotel pack:

"You're wasting your time. These gentlemen have accommodations."

With this, guided by González Blanco, we walked toward a carriage. He kept a pace ahead of us, with that quick trot small people often have. Every now and again, as he talked, he would look back at us, giving us a glimpse of his semi-profile, his white, faded skin, his tight eyelid, black mustache, as even as a toothbrush, and his drooping smile. He accompanied some of his remarks with slight gestures of the hand in which he carried a cane which, instead of adjusting itself to his movements with the naturalness of an object of attire, stood out with the discordance of a symbol.

It would have been around eleven that morning when we got out in front of the hotel where we were expected. Zubarán, who at that moment had stepped out from under the shower, received us in his bedroom, wrapped in a big bath towel which hung down to his feet and which suited him better than the clothing with sleeves and legs which he put on later. He looked, as we introduced ourselves, the incarnation of an ancient Roman. And as one's gestures depend in large measure on one's attire, he received us with an expansive greeting that displayed the toga and its folds, and would not have been out of place in the Forum. His broad, gleaming head evoked Maecenas; his aquiline nose, Mark Antony; his stout arm, Octavius.

I realized later that my evocation of Rome in that first contact with revolutionary Constitutionalism there in Havana obeyed a stronger stimulus than was apparent at first glance. The fact was that Roman thought was very much in González Blanco's and Zubarán's minds at the time. In the polemics they were carrying on with newspapers and writers who had sold themselves to Victoriano Huerta, the most cogent arguments employed by both sides as a rule had little to do with the history of Mexico, but rather with that of Rome, and dealt with decisions and maxims taken from orators, historians, and statesmen of the Augustan age. The usurper was combated in terms of the struggle between Marius and Sulla, and defended in terms of the rivalry between Pompey and Caesar; the clinching argument in every passage at arms was a quotation from Cicero, a paragraph from Livy. All this in bargain-counter Latin, Latin of the paper-back Sempere editions, but not on that account lacking in verve and distinction.

Pani was in favor of our making the trip from Havana to New Orleans in the *Chalmette*, a small ship in which, he had been informed, the cream of Havana society, the most select, the most beautiful, always traveled. I cannot deny that this prospect—to judge by what we had seen on the Malecón and the Prado—would have seduced the most eager revolutionist. But as I had reasons for wanting to shorten our stay in Havana, I did all I could to see that we got reservations on the *Virginie*, which was sailing four or five days before the *Chalmette*.

My eagerness to sail on the *Virginie* was so convincing—thanks to Pani's indulgent attitude—that at the last minute Salvador Martínez Alomía, who was also in Havana, ready to join up with the Revolution, and waiting for the *Chalmette*, threw in his lot with us.

But my overwhelming victory very nearly left us all stranded. Martínez Alomía suffered from chronic conjunctivitis. When the ship's doctor examined him, he stated, without any ifs, ands, or buts, that the inflammation of the eyes looked to him very much like trachoma, and therefore our companion could not come aboard unless he was prepared to pay his return passage in advance, in case the North American authorities refused to allow him to disembark. This demand seemed to us an outrage, above all because we suspected that once the passage money had been paid, the ship authorities would help to see that Martínez Alomía did not go ashore, and we threatened to call a general strike of the first class passengers. Such a threat was not a figment of the imagination, but the unvarnished truth, for as Pani, Martínez Alomía and I were the only non-steerage passengers, we could easily have carried it out.

Our unique and revolutionary tactics won an immediate victory. Martínez Alomía was allowed aboard unconditionally; and with this point settled, Pani and I saw no reason why we should not honor the *Virginie* with our money and our presence.

The *Virginie* was as old as a caravel, as dirty as a fishing smack and as heavy as a granite tub. The huge size of it was one of the reasons we felt as though we were aboard a phantom ship. The long decks were for us alone, decks where no sailor was ever seen; the lounge was for us alone, a lounge where no faces other than ours were ever seen; the navigation chart was for us alone, a chart with twenty flags indicating the twenty positions during the twenty days of the transatlantic crossing. And this strange sensation of loneliness, this feeling that almost the entire boat was for the three of us, aroused a feeling of contact with the mysterious, the eternal, the supernatural. If at that time Buster Keaton had already made his film *The Navigator*, we might have felt the eerie fear that the doors of all the staterooms were opening and closing at the same time at the touch of invisible hands. If Sutton Vane had at that time written his play *Outward Bound*, we might have seen in the steward who served our table Charon himself.

Certainly there was something frightening about that first meal the three of us shared in the dining salon, not so much because of the possible identity of the steward, as of the food itself. Nothing that was served was for human palates, except the wine and, up to a point, the bread. Pani began to drain glass after glass of the wine when he saw the second course, and between swallows he turned on me glances that anyone else would have taken for reproach, but which I, going after the wine with an eagerness that matched his, decided to ignore.

The duality of the bread and wine was enriched by another element when we reached the dessert. It became a trinity of bread, wine, and cheese, thanks to a Camembert, a little overripe but still edible, which appeared amidst the rotting fruit and the rancid sweets. In a word, we stood our ground, and made out so well that when we left the table Martínez Alomía was talking about reciting his best poems for us, and Pani summed up his impressions as we settled down in the lounge:

"You say it will take the *Virginie* three days to reach New Orleans? All right, then for three days we'll live on bread and cheese and get drunk."

To my crossing of the Gulf aboard the *Virginie* I owe two of the most amazing sights I have ever seen: green lightning and the mouth of the Mississippi.

The green lightning surprised me one afternoon while I was talking with Pani, both of us leaning over the rail. It was a beautiful afternoon, a Gulf afternoon; as we talked we immersed our eyes in the beauty of sky and sea. The curve of the sky and the curve of the water rose and fell, each silhouetted against the limits of the other in the transparent harmony of glass as the slow-pitching *Virginie* cleft the waves. The water was blue and gold; the air, blue and silver. I had been watching the last phases of the sun and the moment was at hand when the intersection of the two curves would swallow it up. I wanted to see the last gleam in the marvelous clarity of the afternoon. I did not take my eyes from the portion of the glittering disc, the small segment that gleamed at the surface of the sea with the incandescence of a thousand conjoined stars, from the luminous point swimming in copper liquid, when suddenly a green effluvium—as green as the purest green of the spectrum—rose like a figure X from the sunken glow and covered half the horizon in a momentary, instantaneous flash.

We reached the mouth of the Mississippi at dawn. The waters were still sea, and were already turning into a mirror —a fluvial mirror whose slime was aglow with all the hues of the dawn. Here and there the mirror cracked to make way for the intensely green banks. And between the banks, so level with the water that they seemed lakes bordered by colored earth, the *Virginie* moved at half speed. From a distance our ugly ship, as it sailed through the silence, must have taken on the majesty of a monstrous swan. The furrow raised by its prow was the only moving thing in all that peace-dominated nature—the nature of an incommensurable river, of a river whose conquest of the sea was silent and peaceful.

2 SAN ANTONIO, TEXAS

José Vasconcelos was already steeping himself in Neo-Platonic and Buddhist concepts of the universe, and had declared war without quarter—although not without waverings —on the evil beast in whose body our poor souls suffer the punishment of being incarnated for life. He was, however, too generous to limit himself to a mere inner aspiration, however deep. And as richness and generosity give rise to incongruency, he lived the whirlwind of the sensory illusion as ardently as he put his faith in his inner, purifying, and liberating doctrine. It took him longer to enter the revolutionary camp than, once there, to take up clear and vehemently defined positions—though changeable, as was customary with him.

In San Antonio, Texas, he received us as we stepped down on the platform of the Southern Pacific with shouts of jubila-

tion which were in the nature of a paean to Francisco Villa:
"Now we're going to win! Now we've got a man!"

This, which on the one hand did justice to the early brilliant triumphs of the guerrilla leader of Chihuahua, on the other was a slap in the face, in the very act of greeting us, to the Sonora sector of the Revolution, that in which Pani and I up to then had centered all our hope. In other words, Vasconcelos's affectionate greeting, without his realizing it, rammed down our throats, or at least Pani's, his enthusiasm for Villa. I had come to the Revolution without any bias as far as personalities were concerned—from a distance, the only names that meant anything to me were those of Cabral and Bracamontes—whereas Pani was already an admirer of General Obregón and was attracted by the authoritarian temper of Carranza. His regard for Obregón was so high that he carried in his wallet a picture post card of the general (like those we distributed for propaganda purposes), and often, in a burst of sincere patriotism, he would take it out, look at it, and then say thoughtfully:

"With three men like this, what couldn't Mexico do!"

"*Quién sabe!*" I used to answer, torn between doubts and enthusiasm as I looked at the picture which, as I studied it carefully, said nothing to me. As a matter of fact, until the battle of Trinidad, Obregón's figure completely lacked photogenic interest. In his earlier photographs he looked commonplace, moon-faced, and the carefully smoothed mustache, the straight-set military cap with its gold-embroidered eagle, all bespoke the martial ambitions of a fledgling officer playing up his uniform for all it was worth.

Vasconcelos wanted to put us up in his house, which belonged to a Mexican politician in exile in the United States. We drove through the main streets, prosperous and ugly, and then out along one of the beautiful tree-lined avenues. But once there, Pani and I again declined his invitation. The house was very small, one of the sort anyone can acquire with a minimum effort in that country where it is so easy to achieve the satisfactions of a decent, comfortable life on a modest level. How were two more people to fit in there, and for a week? But neither Pani nor I, as we later realized, had counted on a miracle. In that small house there was a pair of diligent, friendly, hospitable hands that knew how to convert into pleasant coexistence what in another house of that size would have caused material difficulties that defied solution. We saw three white, soft beds lined up in the main bedroom; we saw the front porch turned into a living room; we saw another regime, parallel to the normal household existence, set up exclusively for the three of us, Vasconcelos, Pani, and myself. All this with such skill in domestic economy that later its mere recollection gave me pleasure.

Those diligent hands went into action from early morning, making sure that our stay should not suffer the slightest neglect. We did not even have to get out of bed to learn the latest news of the struggle against Victoriano Huerta; the first thing we saw when we woke up were the newspapers which had been quietly put in our room.

Vasconcelos pulled up the window shade near his bed, unfolded the San Antonio *Express*, and read out loud, translating as he went along the news from Mexico City and the reports of the correspondents in the frontier zones. The news was abundant and nearly always encouraging, for the revolutionary movement was in full swing. The reading was interspersed with the sound of children's voices coming through the windows, and the aromas of morning cooking. While Vasconcelos was reading, I wondered, as I listened to him, what might be the hidden meaning of the intrusion of those hearty, comforting smells. It seemed to me that our political passions were acquiring a new hue as a result of the activities of that Yankee house where we found ourselves, within the confines of those walls built by men belonging to a race less presumptuous than ours in its daily living and which dignified the simple, modest things of life more. The scents of baking flour, vanilla and cinnamon, of coffee were wafted to us.

Shortly afterward, seated at the table, those remote perfumes became embodied in the breakfast set before us—simple, and at the same time, succulent and, I would go so far as to say, esthetic. White, or, at most, cream, was the predominant color. Butter melted on the steaming, fluffy pancakes; the blackness of the coffee disappeared in the white of the milk; the water glasses glittered, and in the big glass dessert bowl the curds for which Morelia was famous floated in syrup.

Aside from our association with Vasconcelos, those eight days we spent in San Antonio were limited to a few visits to revolutionists, nearly always monotonous and, for the most part, dull. We made these calls every morning when breakfast was over and we had spent an hour chopping wood in the back yard, inasmuch as this, if my memory does not deceive me, was an indispensable rite to comply with one of the canons of Vasconcelos's theories about the harmonious employment of time.

The revolutionist par excellence among all the San Antonians in those days was Samuel Belden. He waited for us around eleven o'clock in his office which was half Mexican, half North American. When we arrived he was always busy with some client, either obviously Mexican or of uncertain nationality. But as soon as we appeared he dropped everything, invited us to sit down, and proceeded to listen to us and give us news, the latter more than the former, inasmuch as news and rumors from everywhere seemed to reach him in greater profusion than a newspaper office, as though he were really a center of confluence of the Revolution. In his halting, garbled Spanish—at times unintelligible—a Spanish without the narrative third person and with Anglicized syntax, he told us all he had heard or surmised. We knew from him when Lucio Blanco would be getting to San Antonio on his way from Matamoros to Nogales; what the senator from Texas thought about the Revolution and what his plans were for helping it; what had been done, said, or plotted the previous

afternoon at the Mexican Consulate, and other similar matters which interested us very much.

Belden's direct, brusque manner appealed to us from the
first time we visited him, and led us to treat him with a kind
of pleasant familiarity from the start. When I was introduced
to him I was somewhat overwhelmed by the man's stature;
but then I noticed that as he talked he was in the habit of
lowering his head—a rough-hewn, pale, faded-looking head—
in a way that lifted from his shoulders the excess of height
and bulk. And this lent him a kind of childlike appearance
as two heavy ringlets of thick, wavy hair swung along both
sides of his forehead. When he got excited the swinging of
the ringlets kept time to the swift staccato of his words. I
found it amusing to watch how they shot out of his broad,
fleshy cheeks like machine-gun fire, with metallic repercussions that left something of their movement on the curve of
his thick, strong lips.

Belden possessed a virtue which for us at that time was
primordial: his absolute faith in the Revolution. On closer
contact, however, it became apparent that this faith did not
arise from his concept of the Revolution per se, but from
his belief in Carranza, whose qualities he praised unceasingly
and in whose friendship he took great pride. What he found
so praiseworthy in Don Venustiano was a little hard to de-
termine, although, by and large, one gathered that it was the
quality of greatness. And this greatness so fired Belden's enthusiasm that it led him to boast of the bond which linked
him to it. To give the measure of his friendship with Carranza he employed terms typical of North American material-
ism. He would say:

"If this very minute I were to ask Don Venustiano for ten
thousand dollars, he would telegraph it to me; I'll bet anything you like."

In time this judgment, which was based on a shrewd understanding of the First Chief's psychology, was to give me
the key to many things that took place.

In addition to supplying us with information, Belden

treated us with all the attention he could command. From
his dusty office, whose only furnishings were two tables, four
chairs, and, on long open shelves, the yellow volumes of the
interminable collection of United States jurisprudence, we
would go down to the street. There was not much to see,
but that did not matter. We strolled through the lovely park.
Naturally we went to the bar famous for its antlers and other
hunting and sport trophies. We seated ourselves on the terrace
of the St. Anthony Hotel where Pani, in his character of ex-
Under-secretary of Education converted into Constitutional
revolutionist, received the reporters of the *Express* and the
Light. And it seems to me that we even visited the plaza of
the Alamo, in spite of the unpleasant memories it aroused
of the traitors Zavala and Santa Anna.

To multiply the sights of San Antonio—as Belden called
them—we alternated them, or he alternated them, in his desire to make his city agreeable to us, with certain entertain-
ments. The big act was the Mexican restaurants, patriotic
restaurants with a synthetic national cuisine. We came to
know them all one by one, though the first could abundantly
have given us the measure of the others. They were all characterized by the same bill of fare on the same kind of table;
in all there was the same display of the national colors and the
same picture of Father Hidalgo, for the one complete and
absolute Mexican patriotism is that of the Independence and
the flag; and in all of them, naturally, we ate the same highly
seasoned dishes, so seasoned that at times they became ex-
aggeratedly Mexican or were spoiled by too vivid interpretations of our local color.

3 MY FIRST GLIMPSE OF PANCHO VILLA

To go from El Paso, Texas, to Ciudad Juárez in Chihuahua
was, to quote Neftalí Amador, one of the greatest sacrifices,
not to say humiliations, that human geography had imposed
on the sons of Mexico traveling on that part of the border.

Yet that night, when we arrived from San Antonio, Pani and I went through this ordeal with a certain joy that was somehow bound up with the very sources of our nationality. We realized once and for all that we had been born and would die a part of the soul of our country.

Ciudad Juárez is a sad sight; sad in itself, and still sadder when compared with the bright orderliness of that opposite riverbank, close but foreign. Yet if our faces burned with shame to look at it, nevertheless, or perhaps for that very reason, it made our hearts dance as we felt the roots of our being sink into something we had known, possessed, and loved for centuries, in all its brutishness, in all the filth of body and soul that pervades its streets. Not for nothing were we Mexicans. Even the sinister gleam of the occasional street lights seemed to wrap us round in a pulsation of comforting warmth.

Hoarse, noisy Neftalí Amador acted as our guide. He walked with short and rapid steps. He talked without a pause, stringing together flat-toned words, words redolent of chewing gum, which he ejaculated from between rigid jaws. On the street corners the night light glanced off his pox-pitted face. Every time we had to cross the street, as our feet sank into the mud, he would repeat: "This is a pigsty. When the Revolution wins we're going to clean it up. We'll make a new city, bigger and better than the one across the river."

Beams of light which were powerless to dispel the gloom filtered through the doors to the public mud. Streetcars clanged by. People and shapes resembling people crowded the streets. Occasionally above the mass of noise in Spanish —spoken with the soft accent of the north—phrases of cowboy English exploded. The hellish music of the automatic pianos went on incessantly. Everything smelled of mud and whisky. Up and down the streets, rubbing against us, walked cheap prostitutes, ugly and unhappy if they were Mexican; ugly and brazen if they were Yankees; and all this intermingled with the racket and noise of the gambling machines that came from the saloons and taverns. We stopped for a few minutes before the doors of a large hall where a hundred or more people sat bent over the tables, their attention fixed on a number of placards covered with figures. Raucous voices called out numbers in English and Spanish.

"They play keno here," said Amador.

A few steps farther on we stopped at the entrance to a long hall at the rear of which, among the groups of men and women, could be seen the gleam of green tables with piles of red, blue and yellow chips. It seemed a big place.

"That's for poker, for the roulette wheel, for monte, for shooting crap and seven-up."

And after blurting out those words, one on top of the other, Amador paused for a few seconds and then went on, as if he were answering himself: "No doubt about it, it's a contemptible business; but there's nothing like it when funds are low. When the time comes, we'll get rid of it. We'll drive it out. But not now. Anyway, in the meantime it's the Yankees who keep it going. They come with their money and leave it here for us to buy rifles and ammunition. They're helping along the good cause; though I realize that, as we buy our munitions from them, in the end they get back the money they left here for a little while. Still, we have the arms. But we don't have them either, for we destroy them. And, what's worse, we destroy each other with them."

With this speech, Amador came to the end of the most populous and least badly lighted street, but he began a new monologue for the next one. He flitted agilely from one to another of the various themes our walk afforded him. Pani and I hardly answered a word; we looked, or rather peered, from left to right trying to get a glimpse of the places he was pointing out.

The sidewalks had become still more primitive; they crept along beside walls whose soft colors made the darkness more friendly. The opposite street was lined with low, flat buildings, whose windows and doors were set at rude right angles. They might have been houses in Mesopotamia five thousand years ago or in Palestine three thousand years ago. There was the same relation between their solid mass and the banks of clouds in the dim sky as between the fence of a park and the overhanging treetops.

A little farther on, the walk disappeared completely from under our feet. The light became a mere furtive gleam from some window or door; silence began to rise over the barking of the dogs and the remote sadness of faint yet audible singing. Every now and then, for greater safety, I steadied myself against the wall that ran along beside me; I could feel the roughness of the uncovered, chipped adobes, and the gravel in the joinings.

"In 1911," went on Amador's voice, "during the attack of the Madero forces, one of the fiercest battles took place here. They say it was here that the revolutionists began to breach the walls to advance under cover of the houses. I don't care what anyone says, Tamborrell was a great fellow and a first-class fighting man."

A short pause, and then he added, turning to me: "He died like your father before him, a hero who had performed his duty, which is the saddest of all the forms of heroism, for it is filled with melancholy, not enthusiasm."

We went on awhile longer until we came to a place that in the blackness of the night gave the feeling of being near the river, toward the part where the bank and the lower end of the city came together.

Amador interrupted himself: "Here it is. Right round the corner."

Saying this, he stepped a couple of paces ahead of us, straightening up his shoulders with the air of one who is conducting a party. A short throaty cough replaced his talk.

And, sure enough, just round the corner we almost bumped into a group of the rebels on guard. They were lined up along both sides of the door of one of the first houses, some squatting against the wall, some standing up. From between the two halves of the door, which was ajar, a few faint gleams of light radiated out into the thick shadows, throwing the forms of the soldiers into a kind of distorted visibility. The brim of their enormous hats seemed to weigh them down, making them still more squat. Each one seemed to have across his breast ten or twenty cartridge belts with hundreds and hundreds of shells. The movements of their legs in their tight trousers imitated the swell and fall of a wheezy accordion. Across their shoulders, between their hands, beside their feet, gleamed the rifle barrels, and the rifle butts made a dark, shining, triangular blotch.

As soon as they heard our steps, they jumped to their feet, making a brilliant play of lights and shadows in the pale rays that filtered through the door. One of them, heavy with the weight of his rifle and cartridge belts, shuffled forward to meet us. His dark face was framed by a huge hat, the brim of which, turned up in front and down in back, buckled against the thick folds of his blanket, which he wore in a roll over his shoulders.

"Say, where are you headed for?"

Amador went towards him, assuming a familiar air, and answered him in a voice that was meant to be affable, but which was toneless: "We're friends. These two gentlemen, who are revolutionists, just got here from Mexico City, and want to see the general. I'm Neftalí Amador. One of them was a minister under President Madero—"

"Not minister," interrupted Pani, "under-secretary."

"That's it, under-secretary," and Amador rambled on with a thousand unnecessary explanations.

We had stopped in front of the door. The soldiers, quiet in their places, were listening to Amador's chatter with the rapt attention of those to whom a discussion is all Greek. They had about them that air of humble pride which characterizes our victorious revolutionists.

"Then it's Mr. Amador and two ministers . . . ?"

"That's right. The Under-secretary of Public Instruction in President Madero's Cabinet and the Director General. . . ."

"Say, how do you expect me to say all that?"

"Well, then, just Mr. Amador and a minister of President Madero."

"One minister or two ministers?"

"It doesn't matter, one or two. . . ."

The door opened wider to let the soldier in and then was shut completely. In a minute it opened again:

"Well, come in, if you're who you say you are."

We went in. The door opened into a low-ceilinged square room, with a damp, dirt floor. A kerosene lamp on top of a pile of saddles and boxes shed its dim light and smoke through the room, which was nothing but a shed.

Once across the threshold, Amador turned to the left, slipping between the door and the soldier. Pani followed him. I was the last. Four or five steps more and the three of us were in the corner opposite the lamp, the darkest of all.

There was Pancho Villa.

He was lying on a cot, covered to the waist with a blanket. He had raised himself up a little to receive us, one arm acting as a column of support between his body and the bed. His right arm hung by his side; it was unbelievably long. But Villa was not alone. At the head of his bed two other revolutionists were sitting on turned-up boxes, with their backs to the light. They seemed to have cut short an important conversation. Neither of them moved as we came in, or showed more than a vague curiosity, indicated by the way they turned their heads, half hidden in their enormous hats, toward the door.

Amador's words of introduction were as flowery as they were long. Villa listened to him unblinkingly. His mouth was a little open and there were traces on his face of the mechanical smile that seemed to start at the edge of his teeth. At last Amador stopped short, and Villa, without answering him, ordered the soldier to bring up chairs. But apparently there were only two, for that was all the soldier brought. Pani and Amador sat down. At the general's invitation I had seated myself on the edge of the cot, a few inches from him. The warmth of the bed penetrated through my clothes to my flesh.

It was evident that Villa's intention had been to rest for

only a little while; he had on his hat, his coat, and, to judge from some of his movements, his pistol and cartridge belts. The rays of the lamp shone straight into his face and brought out a gleam of copper around the brilliance of the whites of his eyes and the enamel of his teeth. His curly hair lay in a tangled bushy mass between his hat and his broad, curved forehead. As he talked the short ends of his reddish mustache made moving shadows across his lips.

His attitude, his gestures, the movement of his restless eyes, gave him a resemblance to a wild animal in its lair; but an animal that defends itself rather than one that attacks. He looked like an animal that was beginning to feel a little confidence, but at the same time was not sure that the other animals would not leap upon him suddenly and devour him. In part his attitude was in contrast with that of the other revolutionists. Who were they?—Urbina? Medina? Chao? Hipólito? To judge from their appearance they were perfectly calm, smoking, one leg crossed over the other, and every now and then leaning forward with elbow on knee and chin on fist.

"Why didn't you put a bullet through that son of a bitch of Victoriano Huerta?" Villa interrupted Pani in the middle of his account of Madero's death.

Pani repressed a tendency to smile, for he grasped the psychological import of the situation, and answered very seriously: "That wasn't easy."

Villa reflected for a moment.

"You're right, boy. It wasn't easy. But, believe me, it will be."

And in this way, for over half an hour, a strange conversation went on. Two absolutely opposed categories of mind were revealed. Every question and every answer from one side or the other made it plain that here were two different, two irreconcilable worlds whose only point of contact was the chance fact that they had joined forces in the same struggle. We, poor visionaries—for then we were only that—had come armed only with the feeble experience of our books and our

early ideals. And into what had we walked? Full-face, and
without a word of warning, into the tragedy of good and evil,
which knows no compromise. One or the other had to win
or be defeated; there was no middle ground. We came fleeing
from Victoriano Huerta, the traitor, the assassin, and this
same vital impulse, with everything that was good and generous in it, flung us into the arms of Pancho Villa, who had
more of a jaguar about him than a man. A jaguar tamed, for
the moment, for our work, or for what we believed was our
work; a jaguar whose back we stroked with trembling hand,
fearful that at any moment a paw might strike out at us.

As we were crossing the river back into the United States,
I could not get the figure of Villa, as I had just seen him, out
of my mind. It obsessed me and kept me thinking of what
Vasconcelos had said to us in San Antonio: "Now we'll win
all right. We've got a man!"
A man! A man!

BOOK III

Threshold of the Revolution

1 GENERAL HEADQUARTERS

It was dark when Alberto J. Pani and I reached Nogales. At the station, an ugly shed like those we had seen on our long trip through Arizona, except for its typical Mexican patina, there were several friends and friends' friends waiting for us. They greeted us with affectionate warmth. They took our suitcases out of our hands, smiled at us, hugged us, asked us a thousand questions. This was like wine to the spirit, both to theirs and to ours, for it was proof of a comforting bond of union. They represented our first real contact with the Revolution, and they were evidence to us that the struggle, at least on the border, was a reality. We, who had just come from the city of Mexico, perhaps meant to them a new link in the endless chain of volunteers who renewed the ranks and the faith from day to day.

As a last touch of extreme luxury the mayor of the town had brought his Ford to conduct us to the hotel, which was hardly two steps away. But as the car was too small to hold all of us, we left it in a lot near the station and all went together on foot, a friendly, noisy group.

We crossed one street and walked a part of another to the hotel. The door opened into a hall which became a stairway in the rear: first a long entrance passage and then a long ascending passage, all dirty, shabby, miserable. A familiar fig-

ure appeared at the head of the stairs and stood there with
outstretched arms all the time we were ascending. It was
Isidro Fabela. When we reached the top, he greeted us with
the greatest effusiveness, embracing us and giving way to
transports of affection, accompanied by shouts of rejoicing
that were almost terrifying. The doors of the rooms began to
open and the different characters of the Revolution made
their appearance one by one. Out came Adolfo de la Huerta,
Lucio Blanco, Ramón Puente, Salvador Martínez Alomía,
Miguel Alessio Robles and many others whose identity I
cannot recall now. We knew some of them, but many were
strangers to us.

Rafael Zubarán, the leader of the group that had been
waiting for us at the station, made the necessary introductions. He presented us to General Lucio Blanco and Adolfo
de la Huerta with particular interest. Blanco's noble air and
handsome features, hairline mustache, and hat, a cross between Mexican and Texan—brown felt with a shimmer of old
gold, broad, soft brim, the crown slanting back, with two deep,
worn indentations—made the most agreeable impression on
me. We felt drawn to each other at once. I hardly noticed
De la Huerta, beyond the fleeting impression of his marked
resemblance to a Yaqui Indian and his richly sonorous voice.

Where to put us up was a serious problem. Escobosa, the
owner of the hotel, swore that there was not room for two
more pins, let alone two more people. But finally the difficulty
was straightened out; a corner was found for me in the room
that was occupied by Adolfo de la Huerta and somebody else;
and they put Pani in with Martínez Alomía and I don't recall
whom else. There we brushed off some of the dust, gave ourselves a cat-wash, ran a comb through our hair, and made
ourselves halfway presentable.

"And now to GHQ," said Fabela, as soon as we were ready.
"The Chief knows that you're here and wants to meet you."

The Chief! General Headquarters! I felt a thrill of emotion
as I heard those words for the first time, spoken in that famil-

iar, offhand fashion. When I think today of my formal initia-
tion as a revolutionist my heart still swells as it did while we
walked from the dirty Hotel Escobosa to the offices of General Headquarters.

These were located two blocks from the Customs Building,
in a low corner house facing both ways, the hall of which
opened on to two perpendicular wings of rooms, and at the
back on to a dismal court, lighted by the last gleams of day.
Two sentinels, on duty at the door, presented arms as we
passed. Eight or ten more soldiers who were seated on benches
in the hall got up and stood at attention. The habiliments
of these soldiers were not so picturesque as those of Villa's
men whom we had seen a few days before at Ciudad Juárez
but they had a more martial air—in so far as a martial air is
possible in Mexico's improvised armies—and a more austerely
revolutionary appearance. At least that was the impression
they made on me at the moment.

After a half hour's wait in a small anteroom, we entered
the office of the Chief. There was a certain solemnity about
our entrance. Not less than fifteen people escorted us in,
among them several of the most important figures in the Constitutionalist movement. Rafael Zubarán, Secretary of State
and a personal friend of Pani's, introduced us. My good friend
Fabela went into a panegyric of praise of me with that kindly
eloquence so characteristic of him. Carranza received us with
a friendly and patriarchal air. He had risen from his armchair
and come forward to meet us, and then he remained standing
in the center of the room, surrounded by the group of us.
I do not recall what he said to Pani, but I know it was very
flattering. He held my hand in his for several seconds and
regarded me fixedly from his great height. His glasses, over
which he looked at me a little sidewise, shed on my face not
only the softness of his expression, somewhat bovine, but the
reflection of the electric lights.

I was somewhat prejudiced against Don Venustiano by
what Vasconcelos had told me about him while we were in
San Antonio. His appearance, besides, wakened in me the

memory of the typical figures of the Porfirio Díaz régime; in contrast to the democratic frankness of Madero I seemed to notice in him something very reminiscent of Don Porfirio as I had last seen and heard him. Nevertheless my first glimpse of Don Venustiano did not dampen my budding revolutionary ardors. In that interview he impressed me as a plain, calm, intelligent, upright, and capable man. His habit of combing his beard with his left hand, which he would put under the snowy cascade, palm outward and fingers curved, throwing back his head a little with each movement, seemed to indicate tranquil habits of thought which made unthinkable—so I thought at the time—all violence and cruelty. "This may not be," thought I, "the man of genius that Mexico needs, nor the hero, nor the great, self-sacrificing statesman, but at least he does not play his title false: he knows how to be the First Chief."

It was the custom in Nogales at that time for the more prominent revolutionists to eat every day or nearly every day with Carranza. Pani and I were immediately invited to join them, not by reason of our importance, of course, but out of courtesy toward two newcomers in the city.

"We'll all have dinner in a moment," Don Venustiano said to us. "If you care to join us, I won't make you wait long. I just have to answer two or three urgent telegrams."

We all went into an adjoining room except Carranza, who went over to his desk, and a tall, pale, excessively thin, exquisitely mannered young man who went over to the desk with him and gathered up some papers. Afterward I learned that the young man was Gustavo Espinosa Mireles, and that he was Carranza's private secretary.

We began to talk in the next room, first all together, then in groups, then in couples. Fabela took me over in a corner and began to ask me questions about our friends, the members of the Ateneo who were still in Mexico City. "How's Carlos González Peña? How's Antonio Caso? And Julio Torri? And Pedro?"

In one of the frequent interlocutory readjustments I man-

aged to slip away to the patio. At close view it looked even
more dismal than before, when I had caught a glimpse of it
from the tunnel of the hall. All around it, level with the
ground, ran a narrow corridor covered by the four overhanging
eaves of the roof, which were supported by tall, bare, dry
posts. To one of the posts there was fastened, at the level
of the crossbar, a dim and feeble electric bulb, which opened
its melancholy fan of light over one area, and shed a cone
of darkness over the other. In the illuminated section all was
stark and bare; in the darkness the shadows thickened into
huge piles in the corners. Without being able to say why,
there was something infinitely depressing about that patio;
in contact with its atmosphere the very sound of the voices
that filtered through the walls from the waiting room, mingled
with the talk of the soldiers in the hall, seemed to become
blighted as though by frost.

I walked through the sections of the corridor that came
within the fan of light. Then I prolonged my stroll into that
part that lay hidden in the shadow. Then I discovered that
I was not alone. The shadow of a man leaned motionless
against the shadow of a post. Curiosity drew me closer; the
shadow did not move. I passed by again, closer this time,
and looked at it more insistently, though out of the corner of
my eye. The shadow was that of a tall, slender man. A ray of
light fell on the brim of his hat and bit a spot of gray out of
the silhouette. His left arm was folded across his breast, and
his chin rested on his fist; his other forearm acted as a cross-
support for the first. From the position of his head it was
evident that the man was absorbed in the contemplation of
the sky; the light of the stars fell on his face with a dim glow.

That figure, lost in its meditation, was not wholly unfamil-
iar to me. I walked back from the end of the corridor and
stopped directly before the motionless shadow. Little by little
the man came out of his revery, lowered the hand on which
his head was resting, straightened up, and asked in a mild,
soft-toned voice, that was in strange contrast to the energy of
his movements: "Good evening. Who is it?"

"An old acquaintance, General. Or am I mistaken? Am I not talking to General Felipe Angeles?"

It was Angeles. What was he doing there alone and melancholy, his head lost in the stars, he, the man of action and great initiative? What was he doing there, incarnating the heart-rending sadness that emanated from the patio of General Headquarters, instead of devoting himself with all enthusiasm to the military affairs of the Revolution, for which he possessed a thousand times more ability than the generals who were improvised for this work? I was so taken aback at finding Angeles there in that way that I avoided talking to him about what mattered to me most of all: the successful organization of the constitutional forces; and in the short time we stood there, I let him select the topics of conversation. Naturally, he at once spoke of my father, whose student he had been at Chapultepec. He recalled him with pleasure, affection, and admiration.

"Your father," he said, "not only had the spirit, but he had the voice to go with it, in which his spirit made itself felt and obeyed. It was the voice of a leader such as I have never heard in another; there was something mysterious about its sonority. When the military school was in formation in a whole square of the Paseo de la Reforma, his orders, even when given in a low voice, could be heard from one end of the column to the other. There was no one who did not hear them. To make my meaning clearer, I'll use a comparison taken from mechanics. His voice was like those heavy-caliber missiles which when fired, even at low velocity, describe a long trajectory. He could give his orders in a low voice and make them heard at a distance which others could not have reached with shouts."

Perhaps it was because there was something that touched me intimately in Angeles's reminiscences, but the fact is that his words seemed in keeping with the penetrating sadness of that patio. Occasionally he would emphasize a phrase with a sober gesture of his small hands, dark in the shadows, or the hint of a smile, which never quite shaped itself.

The noise of arms and hurried steps interrupted our conversation. The guard was forming to do honor to the Chief.

"Don Venustiano is coming out," said Angeles. "We'll have dinner now."

When we came back to the waiting room Carranza was there. He wore a broad-brimmed hat, and he towered above all the others. The light burnished his beard, and ran down the single row of buttons on his coat in a stream of gilded drops.

He went out and the others followed after him. Angeles and I formed a part of the group, I with the timidity of a newcomer, he with his habitual timidity. In a little while we were out on the street. The cornets of the guard played a march of honor.

Neither Pani nor I talked much at the dinner, which was excellent from the point of view of the food, and which brought together a most interesting group of people. We both preferred to see, hear and taste. Of course, I (it is to be hoped that some day Pani will write his memoirs) did not miss certain details that might be significant for a budding revolutionist. I noticed, for example, that Rafael Zubarán sat on Don Venustiano's immediate right, as was fitting and proper. Zubarán was Secretary of State in the revolutionary cabinet. I noticed that Angeles, who had recently been named Secretary of War, did not take the first seat on the left, but that this was reserved for Colonel Jacinto Treviño, Carranza's chief of staff. I noticed that Adolfo de la Huerta, in spite of his relatively high official rank, deliberately took his place among the less important diners. And I also noticed that Don Venustiano did not for one moment let the direction of the conversation get out of his own hands. His talk, which bristled with historical allusions—most of them referring to the Mexican Reform period—was listened to with profound respect even when he fell into the most obvious mistakes like two or three he made that night which would have made even a first-year law student smile.

2 THE FIRST CHIEF'S TABLE

Eating with Carranza and his immediate aides finally became, during the time that we were in Nogales, the most important act of the day for me. Aside from this duty, which I performed zealously both noon and night, I had no other steady occupation, and round it revolved my interest and my viewpoint. It was like having an official post *sui generis*, almost palatial, one might say, in spite of the fact that it was on the border of the wilderness.

De la Huerta and I used to wake up very early. This required no great effort on our part, for the Hotel Escobosa possessed, among its scant virtues, the dubious one of becoming flooded with the brightest light of day at the very hour in which sleep, wearied of itself, becomes doubly sweet. Our awakening was followed by a long chat from bed to bed. Sometimes we followed up the conversation where it had broken off the night before. Sometimes we began on a new topic. Sometimes we amused ourselves commenting on some of the extraordinary things I had said in my sleep; De la Huerta had soon discovered that I talked better asleep than awake. Finally we jumped out of bed, dressed quickly, and went down to struggle with the bad breakfast Escobosa offered his lodgers, and then each went his own way. De la Huerta, first secretary of the Department of Interior, went to meet Rafael Zubarán. Having nothing to do until lunchtime, I wandered idly about the streets, looking for someone to talk with, or set resolutely out toward the foothills, to climb them by way of amusement.

At first my status as a mere gatherer at the board of Don Venustiano seemed insufferable to me; a long morning of waiting for lunch; the long wait of the afternoon for dinner. I lacked the resource of Luis Cabrera and Lucio Blanco, who used to arrange noisy billiard matches in the bar beside the boundary line; Cabrera played a shrewd, feline, skillful game;

Blanco's was brilliant, showy, sometimes inspired, sometimes a flop. Nor could I make verses like Salvador Martínez Alomía, before he was selected to prepare the biographical portrait of Carranza. In his hours of leisure Zubarán found solace in the guitar, for which he possessed a positive gift; Angeles, in the severe disciplinary program he had laid out for both body and soul: so many hours riding, so many hours walking, so many jumps, so many hours of study, so many hours of meditation; Isidro Fabela and Miguel Alessio in the secret polishing of phrases and weighing of paragraphs to see which should finally carry off the palm as the Revolution's best orator; Pani in his training as an engineer, which made it possible for him to systematize everything, even emptiness. But I, a fervent believer at the time in the active revolutionary virtues, had nothing to fall back on. Luckily I soon discovered that in Nogales, Sonora, there was a bookstore, though not a very good one. The novels of Dumas seemed to be its specialty, and I undertook to bridge some of the gaps that had been left in my reading when I was thirteen. Later on I found out that in Nogales, Arizona, there was actually a public library, and that even the works of Plotinus were available there. My temporary immersions in Alexandrian mysticism and its spiritual purity, independent of mere knowledge, date from this period, as well as my passing acquaintance with Porphyry and Iamblichus.

At lunch or dinner time I would appear at GHQ. Not before this, so as not to cause any uneasiness, for nothing worried the First Chief's immediate entourage quite so much as the presence of new revolutionists without any clearly defined job. A panic came over them at the thought of finding themselves done out of their positions, which seemed to them full of importance and promise. This does not take from the fact that they were excellent fellows, all of them, from Jacinto Treviño, whose peace of mind collapsed in the presence of Angeles, to the young aviator Alberto Salinas, who would have been capable, decent chap though he was, of

blocking the way of Guynemer himself. I fully understand
Treviño's attitude toward Angeles. Which of the revolutionary generals was not jealous of Angeles? Their name was
legion who were furiously opposed to him—with envy as their
only motive—and who publicly maligned him.

To go to the refectory the group of us used to set out in
close formation, with Don Venustiano at the head, and walk
to the Customs House. On these occasions, as on the night
of our arrival, cornets and drums would play a march of
honor. Apparently it was a matter of great interest to tell
the world that the commander-in-chief of the revolutionary
cause and his right-hand men were leaving their desks to
lunch or dine. Thus the humble inhabitants of Nogales might
know this and rejoice.

That music invariably reminded me of Don Porfirio. (Was
there anyone who had spent his childhood in the Federal
District of Mexico between 1890 and 1900 for whom Porfirio
Díaz, the march of honor, and the national anthem were not
three parts of a single whole?) It upset me to listen to it. It
made me realize how far I was from being a good revolutionary, for there was no sign that my associates felt as I did.
"Were they perhaps concealing their feelings?" I asked myself. Or: "Nonsense. I am reacting like a fledgling politician;
I'll soon get used to it all, and these military trappings and
this personality cult will seem all right to me, or I'll keep
what I don't like to myself."

Paulino Fontes—I became acquainted with him at the time
—was, so to speak, Commissioner in Charge of Housing of
the First Chief in Nogales. In the Customs House, the apartment where we had our meals recognized no authority but
his. I should have known, from the first time I entered that
dining hall, that Fontes, the future Executive President of
the National Railways, was a railroad man by profession, for
the fact is that under his supervision things ran with marvelous precision. The serving of one dish was never delayed one

unnecessary second after the preceding, and the whole thing moved along with such precise rhythm that the guests were like so many trains scheduled on a single line under perfect orders. The infallible Waltham watch, one of those with an engine embossed on the cover, marking the hours with firm hands, seemed to be coordinating everything there: no collision, no accident, no upsets. If some guest arrived late or unexpectedly, Fontes found a way to guide him along the heavy-loaded track, and route him properly without delays for the others or putting too much strain on the equipment. In such cases Fontes made use—in the form of hors d'oeuvres, syncretic and eclectic dishes, and similar emergency measures—of switch roads, Y's, shunts, and with this adequate and unfailing aid, and without anyone's being aware of it, we all completed our two daily trips on time and to everyone's satisfaction. "Will this able man," I wondered, "ever be made the director of the National Railways? Will his administrative ability then be what it is now?" For in Nogales, Fontes was so resourcefully able that he had even managed to create for himself, like a symbolic rite, the act which set the seal of distinction on his duties. All the serving was done under his orders, but he himself passed the tray with the glasses of cognac. I ask myself whether anyone ever had as much respect for him as I did then—respect for perfection which equalized all, the perfection which recognized neither high nor low, great nor humble.

One time we were sitting around the table after dinner, as usual, fifteen or twenty of us, Carranza, Zubarán, Angeles, Pesqueira, Fabela, Pani, De la Huerta, Treviño, Espinosa Mireles. . . . With incomparable ability, Fontes transformed the most unruly appetites into mere exercises in moderation. We were all feeling good. That morning the military band had marched through the town twice playing reveille to celebrate the two latest victories of our troops, at Chihuahua and Tepic. With this motive, Carranza began to pontificate, as usual, and finally set up, as an indisputable fact, the superiority of an improvised and enthusiastic army over a scientifically organized one. A statement of this sort must perforce smack of heresy to any trained soldier, and it did so that night. Angeles waited until Carranza had finished and then, gently in the phrasing, but most energetically in his arguments, rose to the defense of the art of warfare as something that can be learned and taught and that can be better exercised the better one has studied it. But Carranza, despotic in his conversations as in everything else, interrupted his Minister of War brusquely with this bald statement, closing the matter:

"In life, General," he said, "especially in leading and governing men, the only thing that is necessary or useful is goodwill."

Angeles took a sip from his coffee cup and did not utter another syllable. All the rest of us kept quiet, and the final words of the First Chief floated in the silence that hung over us. "Is it going to end like this?" I wondered. "It isn't possible. Somebody will surely put things in their proper place."

But, unfortunately, more than a minute elapsed before anyone made a move to speak. Don Venustiano savored in silence the pleasure of dictating over even our ideas. Perhaps he enjoyed the spectacle of our servility and cowardice. I do not know whether I did right or not. A feeling of shame overwhelmed me. I remembered that I had thrown in my lot with the Revolution, and that to do this I had been obliged to sacrifice all my previous life; I felt myself on the horns of a dilemma. Either my rebellion against Victoriano Huerta was senseless or I was duty-bound to protest here, too, even if only by word.

The silence about the table continued even more dense than before. Was that going to stop me? Decidedly not. I flung myself head first into the small adventure that would immediately classify me forever among the dissenters and malcontents of the revolutionary field.

"Isn't it queer?" I said, without hedging, looking straight

into the depths of the First Chief's benignant eyes; "I think just the opposite. I absolutely reject the theory that goodwill can replace ability and efficiency. The saying, 'Hell is paved with good intentions' seems to me a very wise one, because those whose chief characteristic is goodwill are always taking on tasks that are beyond their strength, and that is their weakness. It may be because I haven't been out of school long, but I am an ardent believer in books and training and I detest improvisations and makeshifts, except when they cannot be avoided. I believe that from a political standpoint technique is a vital necessity for Mexico, at least in three fundamental aspects, finance, public education, and war."

My outburst produced stupefaction rather than surprise. Don Venustiano looked at me with a benevolent air, so benevolent that I at once understood that he would never forgive my audacity. With the exception of Zubarán, who flashed me a glance of friendly understanding, Angeles, who looked at me approvingly, and Pani, who showed his solidarity with me in enigmatic smiles, nobody raised his eyes from the tablecloth. And only Adolfo de la Huerta, trying to turn the whole thing off as a kind of joke, came to my support, or rather to my assistance. He did everything he could to efface the bad impression my presumptuousness had left on Carranza's mind. This was a brave and honorable act on his part, born of his conciliatory spirit, for he did it at the risk of falling into disfavor himself.

3 GARMENDIA'S FIVE SWEETHEARTS

During the sumptuous ball which Don Venustiano gave for the elite of Nogales on the eve of his departure, someone said to me:

"You see how pretty, how charming, how gracious the girls dancing out there on the floor are? Well, take my word for it, they are as nothing compared to those of the little town of Magdalena. You should see them! There are no words to describe them. It will give you an idea if I tell you that the night of the dance Gustavo Garmendia had five sweethearts there . . ."

Colonel Garmendia had just been killed in the Sinaloa campaign; this, which was the first brush stroke in the outline of his legend, heightened the real episodes on which the legend was to be based. But, aside from this, it was plain that the little town of Magdalena stood out in the imagination of Carranza's staff, and also in his own, swathed in clouds of golden charms, even though nobody could clearly define them. "Oh, Magdalena," they sighed. But what had happened in Magdalena? Only an occasional answer went beyond a vague encomium. For the hardier souls it all seemed to boil down to a single circumstance: in Magdalena there were over a hundred pretty girls of marrying age, and not a single marriageable man, if one omitted the Chinese.

There was also the fact that while we were in Nogales there was a very good reason why the girls of Magdalena stirred the revolutionary imagination, and this was that the First Chief often spoke of them and said that he was in their debt. Some weeks before, when Don Venustiano had stopped there on his way from Hermosillo to Nogales, they—so hospitable, so enthusiastic—had organized a dance in his honor which was never forgotten; and for this reason he felt himself under the obligation, on his return from Nogales to Hermosillo, to stop off again in that town and repay his feminine admirers with an even more magnificent entertainment.

Our interest was whetted when, as we were getting ready to leave, we saw those who had been put in charge of securing and sending off the refreshments bustling about Carranza's private railroad car, putting aboard heavy cases of wines—port, sherry, champagne, cognac—and packages and baskets of cold cuts, aspics, preserves, fresh fruit, glacé fruits, dried fruits and all manner of delicacies to be found in the stores of the adjoining frontier city.

We got there in the late afternoon of a superb day. We—that is to say, the young officers (leggings and straps polished to a high gloss, elegant, well-fitted uniforms, gray, broad-brimmed hats, brass buttons, gold insignia)—got off the train overflowing with optimism. The train had been moving through cool valleys covered with chestnuts, evergreen oak, white oak; and something of this atmosphere, the clean perfume of the mountains, seemed to cling to us. The girls, beaming a general smile of welcome, were waiting in groups in the dust beside the tracks. Their greeting flew to meet us.

The local authorities came up to welcome the First Chief and his entourage. The state band, sent ahead by the governor, played the tunes which were our hymn: *La Adelita*, *La Valentina*, *La Juanita*. There were cheers for us, boos for the enemy, bouquets, streamers, confetti. And without need of introductions, friendships sprang up.

Whose was the suggestion that we clear up at once, perhaps with an eye to the future, which of us was married and which single? It was put forward, but the girls refused to listen.

"No, no," they cut us short, with one voice. "We do not want to know, we are not interested. Married or single, it's all the same to us. We know that in the two or three days you are going to be here, no marriage is going to be arranged. So let's just be friends and have a good time without taking it too seriously."

It was a surprising way of talking. I thought it wonderful. What kind of a town was this where girls of seventeen, nineteen, talked with deeper understanding than women of thirty in the drawing rooms of high society? Forming a circle around us, they leaned against one another with a provocative air, giving to their arms sweetly linked together a vague assurance, a decision arrived at beforehand that it would soon be they who were in command and would do what they liked with us. There were blondes and brunettes; some with large green eyes in which the light drowned, others with black, almond-shaped eyes whose blackness was swallowed up in their brightness. Their complexions, fair or dark, were smooth and terse, their foreheads untroubled, their bearing frank and resolute; their dresses immaculate and becoming, their feet dainty and well shod.

There was no lack of gallant young officers on Don Venustiano's staff. Even so, in Magdalena each one could have had on a pro rata basis the same number of sweethearts which legend had assigned to Gustavo Garmendia.

The division depended on their choice; it came from their unalterable decision to be good friends and have fun without taking things too seriously. In this lighthearted fashion the man who two days after arrival did not have more dates than he could take care of was the exception. Under the thick foliage of the square (the early hours of the evening, with the band playing) desires met and agreed. The favorite spots were certain tree-lined streets, long and shaded, in whose distant perspective the rays of a street light broke upon the foliage. There—with the pristine purity of the uncommitted, the "unhitched"—they engaged in a game without beginning or end, which led to nothing and sought nothing beyond itself. And since, at least as far as the girls were concerned, the players were absolutely decent, the arts of the game of love with which the couples amused themselves had less relation to real amorous encounters than to the aroma of such encounters. All the witnesses bear this out. The world of the virgins of Magdalena was a paradise of Eves without Adams, where the Adams could suddenly arrive, but always in the days before that on which evil discovered the body of the serpent for its malign and fascinating purposes.

Suddenly our paradise became clouded over, even though not through any fault of ours, nor to our disadvantage. One afternoon Enrique C. Llorente, and I don't recall who else, arrived in Hermosillo in the company of large groups of beautiful girls of the best families of the capital of Sonora. Because Carranza, who, even in the dances which he enjoyed so much, employed the principle of divide and rule, had decided that there should be representatives of the society of Hermosillo at the dance in Magdalena, and thus the high tension engendered would add to the splendor. And so it did. When the girls of Magdalena found themselves confronted by a phalanx of rivals, it put them on their mettle, and this was to redound to the benefit of the First Chief and his entourage. Because it never entered their minds to attribute such a cruel offense to the political tactics of the Revolution, but to the disposition of the girls from Hermosillo. The result was that they began, without loss of time, a fierce duel to prove that theirs were the better arms. Were they really? The most gallant of our officers tested those of both groups and could reach no decision. "Delight versus delight," they said.

Carranza sent for us the night of the dance, and said to us a few moments before the festivities began:

"This is an affair of an official nature, and for you and for me it means that our duties come before our pleasure. Our real intention is only to see that the girls and ladies of Magdalena, where we were so affectionately received, are satisfied with us, that is to say, with the attentions and gallantry we have come to show them. I have one specific recommendation to make: no lady, young or old, pretty or ugly, is to feel neglected; all of them must receive repeated invitations to dance, to have refreshments, so they will feel that they are being thoughtfully looked after. As you will see, I shall govern myself by the same criterion."

Don Venustiano did not dance, or danced little; but he always felt in his element with the ladies. His endurance when it came to dances and festivities was unlimited. Around four or five in the morning, only the veins of his nose, which became a little more violet, in contrast to the color of his skin, which became a little paler, revealed the night's fatigue. He wooed the ladies with exquisite tact; he took a fatherly attitude toward the girls. During the interminable dances of the Revolution, which began at nine in the evening and lasted until six in the morning, he made trip after trip to the buffet, escorting a different lady each time, and every so often he strolled about the room with a lady on his arm. While doing this—and without ever forgetting that he was the First Chief —he exchanged knowing smiles with his subordinates, even the youngest or lowest in rank, and viewed the entire gathering with sweeping and satisfied glance.

At the dance in Magdalena, he bore himself like a vigorous and munificent patriarch, like the head of a clan looking after the spiritual and physical well-being of his people. Party differences, which were already roiling the political waters, were powerless against his kindly intentions. That night he was even tolerant, something unbelievable. He heard out, with great patience, the speech—too emphatic for the occasion, too frank, too foresighted—in which Juan Sánchez Azcona urged the cooperation of all elements of the Revolution. He gave no evidence that he had noticed the irritation which, shortly afterward, the speech of Fabela aroused in many, that speech which has made famous the metaphor of the "flowering beard" and the apostrophe: "But why should we wonder, sir, that men follow and obey you, when the ladies, as we can see here today . . ."—phrases which certain of the guests, it should be noted, did not understand at the time, nor have ever understood, except as something marginal to Fabela's real intentions, which, under the circumstances, were undoubtedly good. For the vitality which the First Chief displayed on this occasion was in keeping with what Fabela said or insinuated. The question was to make the ladies of Magdalena happy, and Fabela expressed himself in terms which they applauded deliriously, and which must have swelled the breasts of the bolder or more imaginative with deep emotion as they gazed upon that hale man whose long, gleaming white beard seemed less a mark of age than a proud proof of virility. It seemed to me that the lady at that moment leaning on Don Venustiano's arm was irresistibly drawn to him under the effect of the speaker's words.

Like Fabela in his speech, all of us did our part; ladies,

young and old, were completely satisfied. When the champagne was served, it seemed as though the sum of the creative forces of the universe were concentrated in Magdalena. After that, if the party broke up, it was not our fault. Don Venustiano, a gnarled fir whose roots spread wide, was still in his place at six in the morning. It did not surprise Lucio Blanco that a ray of sunlight shone through the window where the buffet was served to share in the conversation he was still carrying on with the mayor's beautiful daughter, a conversation the two were conducting with a verve and sprightliness as though they had just begun it. Neither of them would give in. Enrique C. Llorente went tirelessly on making conquests with his great stiff mustache and beautiful "raven's wing" hair, which so fittingly crowned his handsome figure. Martínez Alomía's walk, characterized by the tropical languidness of the coast, fitted in marvelously with the sober elegance of the North. Rafael Zubarán, with his easy and insinuating flow of words, his perfect manners, his subtle irony, met no obstacles. And so the others, even those who stood out least, either because of their youth or their insignificance. We all did our duty, chatting or dancing indefatigably under the tacit guidance of Carlos Domínguez, the dancer par excellence, whose arm aroused rivalry or jealousy, the one who had brought to the Constitutionalist camps from Paris the Argentine tango and handkerchief in cuff à la Prince of Wales. Little Alberto Salinas was the equal of those who outdid him in stature. In spite of his international obligations (he had been appointed to do the honors to the red-haired, freckled daughter of some Yankee bigwig who was a guest of Don Venustiano) he still managed to make the local belles aware of him and find favor in their eyes.

Strictly speaking, the dance at Magdalena did not end: it just died down to the last spark, the last crackle. The musicians stopped playing when, well into the morning, not one foot was following the rhythm of the waltzes, when for a long time the ballroom had been void of dancers and full of music.

It was after eight when I started back to the hotel. Feminine figures wrapped in silk, with ostrich fans, with satin slippers, were still crossing the streets. The more conscientious of our younger officers were not yet ready to call it a day; they were still chatting at the window grilles.

The next day we left for Hermosillo. The girls all came to the station to see us off, and they did not hide their annoyance at seeing us get into the train with the young ladies from Hermosillo. When the train was pulling out, and most of us were on the platforms or at the windows to prolong the farewells, we heard them call after us:

"Good-bye, good-bye. And when you come back, come alone. . . ."

That night, perhaps by way of consolation, we gave free rein to an exchange of confidences; imagination was at work on memory. And strangely enough, from all I heard I came to the conclusion that the five sweethearts of each of my friends turned out to be—by some weird coincidence—in every case the five sweethearts of Gustavo Garmendia.

4   THE EARLY DAYS OF A LEADER

And so we went on to Hermosillo. Nothing there interested me so much as knowing Alvaro Obregón. Would he be the great man that Pani was already heralding as our outstanding political figure of the future? Or would he be—as Vasconcelos, blinded by Villa's dazzling triumphs, thought him—one of the many whose ambitions clouded the Revolution's horizon? I knew that neither of these opinions was worth anything as a reliable judgment; first, because Pani, perhaps instinctively, seemed to base his conclusions on qualities favorable to his own views and interests rather than on a sense of real human values; and secondly, for the opposite reason, that Vasconcelos, always on the alert to discover extraordinary ability, often jumped to conclusions which he was later the first to rectify. But this, together with the news of new military victories to the south of Sonora, only heightened my curiosity.

Adolfo de la Huerta, faithful proselyte and efficient propagandist, had neglected no opportunity to kindle in me, while we were in Nogales, the flame of the Obregonism then in vogue, overshadowed by and submissive to the Carranza boom.

"You can't help admiring Obregón," was the substance of what he said, "not only as a soldier, but as a thinker, with original ideas, and as a leader, of sincere revolutionary convictions. Besides, he is a man of great natural ability. You should read his manifestoes."

As nobody in Nogales happened to have these manifestoes, De la Huerta made up for the lack by reciting again and again—as though I were to learn it by heart—the message that he himself had carried to Carranza on behalf of Obregón on the occasion of the meeting at Piedras Negras. Obregón had requested the First Chief to publish a decree depriving all military leaders of the right to hold public office, "for," he said "all Mexico's troubles come from the unrestrained ambitions of the army."

I must confess that De la Huerta's admiration for Obregón impressed me at times and even half won me over on the occasions when the canny wisdom of the famous messages was put into evidence. De la Huerta at this period felt strongly the responsibilities of the revolutionary work; and as he was a model of austerity and free from all taint of self-seeking interest, he was able to transmit to others, in his moments of restrained eloquence, his own emotions. His beautiful voice trembled as—though perhaps not in these exact words—he made comments of this sort:

"Obregón knows that his chief work is with the army, and yet he wants to prevent the officers of today from becoming the executives of tomorrow. Obregón knows that he will stand out among our greatest soldiers, and yet he makes no bones

about saying that Mexico's worst troubles come from the ambitions of her military caste."

Really, Obregón's attitude was extraordinary; extraordinary
when he sent his message to Carranza—days after the capture
of Cananea—and still more extraordinary when De la Huerta
was emphasizing to me his patriotic altruism after the battles
of Naco, Santa Rosa, Santa María. Who, lacking political and
human guile—or deaf to them—would not have waxed enthusiastic? It seemed to me that I was being witness to an un-
heard-of event: the formation of a revolutionary leader capable of voiding from the very start the privileges of his
leadership. It was like seeing a lion draw his own teeth and
pull out his own claws.

In Hermosillo the diligence of someone, I can't recall who
—Sánchez Azcona? Fabela? Puente? Malváez?—finally secured
for me one of the manifestoes so highly praised by De la
Huerta and I read it. It was the one Obregón had addressed
to the town of Sonora the day the revolutionary forces first
marched through the Sonoran capital. It began: "The hour
has arrived. . . . Already we feel the convulsions of our be-
loved land which agonizes in the clutches of the matricide."
And then, in the well-known tone of our political proclama-
tions, it painted with terrible metaphors Victoriano Huerta's
crime and invited the populace to take up arms.

My first impression was that this document did not do
justice to its author's mental capacity, or, if it did, from the
point of view of literature and ideas, that capacity was not
worth much consideration. For, aside from the civic indignation—obvious in all of us who were then in arms against the
author of Madero's death—and aside from the germ of an
idea: that armed rebellion was necessary to establish a state
of law; and a noble ideal: not to execute prisoners, the manifesto was nothing but a string of words and literary figures,
striking only by reasons of their high-flown aggressiveness. It
was apparent that Obregón had tried to produce, on the spur
of the moment, a document with literary pretensions and,

lacking talent, or the experience that takes its place, had fallen into the grotesque and ridiculous.

In the first three lines of the manifesto Victoriano Huerta was "the matricide who after plunging a dagger into the heart of his country continues to brandish it as though to destroy all her vitals." In the four following lines Huerta and his henchmen were metamorphosed into "a pack that with blood-stained jowls howls in every key and threatens to dig up the remains of Cuauhtémoc, Hidalgo, and Juárez." Later on, the pack is converted into octopuses, "with which we must struggle for the bloody scraps of our Constitution" and "from which we must tear with one blow, but with patriotic dignity, all their tentacles."

But the worst of the manifesto—or the best from the view of comic effect—was not in the play of similes and metaphors. It came particularly from a certain melodramatic tone, at once childish and pedantic, which permeated the whole proclamation. It was apparent in the opening words: "The hour has arrived"; and it resounded heavily in the final apostrophe: "Cursed be ye"; and it found its perfect expression in this hair-raising phrase: "History recoils in horror at the thought that she must give a place in her pages to this avalanche of monstrosities" (the monstrosities of Huerta).

All my goodwill was helpless in the face of this literature and the spirit it revealed. After the image of "History recoiling in horror" it was impossible to go on with the rest of the proclamation, even if it had deserved it. There came to my mind that delicious old ballad in which, describing a night of storm on the sea, the poet, among other verses I cannot recall, sang these:

"The fish gave loud groans because of the bad weather."

But the ballad, despite errors of imagination that a naturalist would have deplored, had a quaint charm which was not only lacking in the manifesto of March 1913, but would have been out of place.

Eduardo Hay admired Obregón, too, and enjoyed describing the battles of Santa María and Santa Rosa. But it was easy to reach an understanding with him. Colonel Hay would take out his pencil, open his engineer's notebook, and with a deep breath and pedantic air begin:

"The battle of Santa María was carried out, precisely, geometrically, admirably. See, the water was here. . . ."

And it was plain to anyone listening with interest that Hay was right, though his grasp of the battles had more descriptive geometry in it than strategy. Obregón was a good general, as the facts showed; at least, compared with the opposing generals, Medina Barrón or Pedro Ojeda.

As Hay went on tracing lines and dots on his sketch, the military personality of the Sonoran leader began to appear as in profile. It was evident that he was possessed of untiring activity, a serene temperament, a prodigious memory—a memory that broadened his range of attention and co-ordinated information and facts; one saw at once that his intelligence was many-sided, though astuteness was its signal quality, and that he was gifted with a certain psychological insight into the will and intentions of others, similar to that of a good poker player. Obregón's tactical art consisted more than anything else in cunningly drawing the enemy on, in making him attack and wear himself down, and then defeating or wiping him out when his own material and moral support was such as to eliminate any possibility of defeat. Probably Obregón never did essay any of those brilliant sallies that were already making Villa famous; he lacked the audacity and the gift for it; he lacked that faith in the irresistible impulse of the moment which reveals almost incredible possibilities and suddenly makes them feasible. Perhaps he never learned to maneuver either, in the sense in which this is really understood in the art of war, as Felipe Angeles understood it. But he had his own way of fighting, based on very practical and definite combinations, and this he understood and managed to perfection. Obregón knew how to accumulate resources and wait; he knew how to select the site where the enemy would hold all the unfavorable positions and he knew how to give the *coup de grâce* to armies that were destroying themselves. He always took the offensive, but with defensive methods. At Santa Rosa and Santa María, Obregón—counting on the incompetence of their generals—made the Federals defeat themselves. To be sure, this in itself was evidence of undeniable military ability.

At last one night, by the light of a corner lamppost, I met Obregón. He had reached Hermosillo that afternoon to advise with the First Chief about operations at Sinaloa. Culiacán had just fallen into the hands of the Constitutional forces. The troops of Iturbe, Carrasco, and Buelna formed a solid line to Tepic.

We were walking down the street, an idle group of friends, De la Huerta, Martínez Alomía, Pani, Zubarán, myself and several other civilians, when suddenly, a short distance off, we saw Obregón. We all hurried to meet him and gathered around him, under the rays of the street light, to congratulate him on his recent triumph. He was returning victorious once more; he radiated the satisfaction success gives.

Those of us who already knew him embraced him; the rest, on being introduced, shook hands with timid warmth. And then, while some talked with him, the others—or I, at least—observed him with the interest his growing fame warranted. De la Huerta, on purpose, asked him important questions in a light tone, fearful, no doubt, of violating the secrecy of the great revolutionary problems. But Obregón answered jokingly and as though his only desire at the moment was to talk just to be talking. He mentioned his wound, making fun of himself because the bullets did not seem to take him seriously enough: "Yes, I was wounded, but the wound couldn't have been more ridiculous: a Mauser ball ricocheted against a stone and struck me in the thigh."

Out from his eyes, whose golden glints made them reminiscent of a cat's, a continual smile spread over the rest of his face. He had a way peculiarly his own of looking sidewise, as though the smile of his eyes and that of the corners of his mouth were going to converge in a lateral point situated in the same plane as his face. There was nothing military about his appearance. His white uniform with its copper buttons looked out of place on him. His cap, white, too, and with an eagle embroidered in gold above the black visor, was unbecoming, both because of its size and the way he wore it. It was too small and slanted down from the top of his head to his forehead. The appearance of his clothes made it plain that he affected untidiness, and that he affected it as though it were one of his campaign virtues. Since the fighting at Culiacán he had had more than enough time for his orderlies to polish his shoes and puttees and for a barber to shave him. But the dust on his feet and the stubble on his face were the same that had witnessed the triumph at Culiacán.

The famous wound—ridiculous only because it was mentioned—gave Obregón occasion to talk about himself enough for me to begin to know him in spite of the jovial tone of his words. From this first moment he seemed to me a person who was convinced of his immense importance, but who pretended not to take himself seriously. And this pretense lay at the bottom of every one of his acts. Obregón did not live in the world of matter-of-fact sincerity, but on the boards; he was not a man of action, but an actor. His ideas, his beliefs, his feelings were intended, like those of the theater, for the public. They lacked all roots and inner conviction. In the literal meaning of the word, he was a comedian.

BOOK IV

The Ups and Downs of a Revolutionist

---

1 FROM HERMOSILLO TO GUAYMAS

One morning in Hermosillo it was briskly decided that Miguel Alessio Robles possessed unusual qualifications for the post of Secretary of State of Sinaloa, and that my gifts as chief clerk were no less exceptional. Accordingly we were given our passports, supplied with money and letters explaining the object of our trip, and ordered to take immediate leave for the capital of the state that was to enjoy the benefits of our unquestionable but hitherto untried aptitudes for the difficult art of government.

Our trip from Hermosillo to Maytorena was made under almost normal conditions. It was a bright day, a day such as one finds only in Mexico, which makes the distant mountains seem only a step away, and turns the air to pure transparency. The train rushed along in the sunlight without any untoward incident. Every now and then we plunged over the abyss of a trestle, but the passengers' nerves soon grew accustomed to the thrill this occasioned. The engine rocked, the boxcars lurched, the passenger cars creaked, and the passengers laughed excitedly, until we finally got our breath back. From time to time the Yaqui soldiers riding on top of the cars yielded to the irresistible temptation of shooting at the peaceful animals grazing in the fields. In that clear transparent air they made fascinating targets, and we saw cows, horses, and mules falling along the track. At times Eduardo Hay, who was going to Culiacán to take his post as General Iturbe's chief of staff and, who, as ranking officer, was in command of the train, grew furious at these acts of barbarity. Whereupon the train would be halted, a couple of officers would go up to the roof of the train and issue stern orders to the troops, and for a little while we would proceed quietly on our way.

We laid over for more than an hour in Ortiz, so the soldiers could eat and stretch their legs. Alessio and Hay, who were good friends of General Salvador Alvarado, decided that we should pay him a visit. I would have preferred not to leave my seat, for I was loath to arouse melancholy family recollections associated with that place. But Alessio was so determined that there was no gainsaying him, and the three of us set out to find the conqueror of Santa María.

Ortiz at the time was an imposing military center, the headquarters of the forces that were besieging Guaymas; the base of operations, ammunition dump, and quartermaster's department. All of this, run with that great capacity for administration and organization which General Alvarado had always shown whenever he was in direct command, gave the sensation of a really military setup, and on no small scale. There, for the first time, I felt the armed power of the Constitutionalist Revolution, and to a degree unmatched until, in time, I made the acquaintance of the great encampments of Villa's followers in Chihuahua.

Alvarado received us alongside the boxcar which he used as his office. His facile, incongruous remarks, his readiness to theorize about everything, quickly gave me the measure of the man. And I could not help being amused—accustomed as I was to dealing with professional soldiers—at the continuous contrast between his air of village druggist and the martial attitudes he assumed. Nevertheless it was apparent that, for all this, here was a dynamic man, a gifted man, with the capacity for swift flashes of intuition and the ability to undertake great things, though this was weakened by a kind of imbalance between his meager continuity of action and his torrential imagination where action was concerned. It was also apparent at first glance that Alvarado was a megalomaniac, but a straightforward one, that is to say, one of those who neither concealed nor disguised his megalomania. He had on his desk a complete arsenal of pictures of himself, in all sizes, shapes, poses; cabinet size, regular size, mounted, unmounted, in uniform, in civilian attire, bust, full-length, with and without military cap.

Talking about himself was his favorite occupation, and he could keep this up sparklingly and indefinitely. He barricaded himself, in a fashion all his own, behind his glasses, and from that vantage point fired at his interlocutor a fusillade of words and ideas which he underscored with gestures, like a semi-Europeanized Chinese student. His mental activity made my head reel five minutes after I met him. With every twenty words he outlined a plan which, if put into effect, would have changed the face of the earth. His spirit apparently resolved the insoluble conflict between genius and its opposite; at one and the same time he was clear-sighted and obtuse; in one bound he could reach the intuition of the deepest truths while being unable to penetrate the surface of the simplest problems. Later, when his ideative process was analyzed, his genius went up in smoke, the mere outward semblance of a bold toying with ideas, emphatically affirming certain things out of an excess of ignorance about others. In this sense, Alvarado was cut off the same bolt as the other revolutionary personages who styled themselves geniuses and talked of curing the nation's deepest-seated ills with a stroke of the pen from their half-illiterate hands.

Many traits of Alvarado's character warranted respect: his passionate eagerness to learn, his sincerity, his sober attitude toward life. That afternoon, as soon as we began to talk he overwhelmed me with questions about university studies; he wanted to know who Antonio Caso was. He often smiled as he talked, but the smile came from the subconscious areas of his mind, outside the luminous radius of ideas. A quip interpolated by Hay in connection with the battle of Santa María elicited no response from him until the joke had been repeated twice. The point was that neither laughter nor smile entered into the scheme of his thinking except as something pointless, or having no other purpose than to waste time that could be more usefully employed. He felt that the work underlying the revolutionary effort was of such magnitude that it did not permit of wasting a moment or a thought; the slightest detail called for wholehearted attention, the most sober approach.

That afternoon sincerity imbued his every word. He praised, in all that deserved praise, the military organization under his command, and censured all that called for censure. He referred to Obregón in terms he would surely not have employed if they had not come from the heart. And just as we were on the point of leaving, he decided, of his own accord, to present each of us with one of his photographs. He looked at the three of us together—looked at us, his eyes bright with an enigmatic, somewhat Oriental smile—then slowly, one by one, and then asked without affectation:

"Now, let's see, which should I give to which?"

On one of the largest he scrawled his huge signature and handed it to Miguel Alessio Robles. Another, not so large, he signed in a more restrained manner, and handed it to Hay; and, finally, he handed me, after putting a small, meticulous signature on it, one of the smallest and least theatrical. In his opinion he had sized us up, weighed us with his eyes as on a jeweler's scale.

Did it annoy Hay that Alvarado gave evidence of holding him in less esteem than Miguel Alessio Robles? It made no difference to me that he considered me less important than the other two, but I was charmed by that display of frankness which was so outspoken that it hardly met the requirements of politeness.

That night I traveled for the first time over the emergency road that had been cut through the underbrush to join Maytorena to Cruz de Piedra. Victoriano Huerta's troops, which had fallen back to Guaymas, held Empalme also, which was the point of intersection of the railroad from the north and the one going south. As a result the communications of the revolutionists from Hermosillo to Sinaloa suffered a hiatus here. The country around Sinaloa was flat and open and the occasional thickets and clumps of shrubs offered no protection. And, as this area lay open to the fire of the Federals, it seemed more prudent to traverse it at night, and not too early. The majority went on foot; the others in buggies or wagons which they hired at one terminal or the other—Maytorena or Cruz de Piedra—like a ferryboat on the banks of a river.

Alessio, Hay, and I picked out the best of the vehicles at our disposal and we left Maytorena at ten that night. I knew there was no danger or importance to the trip, and yet to me it was filled with charm and excitement. I seemed to find in it some subtle meaning, something that revealed I hardly know what intimate essence of Mexico, in the movement of those men through the darkness, rifle on shoulder, and hip as though grown to the shape of the revolver, sure of their way, indifferent to their fate. An atmosphere of mystery, and the men with faces and souls just as mysterious! The night was clear overhead and dark below; but the swarm of lighted cigarettes, moving restlessly and interminably at eye level, gave a multiple unanimity to the coming and going of the double caravan along our route, channeling into its mobility the heaving of the Revolution.

In the distance we could see the gleam of the Federal campfires, which formed a distant semicircle on our right. Sometimes the fireflies of the soldiers' cigarettes carved out of the darkness with their illumination the wavering lines of dark faces, the gleam of buckles and rifle barrels, the shiny wood of gunstocks, the crisscrossing of cartridge belts over the folds of dirty shirts. The creaking roll of carts flowed around us

like the breaking of the sea. Out of the darkness came the
sad, hungry, incessant baying of the dogs.

In the back of our carriage Hay's orderly drowsed, huddled
among the luggage and bundles. We sat in the driver's seat,
talking, and at our feet the coachman hummed softly.

Cruz de Piedra loomed up before us in the shape of three
or four somber, geometrical masses, among which an occasional lantern winked or moved.

"Now," said Hay, "the important thing is to get some sleep
so we can start out again early tomorrow morning."

And taking our suitcases, we started to look for a place to
rest our bones. The best thing in such circumstances is a boxcar. The first ones we looked over were no good. They had
no doors and smelled bad. Finally we found one that seemed
tolerable. We climbed in. Hay's orderly lighted his lantern
and began to make up his officer's bed: a fine soft pillow, the
cleanest of sheets, and a soft warm blanket. Alessio and I,
who had neither blankets, sheets, pillows, nor orderly, piled
our suitcases up in the corner and, resting our heads on them,
went off to sleep. Fortunately the car was one of the Southern
Pacific's refrigerator cars, and had temperature valves. Thanks
to this, while Hay and his orderly slept warm and comfortable, we, though we were cold, did not freeze.

2   FROM GUAYMAS TO CULIACÁN

The traveler has a choice of two methods for securing breakfast in Cruz de Piedra: one, the everyday manner, the other
the unusual. The first consists in merely buying at one of the
stands that sell supplies to the soldiers a pitcher of coffee and
some tortillas, the big, round flat ones made of white flour
that one folds over and over in layers, and that taste as
though one were trying to chew thin, fragrant paper. The
out-of-the-ordinary method was more complicated: it consisted in getting one of the important personages around the

camp to invite one to eat with him, which meant that one would get better rations than in the strictly commercial breakfasts.

With the meticulous knowledge of a person who takes his campaign life in all seriousness, Colonel Hay expounded to Miguel Alessio Robles and me the advantages and drawbacks of each of the above-outlined methods and finally decided in favor of the second.

"I can assure you," he said, "that if we go to call on Colonel Sosa, whom I have known ever since the battle of Santa María, he will invite us to eat with him and treat us like princes. The visit will not surprise him either, because we really should show him this courtesy as officer in charge here, and besides he'll understand perfectly well what is our real reason."

Alessio and I, exhausted by our sleepless night and the cold, would probably have preferred the immediate cup of hot beverage, bought at the nearest stand, to any rosy promise of a gourmet's breakfast. But Hay, who had slept in a bed, with pillow, sheets, and blankets, spurned the easy way and overrode us. What resistance could we put up against anything or anybody, huddled in the wrinkles and dust of our overcoats, which proclaimed a mile off the kind of night we had spent, on the hard boards and frozen half to death? I was just beginning to respond to the cajolery of a beautiful day. After daybreak, when the cold awakened me for the hundredth time, my spirits had risen at the promise of a bright morning. We had watched how a myriad of horizontal lines came through the cracks of a board, gilding with tiny bosses of gold the facing boards, and how, in the warm penumbra created by this interplay, the immediate surroundings announced their presence and entered with an optimistic and resolute gesture in the beauty of the morning. But in spite of all this, as I say, I was not yet restored.

Of course, Hay was right. Colonel Sosa outdid himself entertaining us. We found him in a most unusual kitchen, improvised of boards, pieces of tin, and boughs of trees. In one corner was an open fire. From a can the foaming, fragrant coffee bubbled over on the blaze. A shiny, sizzling frying pan poured forth smoke and delicious smells. In one corner, almost over the hearth, chunks of beef and pork hung by cords from the rooftrees. And in the other corner dangled festoons of dried beef and red and green peppers.

Introductions were brief, for Colonel Sosa, who was no fool, understood to perfection his duties as a host. After expressing his great pleasure in meeting Alessio and me, he ordered more meat put in the frying pan, more coffee in the coffeepot, and more chile and tomato in the sauce. He drew up to the boards he used as a table the three chairs he owned, improvised a fourth out of a box, and invited us to be seated.

It was a delightful moment; we had found, not only food, but warmth and a cordial welcome. Naturally, to Miguel Alessio and to me Colonel Sosa seemed the most delightful person for miles around. Besides, my attention was caught by a detail that perhaps another might not have noticed: that morning Colonel Sosa was wearing two coats, one civilian and the other military, the first a grayish blue, with greenish buttons, and the other black, with brass buttons and scarlet pipings.

Breakfast over, Hay went to make arrangements about the train that was to take us to Culiacán. Miguel Alessio wanted to get a look at Guaymas, even though from a distance, to see the Federals' gunboats, and he set off for one of the hills near by. I strolled round the encampment, talking with the soldiers and observing the excellent organization that General Alvarado had worked out.

The principle of order was apparent in the camps of Guaymas even in the sales system by which the soldier was protected against the abuses of storekeepers and paymasters, and it was worth seeing at firsthand. For it explained clearly why the soldiers of Sonora—Yaqui Indians, for the most part—were so willing to join the revolutionary army. In 1913, the Revolution, like every liberation movement at the beginning, was an undeniably pure impulse, of regenerating vitality, which made itself felt visibly and actively in the slightest details. If this had not been the case the Federal army would not have failed so completely, for its real attacks were directed not against the revolutionary potential, but against the destructive germ which that army carried within itself from February of 1913.

Miguel Alessio went to observe the Huertista gunboats from the top of the hill which he had chosen as a point of observation, and he spent over two hours there. Hay, although we were not in any hurry, grew impatient, and when Miguel Alessio returned from his trip, he had a serious argument with him, during which several sections of army regulations were cited and several chapters of the Declaration of Human Rights. Human rights won out over regulations to which a man voluntarily submits, and it was evident that Hay, in his eagerness to go by the book, turned the typical revolutionary into an ideal which was a caricature of all the disciplinary virtues.

They finally simmered down, the divergent points of view were ironed out, and the train began its long, weary, interminable trip in sight of the awesome blue sierra between whose crevasses ran the white lines of brooks and mysterious pathways.

"Down those," said those familiar with the terrain, pointing to the whitish cracks, "the wild Indians descend."

And the rough, the immense sierra, whose greatest beauty lay in the interplay of the light with the sharp jags of surface and line, was the subject of many comments on the contrast between the beauty of its brightness and the black legend of its barbarous excursions. At the infrequent stations where the train stopped, there were improvised watchtowers, raised on poles and covered with branches, from which the lookout watched for the Indians, sly and cunning in their attacks.

The stops were in desolate towns sunk—even the more important, like Navojoa—in a dense atmosphere of barbarism, incivility, of satisfaction with the crude, the formless, the primitive and ugly, which made the spirit shrink. They were made up of a few yellowish adobe houses—all of them low, flat, unadorned—sitting complacently in a sea of dust; dust now, without doubt mud in the rainy season. Through the one street of the town occasional buggies and wagons rolled up clouds of dust or, dustier than the very earth, stood where their horses or mules were tied to a stake driven into the ground. It was a Mexican Far West, newer than that of the United States and with less promise of industry, less machinery, less energy; with a greater aboriginal influence, which was revealed in the use of mud as building material, but as barbarous as the other, more so perhaps, its brutality unrestrained by a tradition of civilization, and ignorant of all the amenities invented by human culture. The civilizing influence of the Jesuit fathers had had no time to flourish in those regions; currents of authentic savage life still floated in the tragic, miserable atmosphere, in which every feeble better impulse was crushed out by the uncontrolled passions of men who responded to none but the zoological stimuli. I felt no surcease of this depressing atmosphere until the train entered the gentle regions of Sinaloa. Compared with southern Sonora, even the poorest farms of Sinaloa are outposts of civilization.

In San Blas we found no lodging for the night, but what we did discover at the door of a hut converted into an inn were beds which were rented, in the open like that, to those hardy souls who could brave temperatures of three or four degrees below freezing. Alessio and I were not the rugged type—Hay, with his military equipment, had no problem—but in view of the fact that there was no other shelter, we decided to avail ourselves of that flimsy illusion of rest. The beds in question were fantastic. The frame was made of barrel hoops, which were interwoven in such a firm, unyielding manner that they would not have given under the weight of a locomotive if it had sought rest on them. The hoops, moreover, were covered with rawhide, to form a firm, convex surface, slanting down on each side. We soon discovered how difficult it was to sleep on them stretched out lengthwise, for there was the risk of rolling off on either side. We tried changing position, lying crosswise, but that did not work either. If we lay face up, we were like Prometheus chained to his rock; and face down, we kicked and floundered in empty air, as though we were swimming on a hard, fixed ball. Finally we let ourselves slide to the floor, and huddled there among the folds of our sheets, whiter than ever in the chill light of the November stars.

Neither Alessio nor I was too happy about the mission Carranza had entrusted to us. Just as in Sonora, where the Revolution was already split into Pesqueira and Maytorena factions, in Sinaloa there were the supporters of Iturbe and those of Riveros. The analogy went even farther: in Sinaloa, as in Sonora, the leaders of the groups were fine men; here, too, the schism was based more on personal considerations and with an eye to the future than on any discrepancy of principles. Why were there attacks on Ignacio Pesqueira and Maytorena? On Riveros and Iturbe? The newcomer who inquired about this received a farrago of confused, specious, and totally absurd explanations; but once on location, unless he was extremely shrewd, he found himself forced to take sides, finally accepting one of the versions he heard, and repeating it, in turn, with the same conviction as the interested parties. Basically it boiled down to the dispute—eternal in Mexico—between multiple groups eager to seize power, which is one: the predominance on both sides of immediate, selfish interests over the pure and unself-seeking aspirations, an error which confuses the mediocre impulse to seek the reward of work with the noble impulse which sees the work itself as the reward. But inasmuch as there was no way of avoiding the conflict, a theory was invented to justify it: those closest to Don Venustiano, who, with his Machiavellian

village concept of the art of governing, was the one who most
fostered the discord, claimed that they represented the true
spirit of the Revolution, that they were the real radicals,
and hurled at all who refused to accept them as a privileged
caste of semi-deities the anathema of conservatives and even
reactionaries. In this way the two factions sprang up in
Sonora—one as lacking in ideas as the other, but both obliged
henceforth to accept the position attributed to them or that
they assigned themselves. These two factions, like a plague
of discord, were to spread from Sonora to Sinaloa, then to
Chihuahua, and finally to all the Republic, with the supporters of the Convention, the Villistas, the Carrancistas.

The appointments of Miguel Alessio Robles as Secretary
of State of Sinaloa and of myself as supposed ranking officer
were, by reason of their origin, contrary to the group which
controlled the government of Sinaloa, and were on the point
of putting us in a very embarrassing situation when we
reached the capital of the state. Fortunately, Riveros's supporters, who represented the faction which we, without being
aware of it, offended by our presence, decided to take a firm
stand from the start and devised a simple way of making us
feel their reaction. General Iturbe with his whole staff, General Diéguez with his, and Governor Riveros, with the high
officials of his government, had come to the station to meet
us. And Riveros, as he made the introductions, stressed repeatedly and with manifest intent the titles "Secretary of
State," "Ranking Officer" as he pronounced the names of the
persons who held these posts.

From that moment I decided—and so I proposed to Miguel
Alessio later—not to present Carranza's letters. I did not want
us to set off a new dispute; I did not want this because, aside
from individual values (like that of Iturbe, for example, who
had already won the aureole of being one of the best generals of the Revolution), the two groups of Sinaloa seemed
to me equally revolutionary and equally estimable, regardless
of what they said about one another.

3 RAMÓN F. ITURBE

That night when we came into General Ramón F. Iturbe's dining room, there was none of the display so frequent on special occasions. I could see at a glance that the commander of the revolutionary troops of Sinaloa was a simple, temperate person. The dinner of welcome he gave us was held in a room that was marked by its neatness, its careful order, but where there was no hint of pomp or circumstance. A broad, white table occupied most of the room, in the middle of four almost bare walls, and received and reflected back even more clearly the light from a hanging lamp. The tablecloth, the gleam of the modest, inexpensive china, and the varied transparence of glasses of different sizes alternated with the dark blotches of the bottles of beer, resembling random ninepins.

The only special decoration I noticed anywhere were several bunches of flowers in low vases and two handsome 75-millimeter grenades—two of those recently captured from Huerta's forces—erect, like small pillars, in the ideal foci of the ellipse around which we were to sit. The lamplight burnished the two huge copper casings and highlighted the red surface of the projectiles beneath the tiny headlights which the luminous rays illuminated under the rings of the fuse. Tiny lights, minimal lights, but symbolic of the struggle and of victory. Their presence there fed the hopes of victory— as penetrating and contagious as the discouragement of defeat —and, above all, linked us in brotherhood.

Of the twenty or twenty-five persons gathered around the table Ramón F. Iturbe—this was instantly apparent—was the most intrinsically important, the one endowed with the strongest personality. Diéguez, Hay, Riveros, Alessio, I and all the others were in the picture as reflections or sketches, as partial elements of a superficial chiaroscuro whole. Iturbe stood out in relief. And not because he tried to assert himself, but, on the contrary, in spite of all his efforts to play himself down.

He spoke little and circumspectly. His words, bent upon conveying the exact shade of his thought, followed a slow, winding route, so winding that at first it seemed as though he were trying to disguise or conceal what he was really thinking. Iturbe's culture, which at the time was very meager, had the advantage that he did not dress up what he had to say in the revolting clichés which were like the breath of life to the semiliterate and fake revolutionists. He spoke, moreover, with a certain shyness, with an air of sincere humility of the person who feels that he may easily fall into error, and accepts corrections beforehand. All of which was reflected in his character in a kind of contrast with his other qualities: the contrast between his youthful lack of assurance and the self-confidence living had given him; between his spiritual adolescence and the precocious maturity of his spirit, which was emphasized by his faith in himself and by his deep, intimate conviction that, basically, he was right.

For Iturbe was one of the very few revolutionists who had thought out the moral problem of the Revolution and had entered it with a clean conscience. Though he was very young, his revolutionary ardor came more from conviction than from enthusiasm. And in him this conviction did not reduce itself, as in others—the architects of the Revolution, the leaders—to the desire to create a state of things under their control, but to the need to act rightly, morally, religiously. Not for nothing was Iturbe the only revolutionary general who believed in God and who openly upheld his beliefs, even though apologetically. And this alone, believing in God, raised him high above all his comrades in arms, most of them unbelievers and ignorant, barbarous, audacious, with no sense of human values and detached from all the sources—false or true—which generate the impulses toward virtue.

His youth and his graceless diminutive stature made Iturbe seem, at first glance, a person of slight consequence. Moreover, his slovenly dress testified to such innate carelessness, such authentic indifference to his immediate and corporeal surroundings, that one had to consider the totality of his being two or three times to convince himself that, rather than a shortcoming, this was the quality of a superior being, indifferent to what, basically, represented no definitive value, just as in the generals of Sonora it was an early manifestation of defects and not of virtue, the unshakable clinging to the most militaristic of military trappings. But when one appraised him carefully, Iturbe quickly took on stature and revealed why he was of that small number who were leaders even when they practiced obedience.

His thoughtful and mature temperament was the cornerstone of his personality and was manifest even in the smallest details. That night, for lack of openers, the bottles of beer had to be opened in true revolutionary fashion: fitting the edge of the cap against the trigger of the pistol and then levering this against the neck of the bottle to pry off the cap. Some more, some less, all those present carried out the operation with a certain display of temerity, as though the revolvers (with a .38 or .44 bullet opposite the hammer) were harmless objects. For there was not one of us who did not consider himself very brave, or feel accustomed to risking his life at any minute. But not Iturbe. He pulled his pistol out of the holster without any show; carefully turned it butt up; then taking the bottle in his left hand, and making sure the gun barrel was pointing to the floor or the wall behind him, he moved it in the upward curve of a bottle opener. Seeing the caution with which he proceeded, one would not have believed this was the same man who in the hour of battle, and whenever risking his life had meaning, set no limits to his bravery, as he had just proved during the attack and capture of Culiacán.

BOOK V

Sinaloa

---

1 First Impressions

Eduardo Hay entered at once on his duties as Iturbe's chief of staff. But Miguel Alessio and I had given up our idea of getting appointed to some official post and had become once more the masters of our time and our actions.

To amuse ourselves we wandered about, getting acquainted with Culiacán, which offered the double interest of a city we had never seen and one recently evacuated by Huerta's troops. There was something unpretentious and agreeable in that little city, a brightness that invited one to stroll about it; a fullness of life in mid-December, which, after the dry, dusty days in Hermosillo, revived one, sharpened the wits, cleared the mind, and aroused a desire to establish contacts with all things. During the day everything took on a rare splendor in Culiacán. The waters of the Tamazula had the same blue hue as the sky, broken only by the dark splotches of stones and backed by the sand of the riverbed. On the outskirts of the city, rubbing elbows with the walls of the last houses, grew a rich vegetation: lush gardens, thick canebrakes, meadows that were always green, dotted here and there with flowers. And the sky, whose brilliance almost blinded one at times, shed over those fields and the streets that the groups of houses marked out through them rays of light that gilded everything they touched. In this splendor nothing seemed

ugly or dull. The very mud gave off a radiance that seemed to
ennoble it.

So great was the brilliance and vitality of the natural elements there that it was hard to realize the effects of man's
recent struggle in the city. We had to pass the plundered
stores with their broken-in doors and empty shelves again and
again before we took in their full significance. The abandoned
houses, which the mob had despoiled of all their furnishings,
merely brought to mind the confusion of a passing moment
of disorder, a momentary wrinkle in the social fabric, nothing
of civil war in its wildest riotousness. Small groups of the
city's inhabitants wandered about the streets engaged in the
difficult task of earning a living in a place where there was
hardly anything to eat. Yet, notwithstanding these trying circumstances, they appeared happy, self-assured, optimistic. To
get a new shirt or pair of socks one had to wait for Schwab,
the famous Jewish trader of that day, who used to make trips
to Nogales, Arizona, and come back with job lots of clothes
whose style and prices were incredible, and in which we
looked even more incredible. There were suits of underwear
of colors and designs so weird as to hint of some supernatural origin; shirts that opened down the back; green suits with
rhomboidal stripes, which made us seem first cousins to the
snake family; other suits were such strange combinations of
different elements that they seemed the product of some powerful mysterious imagination, and in them we acquired a
grotesque personality: some were half baseball player and
half cowboy, or a combination of mountain climber and
summer-resort visitor. But this counted for nothing in the
rhythm of the surrounding forces of nature, just as it did not
seem to matter that there was not always bread in the city,
or meat, or coffee, or other supplies. December that year was
like spring. The vital forces thrived and flourished and seemed
to live and multiply on their own strength.

Some weeks later Laveaga, who was to become senator,
but at that time was engaged in the noble duties of the busi-
nessman, appeared on the scene like a god of mythology, in

the midst of that brilliant and sensual existence. For a long
time Culiacán had not tasted beer. Laveaga heard about it
and, bold revolutionary merchant that he was, ran a carload
of it past the Federal troops in Guaymas to Culiacán. The
city received him in triumph and paid the bitter beverage's
weight in gold; and had the natives of Culiacán possessed
the imagination of other ages, a legend and a myth would
have grown out of the rejoicing, which lasted several days.

2 A Night in Culiacán

Much later someone told me, talking about General Juan
Carrasco, an amusing remark of his that endeared him to me.
Once, as he was on his way from Guadalajara to Mexico, one
of his staff officers asked him as the train crossed the bridge
over the Lerma River: "What river is this, General?" And
Carrasco answered, "This, son, is the Rio Grande. They call
it that because it's one of the biggest in the world. I believe
only the Mesesipe is bigger." But the truth of the matter is
that the Sinaloan *guerrillero* already interested me as being
typical of one aspect of the Revolution.

During this time the name of General Carrasco was on everybody's lips. Aside from his military exploits, there was
not a soul in Culiacán who was not talking about the persist-
ent enthusiasm with which he celebrated the Revolution's latest triumphs, especially the capture of the state capital by
our forces. One morning I saw him driving through the main
streets, bearing out perfectly what was said of him. He was
in an open carriage, his gun over his shoulder, and his breast
crossed with cartridge-belts. He was accompanied by several
masculine officers and a notorious feminine one, the famous
"Carrasco's blonde." Behind the carriage, in good Sinaloan
fashion, a band of four or five musicians did their best to
keep pace with the horses, without interrupting their playing.
And the oddest thing about it was that the musicians, in

spite of the double strain on them, seemed less fatigued than
the General and his train. The contrast puzzled me, and I
stopped to get a better look at the spectacle and its actors.

Of these the dominant figure was unquestionably Carrasco; with his tall, shapely body, his small head, his bronzed
face with its angular features, he easily held the center of the
stage. The "blonde," it was quite evident, was doing her best
to play her part and attract attention, but Carrasco put her
in the shade. Without his realizing it, perhaps, and in spite
of his dog-tiredness, the glances of the public were all for
him. Everybody turned round to look at that face, which the
dark line of the greasy chin strap divided in two, shaded by
the drooping brim of his hat, which he wore with a jaunty
grace.

"This is the third day," observed a voice at my side, "that
my General Carrasco has spent this way."

"Three?" I asked, turning round, eager to learn more.

"Three days and three nights," was the answer. "And if I
am making a mistake, it's on the side of less, not more. You
see how the general looks now? Well, there's still five or six
days ahead of him. But when you want to see him is at night."

"Why at night?"

"Because then the soldiers join him."

That very night, a little after ten, I decided to see for myself what my unknown informer had praised so highly. I left
Alessio Robles preparing the speech he was to deliver the
next day at Garmendia's grave, and started out to see the
celebration of Carrasco and his men.

At that hour it was very rare then to see anybody on the
streets in Culiacán. Only around the market place did one
see a few inveterate nighthawks out for the classic dish of
chicken, to be eaten by the smoky light of candles and lanterns. Culiacán was the deserted town of the days following
the siege, houses abandoned, stores twice sacked, by the Federals in flight and by us, when we entered, also spurred on
by the urgent needs of the moment. And the desolation,
which was frightful during the day, but partly hidden under

the cloak of the rich and exuberant natural scenery, even in
midwinter, seemed at night to rise out of the very shadows,
invisible, yet real; impalpable and yet oppressive. After walking several blocks at night, one lost all the agreeable impressions received during the day, and it seemed as though one
were wandering through the inside of a body whose soul had
been torn away. As though it came from the depths of the
dead being, one could hear the beating of one's own heart,
which seemed the only guide, the only contact with the world
of the living.

In the midst of the most complete silence in the open
country or in the mountains, one can always hear or feel at
night the palpitation of life. In a city in ruins the shadows
seem the next thing to the flickering-out of the last breath
into nothingness. Even the occasional flashes of life are
brusquely stripped of their reality, and lose their content.
The half-starved dog that rushes by passes like the specter of
a dog; the distant voice reaches our ear with its human quality transmuted into an echo. The figure that moves through
the lighted space under the remote street lamp is the ghost
of a body, partaking of the insubstantiality of a flat surface,
without a third dimension.

I wandered about the dark and solitary streets for over an
hour. The farther I walked from the center of the town, the
darker became the shadows and the more opaque the silence.
Finally I got lost and had to feel my way along. Then a momentary faraway flash of light gave me my bearings and I
started toward home, trusting to my sense of direction. My
long walk began to seem foolish and futile. Most probably
the celebration of Carrasco and his troops was the invention
of my unknown informant of the morning.

Just as I was thinking this, I perceived, through the veil of
darkness, a faint sound of voices. It came from the direction
in which I was going. I kept on. A few steps more and I heard
several pistol shots, which rose above the sound of the voices,
nearer now, but still confused, a sort of buzzing. I stopped.
It was impossible to make out a thing. I could feel the dark-

ness against my face. To judge from their muffled sound, the shots had been fired in a house. They had followed one another in rapid and uniform succession. "From the same pistol," I said to myself, "and fired by the same hand." I waited quietly.

The sound of the voices kept on. In a minute another series of shots, rapid and regular like the first, rose again above the other noises. These shots were of a different caliber. The voices, like a rising tide, grew louder and formed themselves into a sharp, guffawing cry, which, after several short, rapid, guttural notes, spread into a strangled "Ay," and wound up with a hoarse, obscene exclamation. Then I understood: it was Carrasco and his followers. And I listened with that concentration with which one listens in the dark.

The cry localized for my ears, if not for my eyes, the point from which the shots had come. The house was on the same side of the street as that on which I was walking, about two or three hundred feet ahead. I hesitated as to what I should do. Should I go ahead? Should I turn back? I finally decided to cross over to the other sidewalk, and as I did so, I discovered that the street turned into a mud puddle, or, to be more exact, a river of slime, into which I sank above my ankles. I managed to go ahead little by little, almost dizzy with the darkness, until I touched the wall on the opposite side. There seemed to be no sidewalk on this side. The blackness of the sea of mud melted into the barely discernible grayness of the walls of the houses. It seemed absurd to keep on walking under these conditions, but, as one could see nothing, it was impossible to look for a better path. So I went ahead.

As I came nearer the place where I had heard the shots and the scream, the voices, no less confused and blurred, grew louder. "There must be a lot of them," I was thinking when I stumbled against what seemed to be the legs of somebody leaning against the wall, and I fell forward in the mud. But as I threw out my arms in falling, my hands, as by a miracle, caught hold of the clothing of another body, and I hung on to it. This other body was standing firm, as I quickly noted, and I clung to its legs while my knees sank deeper into the cool, soft mud. My invisible savior seemed to understand what had happened to me, for I felt a strong hand under my arm, which helped me to my feet and released me for a moment, only to come up around my shoulder, squeezing my neck with unexpected affection. The most disagreeable human odor, mingled with the reek of mescal, accompanied the embrace. With a vigorous jerk I tried to free myself from that body, which was hanging on to mine, but the arm tightened its hold. At that moment a ray of light filtered through the door across the way. Whoever was holding on to me said: "Well, now, if you're not trying to get away from me!"

The light from the door fell slanting across us. I wanted to see who had hold of me, and I looked up. My captor was a ragged soldier. His palm-leaf hat rested halfway down on his nose, and the broad, flopping brim touched the neck of the bottle he held in his other hand, the bottom of which rested in the angle formed by the two cartridge belts crossing his dirty shirt. The narrow parallelogram of light that the half-open door poured out on the street revealed many more such hats. It was impossible to guess at the number. It might as easily have been two hundred as four hundred or a thousand. And at the same time I saw this, I saw several men come out through the lighted doorway, among them one tall, unmistakable silhouette: Carrasco. The door closed.

The darkness blinded me now more than before, but, thanks to the awakening of some new sense, I became more aware of the multitude. Within its limits, which I could not see, but divined, there existed the soul of a collective unity. The mass began to move like one body, swaying, weaving about, stumbling, all in the heart of a thick, dull noise. For the same low, vague murmur of the voices kept on as before. Whatever collisions took place while moving were deadened by the mattress of mud. It was evident that the mass was guided now by a single will. A sort of current seemed to flow from body to body. First it reached out like a wave toward the part where I and the brute who held me more and more tightly were standing. Then the wave ebbed. Next I felt that a slow forward movement had begun; it was so slight that it seemed more the intention of moving than a movement.

As we moved along, I noticed that little by little, behind and beside the group my captor and I formed, emerged other groups, which rubbed and pushed against us. There were couples like us, or groups of three or four or six men, their arms around each other. Desperately I tried to get loose again, but my partner, with a rapidity and strength far beyond mine, held me tight around the neck. It was impossible for me to struggle, for he was at the stage of inebriety in which the muscles are of an invincible agility, and, besides, he was tall and strong. My efforts made him laugh, a low, self-satisfied little laugh, but without the least hint of malice in it. Apparently I amused him. Little by little he raised to my face, in proof of his friendly intentions, no doubt, the hand in which he held the bottle. I felt the cold, sticky mouth of the bottle against my lips, and for several seconds the mescal trickled down my chest. Then he raised the bottle to his own mouth and drank down great gulps of the liquor.

The human mass of which we formed a part was moving toward the end of the street. Several tall silhouettes as of men on horseback formed the pivot round which the rest of us milled. The tallest of these must have been Carrasco. Every now and then there floated down from them shouts that had a tone of command, but to me they sounded confused and inarticulate. One of the queerest things was that in the midst of that sea of human beings I had not been able to make out a single intelligible word except those first ones my captor spoke. The only sound made by that whole mass was nothing but whispers, murmurs: the murmur of snatches of songs, the whisper of words. Once in a while a strident cry would rise above the rest; then the buzzing of the hive would resume its sinister dominance. Sometimes, too, a rapid series of pistol shots would envelop us in a reddish intermittent glow, which died away with the last report. Both the shouts and the shots seemed like a sort of climax to vague desires, and they were heard when the formless murmurs, with a harmony of their own, achieved, in their mumbling, a vague resemblance to song.

Strange intoxication of the mass, as sad and noiseless as the shadows which folded it around! Herd drunkenness, like that of ants, happy in their reek and contact. It was the bestiality of the mescal filling the most rudimentary need of self-liberation. Floundering about in the mud, lost in the shades of night and conscience, all those men seemed to have renounced their quality of human beings on coming together. They seemed the soul of a huge reptile with hundreds of heads, thousands of feet, which crawled, drunk and sluggish, along the walls of a cavernous, dark street in a deserted city.

As my companion and I turned a corner, I managed to get away from him. How long was I held in that nauseating embrace—one hour, two, three? When I jerked myself free, I seemed to rid myself of a greater oppression, both physical and moral, than if all the blackness of the night, converted into some horrid monster, had been resting on my shoulders.

3   THE PIETY OF GENERAL ITURBE

General Iturbe, who was in command of the revolutionary forces in Sinaloa, used to invite us to accompany him when he drove out in his surrey. Culiacán lay before us (or, at least, so it seemed, to judge from the happy, satisfied air with which Iturbe surveyed it) like the crowning reward of an arduous effort. Of course, the final triumph of the Revolution was far off—the struggle had barely begun—but at the same time some secret sentiment or presentiment gave us the sensation, driving through the recently conquered city as we did, that we were somehow enjoying to the full and setting the seal of victory on one stage of the contest.

The comfortable vehicle, drawn by an excellent pair, rolled smoothly over the soft dirt of the main streets. After we had exhausted the heart of the city, we went bumping along—bumps which the excellent springs of our conveyance turned into swinging—over the mud and the puddles of the outlying sections. In this way we visited the most out-of-the-way places and took in even the most insignificant details of everything we saw. The city was small for the pace at which we drove and we had to go back and forth through the same streets to make our amusement hold out.

Iturbe, either from a habit of his own or following the custom of Sinaloa, never gave the driver any general instructions when we started out. As we went along, he would instruct him as to the road he should take. Every minute he would say: "Right," "Left," "Back," "Over the bridge," "Towards the chapel." And if he was in the midst of a conversation, he would interrupt himself to give the driver his order and then go right on with what he had been saying. It was a rare ability, which impressed me as a valuable exercise to train the attention to follow two different trains of simultaneous thought with equal efficiency. At first it just amused me; then, little by little, I began to try it myself, taking an active part in the conversation and at the same time analyzing the logic behind Iturbe's itinerary.

The monotony of these drives was made agreeable more than by anything else by a sort of effervescence, as of champagne, in the air, which induced us to see everything with intelligent and understanding eyes. There were, however, two exceptions which seemed to me of great interest in themselves: one, the crossing of the bridge over the Tamazula River; and the other, the invariable halt at the foot of the hill on whose crest gleamed the whitewashed walls of a little chapel.

The long bridge over the shallow blue waters of the river seemed to possess the hidden power to open horizons to the contemplative soul. It was rough, ugly, with nothing artistic to it, but there was always something new and fresh about it, or at least about the landscape around it. It took longer to get there than to feel that one had been translated to a different sphere, a kind of nook meant for the spirit, a temple. Slowly our carriage rolled along between the two red iron arcades whose sinuous parallel lines advanced, as in a series of leaps, from one side to the other. We generally drove over it at nightfall, just at the hour in which the individual character- istics of the different things, so soon to be swallowed up in the shadows, become more accentuated. The hoofbeats of the horses struck a sonorous resonance from the wooden floor which rested on the metal ties of the arches, and the hollow reverberations of the boards awakened answering metallic harmonies, which blended into a rare music. That music made me lift up my eyes to the hills, toward the horizon, and gave me a sense of contact between the immediate and the remote. I could see the sun turning ruddy; the bridge, like a pivot between earth and sky—a sky whose steely bril- liance was turning to red—seemed to divide the universe into two contrasting perspectives. Below, on the earth, these two perspectives were so small and modest that their existence seemed reduced to a mere aspiration, a humble acceptance of those above. On the one hand, the dwellings of the city grouped about the white towers of its largest church—low, poor, discouraged little houses—and on the other, the out- posts of the invading countryside, with its luxuriant, almost rank vegetation, overgrown with underbrush, with advancing canebrakes, and here and there a thick, sturdy tree.

The interest provoked in us by the hill that the chapel topped was of a very different order. Here I could not but meditate on the spiritual connotation of the Revolution. Us- ing my daily contact with the men with whom I was asso- ciated as a basis for my judgments, I tried to forecast what consequences this struggle in which we were threshing about would have for the soul of the Mexican people. And this be- cause what I used to see at the foot of the hill, in the light of the spirit that dominated in most of the partisans of the Revolution, might be considered exceptional, almost unique. We used to get out of the carriage in the midst of piles of masons' materials, stones, bricks, sand, mortar. Iturbe would go over to talk with the foreman; he would inspect what had been done during the day and find out what were his plans for the next day. When he came back to us, he would explain in detail how the work was coming along. The first time we went there he began in this fashion:

"One day—a long while back—when I was still hiding in the mountains, I promised, as soon as I took Culiacán, to build a stairway from the foot of the hill to the door of the chapel. And now, as you see, I am keeping my promise."

As he said this, Iturbe had his eyes fixed on the little shrine on the hilltop, not on us, and he pronounced the last words with a somewhat forced firmness, as though by his tone he wished to make the point, on which he admitted no argument, clear. But he faltered a little over the words, and in spite of his efforts, he could not entirely hide his uneasiness. Reading between the lines, it was evident that Iturbe was afraid of being misunderstood or misjudged on account of his piety. But though this fear affected his words, it did not affect his acts. Iturbe might blush at the thought of his comrades in arms or in political ideals seeing him build a stairway in obedience to a religious impulse, as a simple act of faith in a divine power; but, despite his embarrassment, he built it.

This detail gives an idea of the kind of man General Iturbe was. And, except in the eyes of a few fools, it paints him in a most flattering light. For very few revolutionists of the day dared to confess openly their religious beliefs, even if they had any. The atmosphere and the state of affairs put a premium on the lack of faith. It was, one might almost say, an official duty to deny God. Don Venustiano, who on the one hand dreamed of being like Don Porfirio, at the same time dreamed even more of being like Juárez. This explains his fondness for playing the great patrician in the border cities— a poor mimicry of what was a necessity for Juárez—as well as other more serious imitations, such as the revival of the law of January 25, 1862, in the name of which unspeakable assassinations were committed, despite the fact that Carranza was not a bloodthirsty person. With regard to his religious policy, the First Chief's determination to win himself a certain pedestal in the halls of history set the pace. Those of us who, really or outwardly, followed him flaunted a Jacobinism, a reform spirit of the newest vintage, and all-embracing content. But it was different with Iturbe and a few others. In matters pertaining to the soul he, who was at the time a Catholic and later on became a spiritist, obeyed only his own impulses and refused to be swept along with the rest. He did this in a manner that won him all respect, in this as well as in the military field. In the latter he had completely convinced Obregón that he deserved his rank of general in the Constitutionalist army. Iturbe knew how to command, make his plans, carry them out, and win, as he had proved again and again during the attack on the very city where we were. Nobody could overlook the fact that the capture of Culiacán had been characterized by true military heroism: the serenity of Gustavo Garmendia, the gallant stubbornness of Diéguez, and, standing out over them all, the undeniable leadership, the brave leadership, of Iturbe. After the battle Obregón's praises for the young general of Sinaloa were boundless.

What took place in the civil field was very similar, at least as far as his personal attitude was concerned. In contrast to the mass of servile revolutionists, which was steadily growing larger and more confused, Iturbe, perhaps without realizing it, stood out as an example of independence. His loyalty to his religious faith revealed him as a man who would tolerate no compromise in matters concerning his convictions and his emotions.

I have visited Culiacán in later years, and the streets and the landscape have not always been able to evoke in me the impressions and emotions of the days I spent there as a rebel. But one thing always revived in me, as fresh as the first after-

noon: my feelings at the sight of the construction of the
stairway by which, later on, the faithful should climb to the
shrine of Guadalupe. Before that hill I always felt the same
thrill of profound admiration for the general of the Revolution—although I did not share his beliefs—who possessed
the hardihood of soul to publicly fulfill his religious vow.
Those were other days; the waters of the Revolution's stream
still showed much of their pristine clarity; as yet, ambition,
greed, treachery, and cowardice had not completely muddied
them. Even at the risk of losing with the world, Iturbe fulfilled his vow to God, and to do so employed the official resources that were his to command. His act stands out by
contrast with what happened months later in Chihuahua,
when a Catholic bishop was appointed by military decree of
the Army of the Revolution, amidst applause and shouts of
laughter, and a few weeks after this, in Monterrey, where the
saints' images were ordered to be shot.

4 The Aftermath of Battle

At other times it was not Iturbe, but Diéguez who invited
us to go around the city, although on such occasions we chose,
rather than the city itself, the outlying areas, preferably the
spots which had been the site of recent combat with
Huerta's troops. For these excursions I laid off for a few hours
my civilian revolutionary attire, and somewhat shamefacedly
put on khaki breeches, pigskin puttees, and a stetson hat.

General Diéguez lent our group a jovial tone. All in white,
except for shoes and puttees of black leather, the fashion most
of his officers followed, he came for us, smiling and loqua-
cious. And no sooner had we set out early in the morning
than he began to unwind the reel of his conversation. His
dark skin, tanned still darker by the sun, became a network
of premature wrinkles as the conversation grew more animated, a conversation which was, to a large extent, a monologue; thanks to his personal charm, his words held us en-

thralled, made us forget the monotonous jog trot of our
horses, or pulled us up to observe some detail of the surroundings which he pointed out.

His comments revealed his ingenuousness; his questions,
his good faith. There was an affectionate side to his nature
which made him lean toward his listener as he spoke to him.
Whereupon his interlocutor discovered in the general's face
a new, or complementary, version of what he was saying. The
wrinkled skin around his eyes, like those of a cat, created
polygons of eloquence. A manly mustache vibrated with his
words, allowing a fleeting glimpse of the yellow glitter of his
teeth. There were even those who, as they listened, their
eyes fixed on him, lost the thread of what he was saying in
their bemusement with his physical idiosyncrasies: the ray
of sunlight which fell aslant the cornea of his eye and emerged
enriched with the shades of the iris; the myriad black dots,
as though from a blast of gunpowder, that pinpointed his
frank face which both harmonized and contrasted with his
glistening, tight-buttoned white uniform.

Was there any connection between those black dots and
the attire and smell that were typical of Diéguez? It pleased
me to think so, and whenever I came near him I began,
perhaps for no good reason, to spin the strangest dermato-
logical theories. For General Diéguez always smelled of coffee
—not roasting or ground coffee, but of coffee per se, the
essence of itself, eternal. And this odor could be explained
by his habit of drinking coffee at all hours, at home, in the
office, while campaigning. He always carried with him, on a
strap slung across his right shoulder and hanging over his
left hip, a small, squat, leather-covered canteen with the
amount of coffee extract he would need for the day. From
time to time—often without thinking what he was doing, the
way one reaches into his pocket for a cigarette and lights it—
he would take the canteen in his left hand, unscrew the top,
and take a quick swallow. Then, as he put it back in place,
he would smack his lips several times, as though he had
taken a new lease on life, found himself. He was steeped

in coffee, which was his tobacco, his coca, his vital stimulant, from his forehead to his nails. The color of his favorite drink had given him a strange patina, deeper at the edges and corners of his lips, and concentrated in the pores of his skin, forming an infinitude of black dots over his face.

Diéguez never vaunted his bravery, but all his acts bespoke his calling. He was not boastful or a fake in any way. He was extremely modest about his military attainments, and perhaps for that very reason he savored to the full the soldiering career to which his political ideals had led him. The first time we went out with him, he was determined to visit the places where, a short time before, the clashes in the battle for Culiacán had taken place, and he described the episodes to us with such a wealth of details that it hardly seemed credible that his had been a subaltern, though outstanding, role, but rather that of commander-in-chief and, at the same time, of every officer and private who had participated in the fighting. From the conference of generals and leaders in El Palmito to work out the plan of attack to the dawn entry of Blanco's troops in the city after the night flight of the Federal forces, there was not a detail he ignored or omitted. And his description of the battle was rich in color and specific incident, not the dry language of a military communiqué. His eyes and heart had caught the human as well as the strategic aspects, the episodes that had seemed to him pathetic or comic. But he shed no tears over the pathetic, however much emotion he lent them, emotion which revealed itself in the gleam of his eyes; the others provoked his cordial laughter.

"For there was a little of everything," he said, "in the capture of this town of Culiacán, as there always is in any battle to the observant eye. The funniest thing? Major Alfredo Breceda's panicking during one of the false alarms caused by the movements of the enemy before we began to get the upper hand."

And he narrated the incident. Breceda, eager to see action and cover himself with glory had joined the troops of Sinaloa.

To the single star of major—and which, it was unanimously agreed, was due to merits not precisely those of the battle-field—he hoped to add another, and perhaps even two, indisputably pure and refulgent in origin. How could an aspiration of this sort fail to seem commendable? Major Breceda was well liked, and the encouragement of his comrades and superior officers filled him with pleasure. He was helped, he was singled out. Obregón, himself, undoubtedly to give him every opportunity from the start, took him under his wing; he had him accompany him, as though he were one of his most trusted officers, while he reconnoitered the Federals' positions.

Much of the success of the undertaking would depend, naturally, on the superiority of armament. Breceda was aware of this and, bearing it in mind, he arrived equipped with everything new, of finest quality, polished and ready for action. His foresight was so great that he had not even omitted a camp stove; the one he brought matched the rest of his munitions in beauty and efficiency. It was the latest model, simple to operate, lightning swift, which with equal ease boiled a couple of two- or three-minute eggs, roasted a turkey, or carmelized to a beautiful brown the sugar coating of a custard.

The excellence of his equipment conferred no little renown on Breceda during the days preceding the attack. His rifles and pistols achieved fame even before being fired; his gear excited the curiosity of the whole camp. Especially the stove, that stove which must surely be the source of so many satisfactions, and which brought to mind the maxim that the well-fed, well-looked-after soldier is the victorious soldier, brought compliments, praise, and flattery to its proud owner.

Unfortunately, however, the situation changed when the preparations for attack turned into the real thing, when action relegated to oblivion everything that was not fighting, including the supreme and most enticing of the culinary art. At this point Major Breceda began to lose the sense of what his armament was for; his judgment as to its use became clouded over, despite the perfection of his rifles and pistols. And so it happened that one morning, when the Federals attempted a sortie by way of the railroad tracks, Breceda, his stove on his back as though it were the most precious of his arms, took flight. A magnificent flight, worthy, according to those who witnessed it, of an epic poem. General Diéguez evoked it with his smiling, though not cruel, eloquence, and gave to his telling a kind of melodic cadence, like that of a blind street singer's ballad, interpolating from time to time, like a refrain:

"Major Breceda and his stove didn't stop till they reached Navolato."

And in conclusion he added, as though to excuse his lack of charity:

"Not that the rest of us behaved like heroes. There was neither occasion nor reason for it. That sortie of theirs didn't warrant our moving. Our men fell back a few paces without letting up their fire. But Major Breceda, armed with his stove, didn't stop till he got to Navolato."

When we reached the hills, Diéguez's conversation took on a completely different tone. We went from one end to the other of the bluff which is the prolongation of the Capilla range. We found the remains of the trenches the Federalists had dug. We moved amidst trees whose branches had been lopped off by cannon fire, among slivers of projectiles, bloodstains. And the sight of all this fired General Diéguez's memory like the battle itself. He spoke of his fourth and fifth battalions as of two beings endowed with a soul, as of two chieftains dealing mighty blows. With his extraordinary lucidity he converted us into spectators of the assault on the two fortified outposts, the one captured by the fourth and that which was overpowered by the fifth, and whose resistance held off the attacking forces for over thirty-six hours.

But when he reached this point in his narration, Diéguez always omitted any reference to his own action, brilliant though it had been, to focus attention on that of the others.

He praised the conduct of his subordinates, Major Calderón, Major Ríos, and recalled, in a husky voice, the bravery of Gustavo Garmendia. For it was there, beside one of those improvised brick breastworks, that Garmendia met his death.

"He was advancing as the brave do, at the head of his men, victory in his grasp. He was only a few yards from the outpost; the defenders were plainly weakening. Whereupon, to get it over with as quickly as possible, he led the assault; like the athlete he was, he covered the distance that separated him from the enemy position in a few bounds and reached it alone, or almost alone. . . . A ball hit him in the leg as he was leaping over the parapet. He died on the stretcher we improvised out of a few branches. . . ."

5 A Revolutionary Dance

Obregón's staff officers, who had billeted themselves in the residence of the wealthy Cañedo family, invited us to share their quarters, and this contributed still further to our pleasant existence. The "dream captains" lived—and we, too—like lords, though circumspectly and with perfect order. That beautiful house seemed to us a veritable palace. The magnificent enclosed gallery, large enough for a diplomatic reception and with marble floor and windows that looked out on the garden, was our delight. There were so many bedrooms that it was hard for us to make our choice. In a sumptuously furnished one that seemed to have belonged to two young ladies, Miguel Alessio Robles and I installed ourselves; the "dream captains" made themselves comfortable in several others, and the telegraph operator of GHQ chose his some distance off. We were six in all; we got along extremely well, enjoying complete freedom and the pleasure of being together. Three times a day we gathered around a well-set, well-served table to do justice to excellent meals of the Sinaloan cuisine, and on these occasions we prolonged our state of well-being, conversation, and zest stimulated by the bright light from the garden and the sight of the plants and flowers.

Why did we call Obregón's officers the "dream captains"? Because they were three? Because they were young? Because, like all the young revolutionists during that early phase, they were imbued with pure, disinterested ideals? The name was a bit silly, to be sure; but, anyway, that was what we called them. They were always the "dream captains" to me and, above all, to Miguel Alessio, who often took the word "dream" as an excuse to recite long paragraphs from his favorite orators.

Of the three, it was Aarón Sáenz who managed the house and, so to speak, did the honors. But this in no wise diminished the standing of the other two, Lorenzo Muñoz and Carlos Robinson. The three captains were linked in bonds of friendship; the three, thanks to their individual and collective behavior, communicated to the house the rare placidity of an oasis in the Revolution. As a result of their harmonious understanding, everything moved as smoothly as our feet over the polished marble of the gallery, and if there was ever any friction between them, it never ruffled the surface. By dint of great effort one might possibly have divined, through some almost imperceptible clue, that it was Aarón Sáenz who was Obregón's favorite. He showed his absolute confidence in him by leaving Sáenz in charge of General Headquarters of the Army of the Northwest when he returned to Sonora shortly after the capture of Culiacán.

Culiacán at the time might be said to have been existing in a vacuum. The city was practically deserted; many of its families and, with rare exceptions, the most select of every class had fled toward Mazatlán with the Federals. The pretty faces for which Sinaloa is justly famous were conspicuous by their absence. Nevertheless and notwithstanding, the "dream captains" carried on their search so undauntedly that, a few weeks after the army's entry, those who did not already have a beautiful girl friend were on the point of achieving their objective. Aarón Sáenz made his rounds in a buggy with a fairly decent horse. Had he hired it? Had he found it, too, at the Cañedos' place? One afternoon when I went out with him we aroused no slight hilarity. As his eyes were glued to the window on which his hopes were fixed, and mine on him, the horse was left to its own devices, and we almost ran head-on into the house across the way. As for Muñoz and Robinson, they probably employed less hazardous but equally effective methods.

Once the girl friends had been acquired, or the prospects seemed promising, what could have been more natural than for our captains to have wanted to give a Christmas Eve dance for the society of Culiacán, or, to be more exact, the shreds of society that had stayed on? There were, however, serious obstacles to be overcome. In the first place, Aarón did not know a single dance step; in the second, Culiacán society wanted no part of us, the revolutionists. To be sure, the first of these stumbling blocks was not invincible. Christmas was still three days off, and in that time Aarón could learn. At any rate, that was what I assured him—I who neither before, then, nor after have known how to dance. But the other, overcoming the distaste which the "decent" people of Culiacán felt for the revolutionists, was a harder nut to crack. There were plenty of stories going the rounds that did not make our problem easier: Miss So-and-So had disappeared when the army left; something or other had happened to the Misses So-and-So. In a word, the best thing was to have absolutely nothing to do with the revolutionists, not even speak to them.

There were those who would have immediately lost heart, but not we. The uprightness of our intentions—Alessio's and mine because our only stake in the matter was our affection for our friends, and theirs, which were strictly honorable—made us resentful of the resistance we encountered, and we developed a cynical boldness. We decided to bypass all the intermediaries whom we had at first planned to use and handle the matter ourselves, and for this we found a good excuse. There was a political angle to the affair which came in very handy. Wasn't it a question of a party organized by the officers of General Obregón's staff which the leading families of a city recently captured from the enemy forces refused to attend? In this case it was a matter that needed to be brought out into the open, and this was a duty incumbent on us, the revolutionists. On the other hand, the effrontery with which we planned to go about it was mitigated to a degree by the fact that we were strangers. As we had no official acquaintance with anybody, there was no reason why we should not present ourselves at any house in that very character: strangers who had nobody to introduce them.

So the five of us—Alessio, the captains, and I (the telegraph operator refused to get involved)—went about calling at the homes of the girls we wanted to ask to the dance. Robinson, the biggest of us all—a pleasant giant but who brooked no nonsense—was the first to speak. We had decided on this *modus operandi*, for it was a question not merely of persuading, but of intimidating a little, all with great politeness and restraint. Robinson was backed up by Alessio, who was also formidable in stature, and the other three of us seconded them, if not in bodily size, with whatever our wits suggested.

In each house the skirmish followed the same pattern. Robinson, in a voice perhaps a shade too mellifluous under the circumstances, but with a steely undertone, fired this opening salvo point-blank at the mamas and papas:

"The officers of General Obregón's staff are arranging a little dance on Christmas Eve in honor of the society of Culiacán. . . ."

The battle was then joined with exquisite tact and strategy on both sides. They and we outdid each other in that circuitous phraseology typical of our country, which makes it possible for Mexicans, no matter what region they come from, to thread the complicated labyrinths of human relations without conflict—unless they are looking for trouble. Not once did either of the adversaries come out with a flat "yes" or "no"; the whole gamut of verbal nuances was run, all the while leaving the door open for a word here, a word there, and these, in turn, open to infinite interpretations. Finally, after many smiles and with great courtesy, the situation was made clear: they accepted our invitation—"Who could have thought otherwise?"—but the surrender was not unconditional. None of the officers of Iturbe's, Carrasco's, or Diéguez's troops was to attend the dance, nor anybody for whose proper behavior we could not vouch. What it boiled down to was that only the five of us were acceptable. "Yes, that would be best, for you alone to represent the Revolution at the dance. . . ." In a word, they did not tell us to our faces that they would prefer never to see us again, for verbal subtlety, even among Mexicans, has its limits.

Each interview left us exhausted. But it didn't matter. We were prepared for the worst, and we reorganized our forces and launched a new attack. We fought sixteen pitched battles. And the strangest thing about the whole business was the unanimity of thought and word on the part of all those pernickety families. All of them made us feel that they would prefer to have nothing to do with us, but at the same time they all accepted our invitation "in principle," provided we were the only male revolutionists who were to have the pleasure of the company we were seeking. This tacit agreement finally began to amuse us, and toward the end of our poll we took a kind of masochistic delight in the rebuffs we encountered.

After casting up accounts of what had been said and what had been implied, we reached our final decision without much difficulty. Those people needed a polite reprimand? We would give it to them. We wanted to hold the dance? The dance would be held.

The captains threw themselves heart and soul into the preparations for the festivity, and Aarón not only into the preparations, but also into the effort of learning to dance. This put me on the spot, not through any fault of Sáenz's, but because my qualifications for teaching the terpsichorean

art had the flimsiest kind of basis: that of often having seen
Carlos Domínguez—a real "hoofer"—do his stuff at the dances
Don Venustiano improvised in every town where the girls
seemed to warrant it. Nevertheless I went through with it,
or, to be more exact, we went through with it, for I cannot
say whether I really taught Aarón Sáenz to dance, or whether
he learned by himself on the basis of what I taught him. In
any case, it represented the triumph of mind over matter.
The music—that of the only roll we found in the Cañedos'
pianola—was played over and over again. Its measures which,
fortunately, could be danced to, had a horrible sameness.
Thanks only to the firm hand and feet of Robinson, who
acted as Sáenz's partner, did they adapt themselves in some
degree to the specific contents of the lessons. Looking back
on it, I don't think it came off too well, for the music was a
tango, and what Sáenz was interested in learning was the
waltz and the one-step.

In spite of their reluctance, our guests did their duty. At
nine o'clock on the eve of the twenty-fifth they all appeared,
almost in a group, at the Cañedos' house. Eighteen girls,
among the fairest of the Pacific coast, entered our huge,
marble-floored drawing room accompanied by their fathers,
their mothers, their uncles, their aunts, but by no young
men. To have brought the latter might have had political
repercussions; it would not have been easy to explain their
presence there. Whereas that of the older men was in the
nature of a precautionary measure, just in case of unforeseen
developments.

But those timid conservative families of Culiacán had no
cause for alarm. Aside from the telegraph operator, who did
not look too trustworthy (though in fact he was) because of
his strange getup for the dance—black coat, white flannel
pants, and white sport shoes with black patent-leather trim
—our guests encountered no strange faces when they came in.
And if this was not enough, in a short time we had dispelled
any lingering fears they might have had. We honored the

terms they had laid down to the letter. When the late-comers had all arrived, we ordered the hall door closed, and Robinson, in the name of all of us, informed the papas and the mamas that we had complied with their wishes: nobody would be at the dance except themselves and us—aside from the musicians, of course. Nobody would see them there, for the shutters had been closed; and nobody would molest them, for we had taken every precaution.

This orthodox procedure on our part at first disconcerted them, but as they became convinced of our sincerity, they cast aside their misgivings and hauled down their flag. Moreover, in the dining room, which was visible from the ballroom, a table could be seen, so richly decked that it allayed every feeling that was not one of cheer. The crystal of the goblets shimmered under the candelabra, flowers embroidered the exquisite tablecloth, and in the background, the "dream captains'" orderlies and the housemaids were putting on the last finishing touches.

From that moment the celebration surpassed our fondest dreams. Long before dinner time Aarón had tried out again and again the strange waltz of which I was the choreographer —I suspect that he had already discarded my share in it— and Miguel Alessio, Muñoz, Robinson and the telegraph operator, in spite of his summer-resort getup, were having themselves a ball. At about three in the morning a slight mishap occurred: a fuse blew out and left us in the dark. As we were not prepared for emergencies of this sort, our guests were on the verge of panic. By the light of the matches struck by the fathers, the girls could be seen huddled close to their families, while we struggled desperately to get the lights working again. Those were tense moments during which we felt that the honor of the Revolution was at stake. Fortunately, with the help of two United States pennies I found in my pocket, and at the risk of setting fire to the house, we got our lamps to working again.

My gifts as an electrician won me a standing ovation.

6 MURDER IN THE DARK

General Iturbe offered me, through Colonel Eduardo Hay, a military post in his brigade which held out not a few attractions. I was to be lieutenant-colonel and assistant chief of staff, and I should have no immediate superior except Colonel Hay himself. Nevertheless, I did not accept the offer, in spite of my friendship with Hay and the admiration and affection I was beginning to feel for Iturbe. The motives for my refusal were simple enough: I could not bring myself to trade my precious independence of word and action for the stiff discipline of the soldier, and one of the reasons for not doing so was that I saw no reason for making such a sacrifice. I had no political or military ambitions; and, besides, the principal leaders of the Revolution were far from being, in my opinion, unselfish and idealistic enough for me to want to bind myself to them, even indirectly, with chains that are always dangerous and not always easy to break.

"Anyway," I told Hay, "I think the Revolution has too many officers. Why aren't civil matters given more attention? But I do want you to understand and make it clear to General Iturbe that there is nothing personal in my refusal. On the contrary, on account of you people, I'm sorry not to accept the offer. After Iturbe's brilliant action in the capture of Culiacán, I should consider it an honor to serve under him."

General Iturbe accepted my excuses graciously and did not insist on my becoming a soldier. But at the same time it seemed that he did not want to relinquish the idea of winning me over in some way, and he suggested that, without giving up my civilian status, I should help him in the enormous tasks he had laid out for himself. This new offer seemed splendid to me, and I accepted it without a moment's hesitation, with positive enthusiasm.

Hay and I understood each other with few words and we decided to get busy at once. But the task was an overwhelming one. Where should we begin? In the Quartermaster's Department? In the Military Hospital? In the Paymaster's Division? The reorganizing of the hospital seemed the most urgent thing, so we decided to begin with that; though in those first days such an extraordinary incident took place that it distracted our minds from our work considerably. Some of the details of the strange affair are not quite clear in my memory any more, but I can still recall enough, drawing on the legend that sprang up about it overnight, to outline its main features.

One morning they brought into the Military Hospital of Culiacán a man who was dying, with three bullet wounds in his body. He had been found in the street at daybreak, close to a corner, face down on the sidewalk and unconscious. When they went to pick him up, his hands and face were stuck to the sidewalk with dried blood. The first investigations threw no light on the affair, or so little that it remained practically in the dark. The people who lived near the spot where the wounded man was found said that about midnight they had heard revolver shots closer than usual, and that the next day they had heard that a man had been found in the street shot almost to death. That was all.

Colonel Hay and I made all sorts of conjectures about the matter. As Iturbe's chief of staff he was determined to have perfect order in Culiacán, and he went to the most painstaking lengths to clear up the mystery. But it only grew deeper. For the next morning, in a different part of the city, and near a corner, too, a similar find to that of the preceding day was made. Only this time it was not a dying but a dead man. The result of new investigations: shots late at night, followed by silence and at daybreak the body lying in a pool of blood. It was impossible to advance a theory of murder as the result of a quarrel or hold-up in connection with either of the victims. The first, who died in the Military Hospital a few hours after he was brought in, without regaining consciousness, and the dead man found the next day were both of poorest appearance, with nothing on them except the clothes they were wearing; there was no indication that they were in the habit of carrying weapons, nor did they seem the sort to be mixed up in adventures or brawls. And this was borne out by the testimony of their relatives and their general reputation.

But, strange as all this already was, it wasn't the end. More was to occur that would make the mystery still more puzzling. On the morning of the third day as it was getting light, in a different part of the city and close to a corner, another man was found shot to death, and the circumstances were as mystifying as those of the preceding days.

Our surprise turned to bewilderment in the face of this new crime. Iturbe, who was as a rule cool and self-possessed, flew into a rage; Hay redoubled his police efforts, and Culiacán enjoyed the weird sensation of feeling itself in the power of some unknown fiend, who revealed himself only in the darkness, under cover of which he killed his chosen victim, and who selected a man for every night.

The third crime added a slight detail to the few we had discovered in connection with the first two. One of the persons we questioned said he thought he had heard, several seconds before the shots were fired, a buggy pass by very quickly, but he did not hear it clearly enough, for the street was unpaved, to know exactly what kind of vehicle it was.

"This is a diabolical piece of work," said Hay. "Fifteen or twenty people may have to die in the same way before we can get to the bottom of this infernal plot, in which heaven knows what scoundrels are amusing themselves."

But, fortunately, he was wrong. Not fifteen or twenty victims were needed; two more were enough. For the next night, in view of what might happen, Hay planned certain measures that could not fail to bear fruit of some sort. Patrol squads were stationed in the different sections of the city with orders to rush immediately to the spots where they heard shots.

The patrols worked for a long time without any results. The reports that were heard from time to time were like most of those that continually broke the silence of the night in the revolutionary cities, meaningless and distant explosions, fantastic, unreal, like the far-off baying of a dog; dull explosions followed by a faint, dry, cracking noise as though the bullets had gone through a door or perforated a ceiling. But after a number of profitless chases the most diligent of the squads discovered, close to the corner, a man who had just been shot in the chest and in the abdomen and who was dying. Between the gasps of his death agony he pronounced a few intelligible phrases about the terrible wounds he had received. It seemed, he told the leader of the patrol, that two men, or perhaps just one, had fired on him without a word of warning from a buggy that drove by at a furious pace.

The mention of the buggy together with what we knew about the crime on the preceding night gave us a definite clue. The night before a vehicle had been heard to go by. Today a buggy was mentioned. So it became clear that the author—or authors—of these four consecutive homicides had committed the crimes from one of those low two-wheeled buggies in great vogue in Culiacán, which were popularly nicknamed "spiders."

That night nothing further could be discovered. Nor could Hay's efforts at investigation the next day bring out anything new, in spite of the fact that all livery-stable proprietors, and many private owners of vehicles of this type were questioned. But our lack of success did not discourage us. We were more determined than ever to solve the mystery, and as we were sure that the nocturnal crime would repeat itself, like a natural phenomenon, General Iturbe urged that no effort be spared, and Colonel Hay laid his secret plans to capture the guilty party or parties.

Even Hay's best friends complained of his passion for detail; he was one for whom the trees hid the forest. But on this occasion he proved the value of his obsession, at least for certain things. By working from detail to detail Hay had managed to build up a series of deductions about the movements of the "death spider" that enabled him to predict with remarkable accuracy in what part of the city the next shooting would take place. But this knowledge alone was not enough, for the problem consisted not only in preventing crimes like those that had already been committed, but in catching the criminal, or criminals. And for this the most important thing was not to frighten off the prey. In other words, the plan had to be laid without any fuss, if possible laying a false scent so as to cover up the real preparations.

Hay did it that way. He ostensibly gave orders to station soldiers in two or three places far from the spot he had secretly fixed on. And there, hidden in the shadows and unbeknown to all, he hid his best men close to certain corners. And to avoid any slip Hay took charge of operations himself. This zealousness was not without its dangers; rather, it attracted them. For in his role of director of these nocturnal maneuvers he was obliged repeatedly to pass the spots he had selected as the probable scene of the new crime, and each time he did so, he became a possible target for the unknown assassin.

Everything was carried out as had been planned and ordered. Until a little after ten, occasional "spiders" drove through the streets where Hay and his men were hidden. These were peaceful, inoffensive vehicles taking home some belated traveler or the drivers themselves, worn out at the end of the day. But from that time on, no "spider" was seen, or, to be more exact, glimpsed or heard in the darkness of the night. The silence of the streets was interrupted only two or three times by the hollow step of pedestrians, who scurried along hugging the houses for protection and hurried as fast as they could or broke into a frank run as they turned the corners.

In this fashion it struck eleven, twelve, and nothing happened until well on toward one, when suddenly the empty silence of the night, faintly underscored by the ever-present distant pistol shots, was broken by the sound of a "spider" drawn by a horse galloping at full speed. Ten minutes later a similar sound was heard two or three streets farther away and in a few minutes in a cross street not far off. The horse hitched to the "spider" wore no bells or anything that particularly distinguished it, but from the heavy broken gallop it was soon plain that it was the same buggy driving through the different streets.

Suddenly, after a new gallop, the noise of the buggy stopped. The "spider" seemed to have pulled up short, though it was not easy to say exactly where, for the only two street lamps burning in all that section barely lighted the houses on two corners far from each other. Aside from these two spots the darkness was dense and impenetrable.

Several minutes went by like this. But at the very moment in which a human figure could be seen in the distance rapidly crossing one of the illuminated spaces, the "spider" was heard again. It seemed to have started off suddenly, and in a few seconds its low, yellow shape was seen crossing rapidly under the light of the same lamp that had just revealed the pedestrian. Immediately afterward three shots rang out; a scream pierced the night, and the "spider," which had slowed up, galloped off again like mad.

It could not go far in the direction it had chosen, however, for in the cross street through which it had to pass, the flash of four rifle shots revealed a roadblock of soldiers. The "spider" turned round quickly to avoid the soldiers who were coming toward it. It reached the corner lighted by the street lamp and tried to escape down the street that ran perpendicular to the first. But in a moment this street, too, glowed with the discharge of rifles, which revealed another picket of soldiers. The "spider" whirled round and galloped off in the opposite direction. This time it reached the corner at the same time as the first detachment of soldiers that had cut off its escape. There was a point-blank encounter. Two shots were fired from the "spider." One soldier fell wounded, and another was trampled by the horse, and the "spider" managed to escape again, though not so tempestuously as before. But another squad came running to meet it from the end of the street, firing as it came. Above the noise a voice rang out: "Aim at the horse!"

It was Hay. More shots were fired. Finally the buggy stopped, and from all quarters the soldiers ran forward to surround it.

"I surrender," came a voice from inside the buggy.

And when the soldiers were near, they saw a man sitting with a smoking pistol still in one hand, and the lines in the other, who offered them no resistance.

The prisoner was brought up to the light—where the body of his latest victim still lay—and some of the soldiers recognized him immediately. He was an officer who was notorious for his bad conduct and disreputable escapades, though nobody suspected that these included the horrible sport of shooting down, out of some unfathomable impulse, defenseless and harmless people by night.

7 The Military Hospital

The Military Hospital of Culiacán was at that time in a lamentable state. If an expert in the field had been consulted on how to convert it into a satisfactory institution, he would have turned the job down as impossible, or, if he had taken it on, would have asked for funds in an amount unknown in the orbit of the Constitutionalist cause.

But not being experts, Eduardo Hay and I undertook the task with the nonchalance typical of fools who rush in where angels fear to tread. An iron will guaranteed the successful outcome of our labors—or so we thought. Sustained by a faith in the inexhaustible possibilities of the spirit, we gave our enthusiasm free rein.

This attitude of ours was completely Mexican, in its good and its bad aspects. For the Mexican, like a nation conscious of its physical limitations in the face of nature or the power of other nations, compensates for his weakness by boundless faith in the power of the spirit versus brute force. If this is bad from one point of view, it is good from another. It is bad in the sense that it leads to failure and dooms from the start every constructive effort for lack of solid, secure foundations. What could be more typical of us than our conviction that everything, at a given moment, may suddenly be conjured up out of thin air? And it is good in the sense that it prepares the soul for those rare occasions—rare and decisive—when the odds on the side of physical force may be outweighed by a greater spiritual contribution on the part of the materially weaker side. We Mexicans believe, for example, that a row of heroic breasts can bar the way of a battery of 42-millimeter cannon. Who would deny that we are mistaken? But, nevertheless, the fact remains that in the long run our belief is the only thing that saves us.

Supported, then, by this faith, Hay and I prepared to work wonders, and launched ourselves on the enterprise; he with a certain aloofness, in spite of his vehement nature—the indifference of a casualty of other wars, of one who liked to show his familiarity with field hospitals, of a man who was a veteran and wanted everybody to know it—and I with unwonted enthusiasm, the nervous enthusiasm which feeds on the stimulus of the new.

For it was in the Military Hospital of Culiacán that I first came into contact with the imagination of bullets. Up to then I had believed, perhaps as the result of remote childish ideas and certain sad personal experiences, that firearm missiles were endowed with a certain sensibility, with a certain awareness, which, thanks to some mysterious power, always kept them geared to their exclusively death-dealing mission. A man fired a rifle, pistol, machine gun, and the bullet, obedient to the human frenzy for killing, sped toward its target, sometimes hitting it, sometimes missing it, but always with serious, sinister intent. In the Military Hospital of Culiacán I discovered that this was not the case. There were undoubtedly serious, conscientious bullets, those which kill instantly or wound with simple cruelty; but alongside these there were the imaginative, erratic bullets, those which when released yielded to the universal urge to play, and playfully achieved their design.

I looked at the double row of beds, the beds that filled the wards of the wounded, and rarely was there a bed (or pallet, or chair) that did not reveal the opus magnum of some fiendish pastime. The most gruesome wounds, the worst destruction of the flesh or shattering of the bones impressed me less by their horrors than by the thought of the destructive playfulness that had occasioned them. The same was true of many wounds which at first glance seemed slight. It was no lethal wind that had passed over those bodies, whose existence now centered about their throbbing pain, even though the wounds might later cause death; but a playful, sportive breeze, whose sport consisted in rending flesh and shedding blood, a game of which bullets, like men, are so fond.

Each individual casualty bore witness to the existence of a special category of bullet, to the personality of each projectile at the moment it dealt its blow. But in their totality the wounded afforded a panoramic view, as in a museum, of the special nuances of these categories, these personalities. The bullets which gouged out an eye—as in the case of Major Esteban B. Calderón—and then proceeded on their merry way without further damage were clearly frolicsome projectiles, whose pleasure consisted in exercising their tremendous capacity for evil without exhausting it, thus leaving their victim with the echo of their peal of laughter ringing in his ears for the rest of his life. The bullets which first tore tufts of hair from the scalp and then replaced the hair in a furrow they plowed down the back displayed an exaggerated virtuosity. Those which grazed the tip of a finger or nicked a nail and then proceeded to shatter a collarbone or an elbow took pride in refining to the point of subtlety their destructive potential and later turning it into an atom-smashing blast. The bullets which neatly sheared off the lobe of an ear and then buried the lobe in the nape of the neck and, to round off their work, incrusted the skin of the neck in the heel, were poltergeist balls, bullets which amused themselves

by moving everything they encountered from its place, and
which, the better to achieve their objective, described unbelievable trajectories between totally unrelated points. The
bullets which entered the forehead, but instead of perforating
the skull slipped between bone and skin and came out
through the top of the head revealed a merry dynamism eager
to try out all possible variations.

Interspersed with these bullets, whose art varied from the
simple ballad style to the florid and coloratura, were those
which drew upon their imagination for the purpose of muti-
lating or inflicting pain. These latter concentrated less on
precision or elegance of style than on the extent of the damage wrought. These were the ones which destroyed nose or
jaw; which multiplied at random the orifices of the body;
which perforated the abdomen to bring on peritonitis; which
left in the brain the unending rush of a waterfall or an unbearable brilliance, as if one were looking into the sun; those
which set up for the rest of their victims' lifetime areas of
cold, of numbness, of pain, or weakness in the most vitally
necessary organs. A soldier who would never be able to sit
down again. Another who, in order to eat, had to complete
the buccal cavity with the palm of his hand. That one who
could not bend his left knee or straighten his right. The other
in whom the slightest change of temperature sent tongues
of fire or the chill of an icicle running along his spinal
column.

And there were the bullets whose action turned the hero
into a figure of fun. Those which seemed aimed straight at
the heart, and which sliced off the left nipple and then passed
under the right, leaving it hanging but intact. It was one of
this variety that wounded General Obregón in the thigh. If
it had really wanted to hit him it could have done so; but
instead of inflicting the ostentatious wound the general
longed for as the unquestionable seal on his bravery—this was
to come later—all it left was a contemptible black-and-blue
bruise. The slight was so apparent that Obregón himself
sensed it, and for that reason he instantly cut the ground out

from under the gibe by scoffing at it. As he was incapable of
keeping to himself the fact that a bullet had touched him,
for several days, whenever he had the opportunity, he would
say:

"Could anything be more ridiculous than this wound of
mine."

The sprightliness of the bullets, however, did not stand in
the way of our patients' getting worse and dying. On the
contrary. For despite their whimsicality, they achieved their
objectives with an efficiency which we lacked. The Military
Hospital of Culiacán was a hospital only because it was overflowing with wounded. Aside from this detail, there was no
more reason to call it a hospital than by any other name.
What did the skill of the doctors or the care of the nurses
avail there, when they were powerless for lack of facilities and
equipment? There were not enough beds, or linen, or medicines. Gauze had to be doled out; disinfectants were lacking;
the paucity of surgical instruments, many of them incomplete
or worn out, delayed or nullified the operations.

This state of affairs was such a source of humiliation to
the Constitutional army that General Iturbe, despite the cool-
ness with which he faced up to the most trying circumstances,
could hardly bear it. Morning after morning his visit to the
hospital outraged him. Behind every affectionate word he
spoke to the suffering patients, one could hear the question:
"Is this the kind of care the soldiers of a conquering army
deserve?" And after asking himself this a hundred times, he
came up with the answer hours later, following a line of
thought which, though he did not formulate it in these terms,
ran something like this: "Among the most typically Mexican
military concepts, the overriding one is that which reduces
any army to a group of naked men armed, if possible with
guns, and if not, with the first thing that comes to hand.
Equipment? What for? Without overcoat, without shoes, the
Mexican soldier crosses the mountains and braves the icy
cold to seek out the enemy. Provisions? What for? Without
bread or water the Mexican troops (like those of Santa Anna)

crossed unending deserts, and with empty stomach, parched
mouth, fought the battles of La Angostura. General Staff?
What for? Any self-styled genius can constitute himself a
tactical expert and talk of marching on Washington with
fifty thousand men. Ambulances? What for? Resigned, long-
suffering, heroic, our soldiers, lacking aid, bleed to death or
die of infection on the battlefield, like that colonel who conscientiously fulfilled his duty at Malpaso, or like Gustavo
Garmendia, who died at the foot of Capilla range."

To tell the truth, it was not much that Hay and I accomplished at the Military Hospital of Culiacán. We requisi-
tioned, wherever we could find them, mattresses and pillows. We entered two or three private homes and made off
with their sheets, pillowcases, and other supplies. We scoured
the few stores which had survived the disasters of civil war
and managed to round up a few comforters and pallets. But
though this helped a little, the main problem remained un-
solved: scalpels, scissors, gauze, bandages, and medicines.
There were none in Sinaloa or Sonora. Like the rifles and
bullets with which we killed each other, these were to be
found in the United States, but not free. They had to be paid
for, and in gold. And how could we get this gold? Iturbe
called us in for a long conference and decided that we would
get it, at least in part, even though the troops' pay was in
arrears, and even though our paper money was worth still less
than that of Carranza.

BOOK VI

Revolutionary Journeys

---

1 THE TRAIN

When the day came that I was to leave Culiacán, my friends
came for me about ten in the morning, and the group of them
accompanied me to the station.

The train was already in when we got there. It was a typically revolutionary conveyance, dusty, outlandish, made up
of coaches and boxcars of the most varied kinds and in a state
of very evident decay, which gave it much of its picturesque-
ness. Moreover, that train looked as though it were bowed
down by the fatigue of its long trip from the vicinity of
Guaymas, from which it had just arrived, and its resignation
was apparent as it made ready for the return trip.

For it was customary at that time in the railway service
between Sinaloa and Sonora for the train arriving in Culiacán from Cruz de Piedra (that from Culiacán to Mazatlán
had been suspended) to set out at once on the same trip in
reverse. Thus, by turning the engine around, the northbound
train immediately became the southbound train, and in this
way some of the many shortcomings due to the scarcity of
rolling stock were avoided.

This system had the advantage for Culiacán of linking into
one the only two customary railway events, which occasioned
in that city periodic excitement of a completely small-town
character. Every two, three, or four days (for at the time the

movements of the trains were as uncertain as if they were
dependent on sail or the state of the weather) a sudden buzz
began to fill the streets. There was a great clicking of hurrying heels; more carriages, more "spiders" traversed the
muddy streets; more doors and windows were thrown open;
more voices were heard—long farewells, effusive greetings—
and the whole atmosphere took on an animation, as though
there had been a rise in temperature. It was the train, the
train which had arrived and was leaving again.

My farewells at the station were prolonged, for, as always,
the train proved true to its nature and took over an hour to
start moving. General Iturbe flashed his agreeable smile at
me a hundred times, underscoring it from time to time with
some friendly phrase or good wishes for my trip. Alessio
Robles uninterruptedly made me the recipient of phrases and
embraces, each more vehement than the other, which were
admirably suited to the anarchic rhythm which enveloped us,
made up of shouts, excitement, disorder, tumult. Aarón
Sáenz and the other "dream captains" took turns during this
final hour at giving me further proof of their exquisite hospitality. And Colonel Hay, taking me aside and with a supreme effort to make himself heard above the cries of the
vendors of milk and tamales, repeated—always for the last
time—his list of official and private commissions, ranging from
a talk with the First Chief in Hermosillo and the .38
(automatic) revolvers for the staff officers, to the mysterious
little package I was to hand to a certain person in El Paso,
Texas, a stranger to me, who would approach my Pullman
making a sign that had been agreed upon with a handkerchief. Finally the whistle blew and I jumped on to the steps
of one of the cars. The movement of the train was so slow
that for several minutes my friends could continue our conversation, walking along beside the train. The uniformed
group they made, topped with their light hats, moved aloof
and compact through the swarming crowd gathered along
the track. Finally the train accelerated its pace; the tall figures of Alessio and Robinson and the others who surrounded

them were slowly left behind. The station buildings grew
more squat; the panorama of Culiacán began to revolve
round its own center and to diminish and shrink away as
though irresistible ropes were pulling at it from the background of the horizon. A rise in the land came between us
and the town, then a descending curve made the earth rise
toward the sky like the surface of the ocean when a ship
rolls, and finally that landscape faded into another, became
another.

The crowd of passengers was so great that it took me some
time to find the boy who was traveling with me in the capacity of orderly. I came upon him barricaded behind the
bundle of his belongings and my suitcases and ready to hold
with military valor the two seats he had taken by assault. As
I approached, he was defending himself skillfully against the
attack of two officers who were determined to secure possession of those two valuable places—valuable because the trip
might as easily last twenty days as two. His adversaries were
a captain and a very resolute major. But my orderly, who was
both brave and resourceful, made use of the insignia of their
rank, with which they sought to impress him, to strengthen
his own position. To their offensive of three bars and a star
he answered with a defensive, which, though false, was irresistible: three stars and an eagle. To keep a good seat in
the train he had conferred on me the rank of his liking: he
talked of nothing but the privileges of his "colonel" and at
every possible juncture introduced the name of General
Iturbe. My arrival calmed down the aggressiveness of the
officers, who accepted me as their superior in rank, and we
displayed the utmost courtesy toward one another, they
saluting me as colonel, and I inviting them to share as best
they could the space which, thanks to the militant attributes
of my orderly, they looked upon as mine.

In spite of the dispute it had occasioned, the space in question was far from being the last word in comfort. One of the
windowpanes was out; the curtain, which was torn down the

middle, hung dejectedly by one corner from a roller without springs; and the seat itself, with its back torn all the way across and its cushions destroyed to the very bottom, invited one to assume a standing rather than a sitting posture. But we had only to let our glances travel over the rest of the car to make our places seem delightful, for if two or three windowpanes, an occasional curtain, and—to judge by the satisfied expression of their occupants—several seats were intact, everything else was enough to frighten one. In the majority of places, not the glass, but the window itself was missing; in many the tear in the curtain was a prolongation of the tear in the roof; and in many not a trace of a seat remained.

This state of things was eloquently reflected in the passengers. To the destruction—or great deterioration—of the material instruments and mechanisms had followed a corresponding descent and deterioration in the spiritual make-up of those who still employed the damaged instruments. At every point life on the train showed clearly a return to the primitive. The structured complexities of civilization were only partially effective. The distinction between freight and passenger cars had disappeared; coaches and boxcars were used interchangeably for the same purposes. As a result the difference between people and bundles had disappeared; in certain places men, women, and children were piled up like bundles; in other places suitcases and trunks were riding in the seats. But, even more, all the distinctions that link one's ideas of bodily decorum to such things as chairs, tables, and beds were gone. The passengers seemed nowhere so much at ease as in the freight cars, where they stretched out or sat up on the floor as they pleased. And there, as in the aisles and on the platforms of the coaches, a new pleasure, long forgotten, was rediscovered: that of eating on the floor, amidst all the dirt and rubbish.

At first a few passengers, not caught up as yet in the rising tide of barbarism, attempted to stem the disorderliness a little; but they soon desisted. The tendency was like a snowslide; only violent measures could have held it back.

About the middle of the afternoon the train's stops became more and more frequent, and the movement of the train—when it did move—went from slow to imperceptible. These inexplicable stops were maddening. The passengers would swarm out of the cars and spread out in the fields on both sides of the road. The more impatient or the more inquisitive would go over to the engine to inspect it or to talk with the engineer or fireman, and then come back to inform us as to the result of their investigations. The train did not run because the engine could not get up steam, and the engine could not get up steam because the water ran out of the boiler into the fire. The struggle, therefore, between steam and distance had been changed into a struggle between fire and water. And meanwhile we remained motionless.

There were moments in which the fire gained ground over the water. On such occasions the whistle would blow and the train would begin to jerk forward with the feeble, discouraged impulse of its worn-out machinery. But its motion was so slow that the passengers did not even bother getting back into the train. They either walked along beside it or remained seated on the embankment, with the fatalistic assurance that the train would soon stop again.

It became evident that at this pace it would take us four or five days to reach San Blas, the only place where the engine could be repaired. This seemed too much, so the train crew and the passengers held a conference. "If we had some wood to mix with the coal," said the fireman, "we might get somewhere, for mixing the two together you get a hotter fire." To which the passengers replied that if there was no wood on hand, we would supply it. And no sooner said than done. An army of destruction scattered over the fields and set to work. It gathered up dry branches, boards, fence posts, and the cross supports of telegraph poles and in less than half an hour had piled up in the coal car several tons of firewood, with the aid of which the trip was accelerated somewhat.

The supply of wood was replenished several times that afternoon and that evening; the same operation was repeated the next morning and afternoon, and, thanks to this, the second evening we were rewarded by the sight of San Blas and a roundhouse.

2 SHADOWS AND SPIRITS

The state in which we reached San Blas did not unduly impress its inhabitants. Was it because this town, like all those of the Pacific coast, had become accustomed to the Revolution, and nothing that happened could any longer surprise it? Or was it that, when all is said and done, there was nothing pathetic or strange about a train that had been moving for several days at the rate of five kilometers an hour, and finally pulled into the station, shaken and battered, like a ship with its mast swept away making port?

Be that as it may, we felt disappointed. We thought we had introduced a new variant of shipwrecked travelers: the castaways of the train. We prided ourselves on a modern type of heroism: that which could make locomotives travel contrary to the immutable laws of Nature. But when we finally made it to San Blas—and this confirmed our worst suspicions—there was no Red Cross delegation there to meet us, no white stretchers, no field kitchen giving off the pleasant aroma of coffee and the satisfying sputter of frying fat.

Our frustration grew when we heard the instructions issued to us.

"It will take at least a day for the repair shop to get the locomotive into shape," the conductor informed us as he walked through the various groups. "At least a day, for there are no hammers left in the San Blas roundhouse. And as the station is not equipped for emergencies like this, those passengers who so desire can take up quarters, until the trip resumes, in the place I am going to show you. Everybody follow me!"

Shortly before we left the train, night completely shrouded the sky with shadows. Now the glimmer of lanterns dotted the dark station, repeating their glow, weakly and at ground level, throughout a wide circle of the gloomy ambience, finally to hang themselves against the curtain of darkness. So feeble was their light that it set up an inversion of values to our dazed eyes: the nearer the light, the wanner; the farther off, the brighter.

The bolder or more rebellious passengers set off through the streets of the town in search of comfortable accommodations. They could be glimpsed in the lantern light, shrinking from the cold, bent over by the weight of their luggage. In their swift transit, the faint glimmer of the lanterns now diminished, now enlarged their figures, distorting them, throwing them into momentary contrast with the almost motionless groups around the stalls of bread and frying food. The more humble or more sensible followed the conductor toward the lodging he had promised. This was not far off; but as a merciless competition immediately developed as to who should be the first to grab the best places—the best there might be—the nocturnal caravan of castaways of the train went loping through the darkness, a confused mass of shadows moving to the flickering light of the lanterns.

The first arrivals made no spectacular conquest, nor the last either. The light of matches and an occasional lantern quickly revealed the fact that the hotel provided by the railroad authorities was not much more inviting than the street. It consisted of the halls and corridors of a building which was either half in ruins or only half finished, whose walls, either not yet plastered, or from which the plaster had crumbled, rose from the damp ground to lose themselves in the night. In a few places there was a vague indication of flooring and rafters, which gave a faint feeling of shelter from the elements. In others the cold January wind shrilled like a fife, fighting with itself at the corners of the walls and the intersection of the halls; whistling as it buffeted the bent-over bodies of the castaways. But there, as everywhere else, one had only to look up to convince himself that the only real

roof was the sky clotted with storm clouds in which an occasional star winked for a moment, and then disappeared
again.

There was a brief period when the darkness was filled with
the sound of voices and the crying of children. Then, in typical Mexican fashion, resignation took over—that fatal, facile
resignation, in whose sheltering folds the crowd gradually
enveloped itself. The hundreds of mobile shadows began to
shift places and settle down. What had been a confused and
moving verticality, in the India-ink shadows took on hori-
zontality, and on the invisible floor an infinite series of parallel lines assumed the quality of ties of a nightmare railroad.

Finally, almost absolute quiet followed. The wind went on
whistling and slithering between the recumbent bodies. The
shadows grew thicker. Only at the end of the hall a tiny
shadow projected by the gleam of its lantern moved from
time to time. It advanced a few paces and stopped; stooped
for a moment over one of the stretched-out figures; lowered
the lantern; bent its head for a few seconds, raised it again;
then moved on. Thus it proceeded from form to form, with
lantern alternately in the air and at ground level. It was the
old Frenchman, a diabetic septuagenarian who in spite of his
weakness possessed astounding nervous energy, and who during the entire trip had never stopped talking about saccharine
and doing all sorts of small favors to passengers still weaker
than he. His humanitarian vocation was matched by his organic capacity to manufacture sugar. He was sweet in
body and soul, with a sweetness that surpassed the weight of
his years, sweet even when the freezing wind and fatigue
overpowered strong men and laid them low. There he went,
from pillow to pillow, ready to remedy all ills, and handing
out, left and right, with his small, shaking, generous hand
everything he carried in his basket or his pockets.

I was by way of being an authority on the subject of nights
in the open air. Moreover, I had had my fill of the rawhide
and barrel-hoop beds that were the specialty of the lodging-
houses of San Blas. So my orderly set up my cot in the lee

of the first house we came to, ignoring my suggestion that he look for a portico or something of the sort. Fully dressed, I got under the blankets, or, to be more exact, I rolled them around me. But even so, the cold was so penetrating that I struggled in vain for an hour to get to sleep. From somewhere there came a plaintive, indefatigable music—indefatigable from utter straining—which in the dark silence of the village was more disturbing than a storm. It consisted of a violin, a clarinet, a bass viol, whose mournful notes at times harmonized, at times were sourly dissonant, and every once in a while were completely drowned out by the stridence of a guttural, savage cry, a prolonged cry which concluded in a burst of laughter followed by an *ay* as cold, sharp, and piercing as a dagger. The three instruments were playing a popular tune, going back over it again and again, and then proceeding without a break to another, and a new cycle of repetitions. The wind snatched up the twang of the clarinet, the wheeze of the violin, the throb of the viol, and dragged their eddies through the streets, plunging me in a sea of remote discords.

As sleep was out of the question, I got up from my cot, wrapped in the blankets, and went to see where the music was coming from. Only a few steps away I found it, or rather, those who were making it, three sleepy, half-drunk musicians sitting on the ground in a sheltered corner. They formed a semicircle facing another man who was still drunker than they, but who, no less intent on the rhythm, stood swaying back and forth, supporting himself against the wall with one hand, and holding in the other a bottle with a good supply of cheer. The street light threw into relief his young and dirty face, drew a crystalline sparkle from the liquid in the bottle, and died away in weak reflections on the keys of the clarinet and the greasy luster of the bass viol.

The drunk man, as I soon learned from the conversation I struck up with the three musicians, was a railroad worker from the town of Huamúchil. He had come to San Blas more than a week before, and since then he had been celebrating

his saint's day without yet feeling that he had done it justice. He was, beyond the shadow of a doubt, a firm believer
in the chain carousal, then so much in vogue on the banks of
all eleven rivers of fruitful Sinaloa. He had already exhausted
four orchestras, counting the one which at that moment was
adding a musical flourish to his intoxication, and he seemed
capable of wearing out four more. The strains of *La Valentina, La Juanita, La Julia* contributed to his taciturn state of
well-being, establishing an intimate contact between him and
the creative powers of the universe, and revealing unsuspected
lodes of vitality in his body and soul. He reeked of liquor
ten yards off; his very hair oozed alcohol. But between swig
and music, music and swig, he managed to keep himself in an
upright position, so as not to tear his soul from the Elysian
fields where it was at the moment sojourning. The pulque
and mescal could not overpower him; his organism refined
them of their dross, leaving only their divine essence. He was
miraculously immune to all that overpowers and destroys as
the blood boils in the flame of the pulque. For twelve days
and nights he had been going about the streets, drunk and
alone, followed at a distance by the band of musicians who
played for him and got drunk with him at so much an hour.
But he looked as collected and robust as though he had only
started on his binge.

When he took in the fact that a stranger was talking to his
musicians, he ordered them to follow him and walked away.
He was weaving a little, but his step was firm; they were
dragging their feet, stumbling, the rhythm of their movements and their music completely eluding them.

We left San Blas the next afternoon, and two days later,
at nightfall, reached Cruz de Piedra. Shortly after our arrival a young officer, with a frank, though shy air, came over
to me saying, "I am General Rafael Buelna," as he shook
hands with me.

That sudden introduction disconcerted me, most of all
because it brought tumbling to the ground all that my imagination had built up around the name of Buelna. He was

not, as I had supposed, a guerrilla fighter of the type of Juan Carrasco, but an adolescent who gave the impression of having mischievously stolen the military trappings he wore. And my surprise would have continued if I had not noticed, as I looked him over slowly, that there was a marked discrepancy between his outward appearance and his inner self. As he talked the contrast between his still beardless face and his thoughtful manner grew.

"I have a parcel for you," he went on, "from General Ramón F. Iturbe."

And turning to the two officers who accompanied him, he said to one of them, as he handed him a bunch of keys:

"Son, go to the dispatch cases and bring me the little parcel wrapped in newspaper that General Iturbe gave me in Culiacán."

The officer went off and was soon back with the package Buelna had asked for. The latter handed it to me.

"It must be something important," he said, "for General Iturbe insisted that I was to get it to you as soon as possible. Do you want to open it and see what's in it, and let me know if you are satisfied?"

A feeling of mutual sympathy led to our prolonging our chance meeting. I told him I was on my way to Hermosillo. He suggested that we make the trip as far as Maytorena together. And from that moment we shared our thoughts as though we had known each other all our lives.

Buelna reflected not the enthusiasm of the Revolution, but its sadness. He seemed weighed down by a great sense of responsibility, which, on the one hand, obliged him to carry out certain tasks, and, on the other, demanded a stern accounting for them. He was one of the very few who were conscious of the tragedy of the Revolution: the moral impossibility of not supporting it, and the material and psychological impossibility of achieving through it the regeneration that would justify it. And inasmuch as he had given deep thought to the struggle, and lacked the ability to express this in adequate form, he assumed a forbidding air, affected a brusque

manner of speaking which was completely foreign to him, and
which he laid aside with his intimate friends. When this took
place, he turned into the boy who had run away from school,
the student who had only begun his education. One sensed
in him the man in love with an imaginary, ideal world endowed with the generosity, the selflessness of his readings;
of the world of reality, there was the eternal hope which
makes it possible to live today's black hours with the illusion of achieving the bright tomorrow.

3 NIGHT FLIGHT

When we got to Maytorena, Buelna said to me, "If you feel
up to it, why don't you make the rest of your trip with me?
No train can match my motorized handcar in comfort or
speed."

The suggestion did not displease me; on the contrary, I
liked the idea. For there was no question but that it was
better to leave Maytorena at once, with the relative assurance of being in Hermosillo early the next morning, than
to spend another sleepless night in camp and run the risk
of endless delays on the ordinary trains. To be sure, a trip of
two hundred kilometers on a gasoline-propelled limber was
not too tempting, especially on a January night with the railroad track in such deplorable state. But bad as this was, it
seemed preferable to the prospect of spending the night in
the open at Maytorena awaiting the departure of some uncertain train.

Buelna had extravagantly praised the qualities of his motorized vehicle, or, to give it the name he used to describe it,
his "flying machine." Was he in earnest about it? When we
went to see it lifted off the wagon on which it had made the
trip from Cruz de Piedra, I saw at once that there was nothing special about it. It was a primitive contraption, unpre-
possessing in appearance, without personality of any sort. It

consisted of four wheels, the motor, and a platform with
three or four cross-benches which would hold, at most, five
or six people. Its size and flimsiness could be judged by the
ease with which it fitted onto the vehicle from which they
were lowering it. A spavined mule could have hauled it.

"This little machine," I thought to myself, "may land us in
Hermosillo or in heaven."

Buelna must have read my mind, for he said:

"Don't you be forming a poor opinion of my machine because it doesn't look like much. Really to appreciate what it
can do, you have to ride it at eighty kilometers an hour, at
least eighty."

Buelna left the car in the hands of his orderly and a me-
chanic; he told his two officers to have their dinner, and we
set out to do the same, which was not a difficult enterprise,
for Maytorena was a well-provisioned camp, and we found
what we needed without too much effort.

After we had eaten, Buelna remarked, "There's no point to
getting to Hermosillo at three or four in the morning. If we
leave here between one and two, we'll be there, without
rushing, around seven. It's twelve now. Shall we stretch our
legs a little?"

For a good while, almost feeling our way, we walked
among the tents set up here and there on both sides of the
station. At that hour the silence was solemn, if not profound.
In the distance the steady barking of dogs could be heard,
and still farther off, the monotonous creaking of wagons on
the road from Cruz de Piedra. At intervals the sound of soft,
slow, slurred singing came from the soldiers' tents. One could
sense the men in the darkness, humming their songs with
eyes half closed. In the open fields the scope of the silence
grew, broadened, became infinite. The night, though starry,
was dark. The glittering dots shone overhead with a quiet,
eternal intensity. At ground level the humble, ephemeral,
moving lights of the cigarettes of soldiers, not yet asleep,
glowed.

At times the barking of the dogs was not so distant. One would emerge out of the bushes, followed by another, until we were surrounded by a veritable pack, baying at us fiercely out of the darkness. They kept closing in on us until we had to drive them off. Having an innate fear of dogs, I would wait until the last minute; Buelna would make for them automatically and, without interrupting our conversation, aim a kick at them, and then come back to me. For a little while the dogs would be cowed, and then they would begin to encircle us again.

We must have spent about two hours in that fashion, now stumbling over bushes, now stopping to contemplate the distant serenity of the sky, or to observe, in the direction of the coast, the campfires of the Federal troops. The ruddy glow of those lights, blazing at intervals on the peaks of an invisible horizon, had a deep and stirring significance for us. They were more than the symbolic reminder of the struggle; they were, under the blanket of stars, the expression of a contrast: the minimal gleam of the national impotence, the sign of the pettiness for which the aspiration to greatness had settled. "Federals! Revolutionaries! Not the tiniest glimmer of light of the smallest of all the stars!"

Suddenly I said, "How many things those campfires call up!"

"How many indeed . . ." answered Buelna, without taking his eyes from them.

When we got back to the station the handcar was ready to go. Buelna and I took the back seat. In the middle, where he could reach the throttle and the controls, sat the driver; at his side, the general's orderly; and in front, the two officers.

We were about to take off when I noticed that we had no lights.

"Wait a minute," I said to Buelna. "You mean to say we are running without lights?"

"Of course," he answered.

"All right," I said, "but I think you should know one thing. From here to Hermosillo there's not a single one of the larger bridges standing; there are places where the road plunges down the slopes of the ravines to the riverbeds. Some of those shoo-flies are terrible."

"That doesn't matter," said Buelna. "The line from Culiacán to Cruz de Piedra is in the same shape, and that's the way we came. Nevertheless, there's no harm in taking precautions." And turning to his orderly, he added:

"Get out the lantern and tie it in front of the motor as best you can."

The orderly rummaged around in one of the bags, and finally brought out something that I supposed would be a searchlight. I was wrong. It was an ordinary lantern. When he had hung it in front of our car, it did not light up the track for more than half a yard. But I didn't want to raise further objections.

"This doesn't look to me like much of an improvement," Buelna remarked.

"No, General, it isn't," answered the driver. "Maybe we ought to put a paper behind the lantern to act as a reflector. That way we'd have more light."

This time one of the officers rooted in the bags until he found the sheet of white paper that we needed. But this new device did not impress anybody; the reflector added almost nothing to the range of the light.

"How well do you know this road?" Buelna asked the driver.

"I've never been over it, General."

Whereupon Buelna turned to me, "Do you think you remember where the most dangerous shoo-flies are?"

"How could I?" I answered. "I've only made the trip once."

"Very well," he said, putting an end to the discussion; "we'll do the best we can. We're not going to let a trifle like this interfere with our plans. A little care is all that is needed. Watch it, son. If you feel the road dropping too much, slam on the brake."

And so we did the best we could.

It must have been around two when we set out from Maytorena. As soon as we had left the station, we realized

that the night was as black as a pocket; instead of lighting
our way, the lantern blinded us. We could tell by the sound
when we had passed the last of the boxcars lined up on the
sidings. We could tell by the movement when we had crossed
the last switch, and again by the noise when we had left the
last house behind. Then, surrounded by darkness, our ears
underwent a rapid training.

The motor, which was cold at first, warmed up quickly and
started to accelerate, firing with perfect regularity. Our car
began to rush dizzily along the invisible rails. It cleaved the
darkness, turning it into wind which lashed our faces. Its
motion was swift and smooth enough to lull one to sleep. The
two officers stretched out as best they could on the seat, ac-
commodating themselves to one another, huddled up and
went to sleep, with only inches between themselves and the
track and death. The orderly rested his arms on the back of
his seat, leaned his head on his arms, and went to sleep too.
Buelna and I kept up our conversation. A little later the
driver began to nod.

What a mad journey, the outcome of one of those chance
meetings, which gave rise to something worse than rashness:
total unawareness of danger. Or something even worse than
unawareness: vanity and fatalism. None of the six men traveling in this manner had the need or desire to kill himself.
But there we were, flirting with death, some out of obedience, others out of an unwillingness to confess that the game
was not worth playing because it was dangerous. Basically we
all had the same sustaining thought, or shadow of a thought:
no man, for all his foresight, can outwit his destiny. It is a
thought typical of primitive and heroic peoples.

There came a moment when Buelna and I could no longer
talk. The motor, in complete mastery of its perfect rhythm,
grew by what it fed on, and gave itself over to the full enjoyment of its finest hour. The "flying machine" really seemed
to be flying. And there was something truly awesome in that
wild flight, without purpose or objective, over rails of darkness. It was a unique experience, that vertigo of speed with-

out any point of reference, under the impassive stars, the vertigo of pure speed, perceptible to the ear and the muscles. As immobile as though we were not moving, ahead of us shone the two arrows of light which the lantern cast upon the rails.

Suddenly the fleeting gleam of another arrow was added to ours, and coincided with the double click of the wheels as they crossed a switch. With this our smooth noise was violently shattered—some boxcar? a house?—or was channeled for a brief moment. New fleeting gleams, new clicking, and then our noise resumed its steady rhythm. From time to time the motor swayed to one side or the other, upsetting our equilibrium. We sensed that we were describing a majestic curve in the dark, or changing direction. Every so often a sharp descent, a hollow sonority, informed us that we were crossing a culvert, a drain. The unexpected leap of the shoo-flies lasted for breathless moments that were terrifying and delightful. We could feel the motor seeking the rails that had suddenly disappeared, shoot down the abyss at even greater speed, to the bottom of the canyons and the riverbeds. It was like a fall in a nightmare, which lasts only a moment but seems endless, between shapeless masses of vegetation and the silhouettes of cliffs toward which the car seemed to be rushing head-on. But always, when the distress caused by the descent was growing unbearable, without transition it turned into the breathlessness of ascent, climbing incredible slopes, like a ship rising on mountainous waves, which here were hard, black, formless. It was a chute-the-chutes in the loneliness of the countryside and the night; but so absurd, so unpredictable and inexplicable in its curves and rise and fall that at times it seemed like a journey in infinity, without beginning or end. What was I doing there, in that dance of mad fugues, in the company of five strangers as witless as myself?

My efforts to penetrate the darkness were finally rewarded. I could see as clearly as though the sun were shining: a perfect road, lined with trees on either side, telegraph poles, carefully laid ties; villages below, mountains against the hori-

zon, silver-rimmed clouds in the sky. The track with all its
ups and downs, its curves, its swerves, its crossings did not
represent the least danger. It was a smooth, clear track on
which one could not imagine the slightest obstacle. There
was nothing to worry about; one could sleep . . . sleep. . . .

The car gave a leap, then dropped back on the rails. It
hesitated as though the wheels had become locked together.
It seemed to stumble. It reared up and gave another leap.
Once more it fell back, dragging itself along. The motor died.

Buelna and I were standing up, holding tight to the seat.
The driver was tangled up among the controls. The orderly,
his body half out of the car, was holding on to the front seat
by his legs. The officers had disappeared.

We could feel something under the platform. Though we
did not put our thought into words, we supposed it was the
officers. We got off, quietly untied the lantern, and tried to
see what had happened. Caught between the four wheels
huddled a huge, shapeless mass. It was something furry,
damp, warm. It was not the bodies of the officers; it seemed
to be an animal. Leaving the car and half feeling our way by
the dim light of the lantern, we looked along both sides of
the track. The officers were not there either. Then we walked
back over the ties. Ten or fifteen meters away we discovered
a small bridge. We crossed it, and went on looking. There
was no sign of the officers' bodies anywhere, nor the slightest
trace of blood.

"They must be down below," I said to Buelna, speaking for
the first time, "in the creek."

"Probably," he answered.

And, sure enough, after a short search in the gully we found
them, unconscious and bleeding profusely. It was no small
job to get them out and carry them up beside the car. One
of them soon regained his senses. The other seemed near
death.

After a long struggle we managed to get the motor free
from its encumbrance. It was a mule that had been killed
when the car struck it. It had undoubtedly been lying asleep

across the track at the entrance to the bridge when the motor hit it and dragged it under the wheels.

In spite of everything our machine had not lost even a screw. We lifted it back on the rails, accommodated the injured officers as best we could, and started off again. In a little while we pulled into a big station. Could it be Hermosillo? In the darkness we could make out thick masses that seemed buildings, and streets in the distance. Curiously enough, there was hardly a light visible.

We stopped, and Buelna and his orderly got down and walked over to the station sheds. The driver and I stayed with the injured men.

In a few minutes I heard a voice calling:

"Guzmán! Guzmán! We are not in Hermosillo; this is Torres."

Buelna and his orderly returned and we immediately resumed our trip, but this time slowly. We traveled in this fashion for several hours. Day broke, a day so clear that everything was bathed in light; we could see jack rabbits running on either side of the track. Buelna could not resist the impulse to do some target shooting and he amused himself by knocking them off with the Mauser.

Two kilometers from Hermosillo we ran off the track again. The driver did not notice that the switch had been thrown, and as the car ran over it, it leaped the rails and landed up about two meters from the track. But that was not the last of our tribulations on this memorable trip, for we had not recovered from this accident when, in the very station yard of Hermosillo, the passenger train leaving for Maytorena bore down on us. A few seconds more and we would not have had time to swerve the car where our injured men lay groaning piteously.

At about eight in the morning I reached the Hotel Arcadia. I was covered with dirt and bloodstains. While the clerk looked through his register and found the key for the room I had asked for, I sat down in a chair next to the desk and fell asleep.

4 THE REBELS IN YANKEELAND

To approach Nogales, Arizona, coming from our impoverished
cities and our fields laid waste by war, was like beholding a
radiant and unsuspected vision. As I looked at it once more,
I understood better than before why the revolutionists who
entered that frontier town fell under a kind of spell. It was
the attraction of commerce, vitality.

We went to Nogales to warm ourselves a little at the fire
of man's industry, and to buy with our paper money (which
was accepted in nearly all the stores) even shoestrings. The
shop windows of the town's main street—unpretentious, but
full of goods—made us stop in surprise and admiration. We
were fascinated by the rows of kitchen utensils, the shining
frying pans, the coal and wood stoves, the shotguns, the clothing, the leather goods, the shoes, the pliers, the hammers,
the bicycles, the automobiles; and our admiration was all-
embracing, undiscriminating, as though civilization, even the
semibarbarous variety of the cowboys, had been invented for
our special delectation.

The storekeepers of Arizona had quickly grasped the fact
that the Mexican Revolution was a gold mine for them, and
they were eager and willing to satisfy many of our needs. In
Nogales they outfitted us for life and death; they sold us the
wine that was served at the official banquets of the First Chief
as well as the steel or dumdum bullets for our revolvers,
both in exchange for pieces of printed paper. Later they used
this to acquire the remnants of the country's wealth which
the Revolution sold for whatever it could get because it was
in dire need of money, and because this wealth had belonged
to the privileged caste. And so the revolutionists came back
from Yankee Nogales to Mexican Nogales with everything we
needed to go on killing one another, as well as to regale ourselves a little between combat and combat. And at the same
time the cattle of the ranches of Sonora poured across the

frontier in a single herd, an endless herd, to enrich at prices far below their value the livestock dealers of the Far West. The Yankee ban on the exportation of arms and munitions to Mexico—the arms embargo, as they called it—did not interfere with this flight of the national patrimony. Rather it intensified it, for the risks involved in the smuggling, and the climate it created, which raised the price of our principal import, were reflected in everything else. We paid dearly for everything, especially those articles which flattered the sartorial vanity of the young Constitutionalists: the handsome gray broad-brimmed hats, the khaki-colored cashmere suits of military cut, the yellow pigskin puttees, the shirts of olive-drab wool.

The international crossroads of the main street, which was Mexican on one side, North American on the other, and the street that intersected it perpendicularly, the southern part Mexican, the northern, North American, saw us pass dressed in one fashion and return in another. There those on the way to make their purchases and those who had completed them met; it was a kind of fair, with all the parcels, and the friendly, inquisitive joking.

"I suppose you've bought out all the stores on the other side," said Rafael Zubarán to Juan Sánchez Azcona, who had just arrived from Hermosillo and was about to cross the line in the company of his son, a second lieutenant in the Constitutionalist army.

"Bought them out? Don't you believe it," Sánchez Azcona answered; and he pulled out his wallet containing various bills carefully arranged in order of value, crisp and still smelling of ink from the presses of Monclova, which did not amount to two hundred pesos. "Just shirts and socks."

Those brief conversations at the frontier often highlighted the paradox we felt existed in this contiguity of the two countries. We shook hands across the imaginary dividing line; we stood with one foot in each of the two jurisdictions. General Felipe Angeles, who, like all truly good and sincere

men, had much of the child in him, made a game of going
to the United States and returning in a single step.

"I'm going to the United States," he would say, putting
one foot forward. And then, drawing it back: "I'm returning
to Mexico."

One day he came and went in this fashion twenty times—
"to break all records." And as he did this, he wore that melancholy smile of his, pleased at having found in me a spirit
that understood him even in such trifles.

After a brief stopover in Nogales, Sonora, I continued my
trip toward the large eastern cities.

In New York I met Alberto J. Pani, Luis Cabrera, Roberto V. Pesqueira, Juan and Francisco Urquidi, and several
other revolutionists. All had been invested with more or less
diplomatic or consular duties, or were heading commercial
missions, or were on utterly senseless and absurd assignments.

Cabrera's arrival had made it possible for Pani to shake
from his feet the dust of Washington, where he had been having a very thin time of it on the fifty cents per diem which
Pesqueira, a confidential agent of "the cause," allowed him
for his expenses. Now established in New York, Pani affirmed
his right to live, if not in the luxurious style of the official
representatives of the Revolution, at least with decorum. He
went from the furnished room for which he paid a dollar a
week in Washington to a good room in the Hotel McAlpin,
with a bath and the other comforts of an up-to-date hotel. In
a word, on that corner of Broadway and Thirty-fourth Street,
he was making up for all the privations he had undergone.

Cabrera, too, was stopping at the McAlpin, but not Pesqueira; he was at the Vanderbilt. I took a room at the Mc-
Alpin.

Roberto Pesqueira lacked the preparation, or perhaps he
was too young, for the position which circumstances and the
greed of the Sonoran faction had assigned him. His qualifications consisted of a knowledge of English and a certain

amount of experience in dealing with North Americans around Douglas, Arizona, where the supreme centers of action and culture were the Green Copper Company and other similar organizations. But as he did not lack natural gifts or the ability to size up a situation quickly; his instinctive tendency to listen to good advice and act upon it, without his vanity being hurt, made it possible for him to carry out his mission, if not brilliantly, at least with a certain effectiveness. Though it is also true that in Washington he had had Pani at his side for more than a month without realizing how useful his collaboration might have been. Was this because Pani was almost unknown among the revolutionists of Sonora? Or was it that Pesqueira, like the rest of the Sonoran faction, had an inkling of the chinks through which the political fruits of the Revolution might slip away from them? Months earlier in Sonora it had taken Felipe Angeles longer to enter the Constitutionalist camp than for Obregón to declare war to the death on him. Angeles, by reason of his military ability, and, even more, because of his virtue, was as much of a danger to the budding *caudillos* as the truth is to those who live by pretense. Similarly, though in a different field, Roberto Pesqueira may have sensed that Pani was destined to play a more important role than he in the lusterless diplomatic and financial activities of Mexico at that time. Basically, this was only the first episode in the struggle which the civilians of Sonora were to carry on against Pani for several years, and from which he would emerge victorious only with Obregón's support. Far from representing a threat to him—such rivalry was out of the question—Obregón was to find in Pani an extremely useful instrument. Not so others: neither de la Huerta, for example, nor Calles, during the time when these two were allies.

As for Cabrera, Pesqueira's attitude toward him was completely different. From the start Cabrera had acquired a place among the top leaders of the movement by reason of his merits. It was in the upper echelons that he would encounter rivals for honors and power; therefore Pesqueira, who was on a lower level, could subordinate himself to Cabrera without fear and follow his indications.

It was Cabrera rather than Pesqueira who at the time gave the impression of being the head of the diplomatic mission of the Revolution in the United States. The Hotel McAlpin echoed with his name and authority. No sooner did he appear in the lobby than a horde of people eager to talk with him got up from their chairs. There were always two or three important persons waiting for him on the sofas of the mezzanine floor. The bellboys were always paging him; the angular pens of the automatic writing machines—those which transmit messages from one floor to another—were in continual movement to keep him informed; his room telephone never stopped ringing, and night after night he had to hang on the doorknob of his room the sign "Do Not Disturb," and leave word that he was not to be called until a definite hour. To be sure, most of that activity represented nothing tangible; it was the milling about of innumerable agents moving heaven and earth to sell a rifle they did not own, or to offer some service which it was not in their power to render. But under all the sound and fury there were real and important matters which Cabrera attended to in his nervous, quick, precise way.

I spent a few sybaritic days at the McAlpin—sybaritic in middle-class or, to be more exact, in Elks' Club fashion—following the example of Alberto J. Pani's quiet sensuality. Pani and I began the day by having our breakfast in the big dining room on the second floor, a huge, sumptuous room overpowering with its gold leaf, its pillars, and mirrors, where the guests spoke in a low voice, the waiters moved softly, and the doorman, convinced that this represented the last word in refined living, jotted down on a pad the name and table of each guest so he could quietly notify him in case of some urgent message.

That vast dining room, whose luxury was so out of keeping with the one suit and single necktie which comprised my wardrobe of a nomadic revolutionist, did not inhibit me, but it did lead me to consider it, not so much in relationship to me as in a relation of contrasts. It was different with Pani, or so I thought; for the very reason that his icy calm made an exception only for those things which impinged upon the senses, he enjoyed that great dining room fully and completely. In his eyes it was the answer to architectonic problems—the main dining room of a hotel with two thousand rooms—but, above all, it was the setting for the meticulous service of those who, for the time being and at so much an hour, could feel themselves the great lords of a hotel. This was our case. We were one hundred per cent revolutionists, beyond the shadow of a doubt; but this did not prevent our sipping with delight the glass of orange juice the waiter served us on a heavy silver tray where the facets of the cut glass and the melting ice took on rainbow coloring. And the rest of the breakfast was in keeping with its beginning. The buttered toast for the eggs arrived daintily set in an aluminum rack; the rolls for the coffee were wrapped in snowy napkins which not only kept them warm, but seemed to add still another aroma to the already delightful one of freshly baked bread.

Our breakfast of hotel aristocrats set the tone for the rest of the day. It led us, without our realizing it, to seek out in the subsequent hours the equivalents of our early morning ritual. The same spirit presided at our lunch, at our political meetings, at our dinner. And if we decided to go to the theater, we consulted the entertainment section of the New York *Times*, and refused to settle for anything less than *Hamlet* with Forbes-Robertson, or *Die Meistersinger* at the Metropolitan.

The McAlpin often supplied the final fillip to our day. This was when we had midnight supper in the grillroom. Cabrera, Pesqueira, Urquidi, *et al.* accompanied us; all of them were fascinated by the rhythm of the one-step, the hesitation waltz, and the African blues. The tiled walls of the grillroom, an underground cabaret, elicited from Pani phrases of admiration and technical observations which we listened to and commented on between mouthfuls of Welsh rarebit or oyster cocktail.

It was there I had my first view of the tiresome business of restaurant dancing—piecemeal dancing, between course and course, almost without room to move. There I also learned that pleasure, if it is genuine, must have a certain disorder or Dionysiac flavor.

Roberto Pesqueira, in his impeccable tuxedo, got up from the table every once in a while to dance. We watched him. Cabrera, Mexican to the marrow of his bones, would take out of his vest pocket a mysterious little box and pass it around so we could help ourselves from it. The box contained a variety of chile powders.

"I always carry this with me when I travel," said Cabrera. "I can't live without Mexican seasoning. I have it specially prepared for me."

Nor could he live without recalling that he was a grammarian and a philologist. If at the end of dinner someone ordered a *plus-café*, he corrected him with a smile that ran from his glasses to his mustache, from his mustache to his plate:

"*Pousse-café, pousse-café,* not *plus-café.*"

5 On the Frontier

On my way back from New York I would have liked to stop off again in Sinaloa—Sinaloa of pleasant memories!—if for no other reason than to give Iturbe a firsthand report on what I had accomplished in the United States. But unforeseen circumstances detained me in Nogales and in the end obliged me to change my route.

I learned in Nogales that the First Chief, who had returned from his trip to the south and was on the point of moving on to Chihuahua, had arranged to have me assigned to one of the divisions of his staff "for duties that I would be informed of in due time." I also found that the "dream captains" had instructions to invite me, in General Obregón's name, to accept a post in General Headquarters of the Army of the Northwest.

The idea of joining the First Chief's entourage did not appeal to me in the least. Within Don Venustiano's orbit intrigue and the lowest kind of sycophancy grew rank; the trimmers, the tale-bearers, the bootlickers, the panderers had the inside track. And even though there were moments when this nauseous atmosphere was dissipated by the presence of men of a completely different caliber, men like Zubarán, Escudero, Silva, de la Huerta and a few others, in the long run it was the foul reek that prevailed, or became thick enough to fill one with disgust and the desire to flee it. The honest men, those who were ready to stand up and be counted for their principles, were wasting their time in that completely partisan circle, unless they had such important duties that they could not be abandoned. It was idle to conceive false hopes. By this time I had learned a lot and knew that Carranza, old and stubborn, would never change. He would go on responding to flattery rather than acts, to servility rather than ability. To the day of his death he would be influenced by abjectness, pettiness, for he himself, whose make-up was totally devoid of greatness, was not free from essential paltriness. His calculating coldness, which the incense bearers called the gift of a great statesman, was useful to him in measuring the picayune, not the great, with the result that he ruined his finest moments. Who ever saw in him any display of real enthusiasm, official or private, toward the great events of the Revolution? He was not magnanimous even in rewarding. When Francisco Villa, for example, won three or four battles, one after the other—decisive battles, the kind that as if by magic broadened the revolutionary horizon by a hundred leagues—Carranza began to count on his fingers, and if he finally made up his mind to reward these exploits by a promotion, it was grudgingly. He took care to promote one of his own generals—even a defeated one—five or six days earlier to keep Villa a little lower than his rightful place on the roster. Whereas it was notorious that the day after some bootlicker had heaped dithyrambs of praise on him or a go-between had rendered him useful services, the rewards were clamorous—clamorous and indecent.

My feelings at the prospect of joining General Obregón were completely different. To be sure, I did not really care for him. At our first meeting he had impressed me as being insincere, a humbug. Later (it may have been that he did not like me too well, either) it had been impossible to establish a spiritual bond between us, that understanding without words that creates worthwhile and enduring human relations. Nevertheless, I was not blind to his great ability and many good qualities: his dynamism, his capacity for swift, untiring action, his straightforward, if not great or heroic, approach to politics and war, and, finally, a certain frank, honest way of dealing with his immediate aides, a manliness in his relations with his subordinates that demanded nothing in the way of genuflections or abasement. In Obregón's presence the bootlickers grew circumspect, and any intrigues were quickly snuffed out or subsumed in the only one of any importance: that which he carried on vis-à-vis the First Chief to insure his own future predominance and that of his group. Hence, among his general staff and in the other official branches under his control there was a healthful atmosphere, a joint effort whose objective was the work in hand and not jockeying for position. Officers like Serrano, Garza, Sáenz, Muñoz, Robinson—and the same held true of civilians—conducted themselves with irreproachable revolutionary probity, or, at any rate, gave the impression of so doing, for around Obregón, the winner of battles, people were kept too busy to waste time conniving.

The "dream captains" considered my incorporation—as a civilian—to the Headquarters of the Army of the Northwest such a foregone conclusion that in Nogales they bought me a semimilitary outfit, complete from pistol and horse to campaign cot. In so far as the decision depended on me, they were absolutely right. As between Obregón and Carranza, I did not hesitate for one minute; my mind was made up to go with the former. But in the end (fortunately? unfortunately? it is foolish to try to fathom the designs of fate) it did not work out that way. One afternoon I went to call on Don Venustiano. I explained to him as tactfully as I knew how that I preferred to go with Obregón rather than with him, and asked his authorization to do so. He talked to me about Iturbe, and concluded by saying, "Too many people want you. Let me think it over." And three days later de la Huerta notified me that the First Chief had ordered my transfer to Ciudad Juárez, "where Zubarán would entrust me with an important mission," and had vetoed my going with Obregón's troops, as I had requested.

Was that not a tyrannical act, without purpose or reason? It was indeed. But I accepted it without a word of complaint. I did not even tell anybody, except de la Huerta, the real nature of my interview with Carranza. It offended me, as a free man, to let it be known that the First Chief was forcing me to remain in the very post I had openly rejected.

So we were all going to Chihuahua, though not all together. Don Venustiano would be crossing the sierra on horseback, traveling by way of the Púlpito canyon as far as Casas Grandes. He would be accompanied by a group of his closest associates—unquestioned friends and first-rate riders—and escorted by a whole battalion. The rest of us (whom de la Huerta nicknamed "small fry") would cross the frontier at Nogales, and travel by train through Yankee territory as far as our own frontier opposite El Paso, Texas.

In the end, I was not included either among the riders or the "small fry." I was assigned to a third category: the group which made the trip by automobile from Naco to Agua Prieta; from there we went, by auto, too, to another place whose name I do not recall, and, finally, by train through North American territory until we joined the two other groups in Ciudad Juárez.

Rafael Zubarán shared with me the discomforts and small surprises of that trip on which it seemed that we were play-

ing hide and seek with the two national sovereignties. At
every turn in the road we changed countries; at every rise we
encountered the other way of life, which received us with a
definite gesture of one kind or another. There were places
where they looked upon us as tramps; others where they
treated us like millionaires. The incidents of the Revolution,
too close for comfort there, struck certain Yankees as acts of
sheer barbarism, while to others they held out hopes of gain.
In Naco we ran into an atmosphere of strange suspiciousness
which almost closed the doors of the only hotel there—none
the less bad for being the only one—in our faces. We had to
stay out in the cold of the February night for a long time,
shivering and watching the starlight become blurred with
rime in the freezing night.

In Douglas a great and lavish rustic gentleman, whose name
was Douglas too, offered us hospitality that we refused in embarrassment. Mr. Douglas had a hotel, also called Douglas,
and his manners were those of a miner who had struck it
rich. No sooner did he hear that Zubarán and I were on our
way to the office of his hotel to engage a room than he came
to meet us, introduced himself in a few brief and simple
words, and informed us that that big hotel was his—as was the
whole town—and that he would put us up there better than
if we were the "president of a railroad," and it would not cost
us a cent, for he would take care of everything. Zubarán po-
litely but firmly refused the offer, but he could not prevent
Mr. Douglas from blunting this rebuff by ordering his employees to see that we had the best of everything.

"This gentleman who is so determined to entertain us,"
Zubarán said to me, "is not only a miner, as you suspect; he
is a super-miner, a tycoon of the entire mining industry of
this Yankee-Mexican area. Among other things, he represents
the biggest mines of Sonora. Naturally, we mustn't offend
him; but we're not going to accept even a glass of milk from
him without paying for it."

It was a kind of lay, masculine "shelter for wayward girls"
that Adolfo de la Huerta picked out for us in Ciudad Juárez.

I wonder if the idea was ever so stressed as on that occasion that we revolutionists had taken a vow of poverty. Nobody will deny that de la Huerta was always austere in his way of living, but that place was abominable rather than austere. It consisted of a quadrangular patio, about eighty to a hundred meters square, on whose edges four wings of rooms rose, independent of each other and with no communication with the world except the flimsy, sagging door of each room which opened onto the patio. The walls, of the cheapest type of adobe, had once been plastered over; time had cracked off great patches of the plaster. The floors were caving in; the ceilings, on the point of collapsing. At one time the patio must have been paved with cobblestones from the Bravo River; now the few that remained were buried in mud.

In the middle of the patio a meager, rusty water pipe rose straight up from the ground, and at a height of four or five feet bent downward to drip a trickle of water into a cracked cement tub. The faucet hardly worked; a thread of liquid dripped from it continually, and when the tub ran over this contributed to maintaining the patio's odd appearance of a small swamp. At night the February cold froze the liquid thread, transforming it into a beautiful icicle; the tub became an iceberg, the patio glittered as though its mud were shot through with needles of glass. And all this, which in the darkness of night could only be surmised, in the morning became a glory—the glory of nature which shows itself even in the most unlikely spots.

What was our life like at that time? Something infernal which I can hardly recall. I remember our waking hour. We had spent the night in beds that beggar description; the bedbugs ate us alive; the cold numbed our blood, and after all this, when we got up we had to go half dressed into the middle of the patio to wash. The film of ice over the mud cracked under our feet; the beautiful icicle on the faucet put up the resistance of a piece of transparent marble fantastically carved and polished. And at such moments some of us—the more sensory—gave ourselves over to a strange and cruel bodily

pleasure: thawing ourselves out with the smooth solid caress
of the frozen water, for this was the best we could hope for
in that hostel of beggars where we were living.

At the sight of the capricious, anarchic beauty of the forms
of water carved out by the night, our very suffering from the
cold became mitigated as we saw the reason for it.

BOOK VII

The Initiation of a Villista

---

1 PANCHO VILLA'S ESCAPE

My first weeks in Ciudad Juárez were a sort of baptism by immersion in the world that revolved around General Villa. Besides the general himself, I came to know his brother Hipólito, Carlitos Jáuregui (the youngest of his partisans, and the one in whom he reposed the greatest confidence), Juan N. Medina (until shortly before, his chief of staff), Lázaro de la Garza (his financial agent), and many other of his immediate subordinates and satellites. All of them—each in his separate way—drew me nearer and nearer to the Chief of the Division of the North and enveloped me in that atmosphere which his mere presence created.

One night when Carlitos Jáuregui and I were waiting for Villa in Juárez, he told me how he had come to be associated with him. For greater comfort we had climbed up on a pile of boxes and bundles near the tracks on the lower level of the station. It was a soft, warm night in May. Jáuregui had been leaning against the boxes and had slid down until he was stretched out, face upward toward the sky.

He kept his eyes fixed on the stars as he talked. I was leaning against some bales, and I listened without interrupting him, at the same time that I amused myself watching the orbits described by the little red lights that moved in the pitch-blackness of the night on the platform across the way. They were the cigarettes of the soldiers and officers waiting for the military train.

"When Villa was a prisoner in Santiago Tlaltelolco," began Jáuregui, "I was working as clerk in one of the military courts. I have never been in such straits as I was then. I was making about forty or fifty pesos a month, and the life I lived on this was so miserable that my despair must have shown in my face, in strange contrast to my youth. In order to make a little extra I used to go to the courthouse in the afternoons, after office hours, and do copying for the lawyers or the prisoners. My desk was near the iron grating that shut off the prisoners. So from where I sat I could see a part of the prison corridor, which was generally deserted at this time of day.

"One afternoon, as I happened to look up absent-mindedly from my desk toward the corridor, I saw Villa standing behind the grating. He had come up so quietly that I had not heard his steps. As usual, he had on his hat, and his serape around his shoulders.

"'Good afternoon, friend,' he said, pleasantly and affectionately. He didn't look quite the same as the mornings he had appeared before the judge or had been called to testify. He seemed less suspicious and crafty, and franker. What was the same in him was the touch of tenderness in his eyes when he looked at me. This look, which I shall never forget, I noticed from the first time the judge had ordered me to enter the declarations Villa was making in the record. 'I wonder if you'll do me the favor of copying a letter for me?'

"We talked for quite a while; he gave me the paper he wanted me to copy, and agreed to come for it the next day at the same time.

"The next day, after I gave him his letter, he looked me in the eye for a long time, accentuating still more the affectionate note of his smile and his expression.

"'Say, buddy, what's the matter that you look so sad?'

"'Nothing, General'—I don't know why I called Villa 'General' from the first time I saw him—'I'm always like this.'

"'Well, if you're always like that, it means that there's always something the matter. Come on, tell me about it. Maybe I can help you out.'

"His tone, half rough, half affectionate and paternal, won me over. Carried away by the friendship he showed me, I described my miserable, half-starved existence to him. He listened to me with the closest attention, and when I had finished, he put his hand in his trousers pocket.

"'Friend,' he said, 'it's not right for you to go on suffering this way. I'm going to see to it that things change. As a start I want you to take this.'

"And he held out, through the bars of the grating, a bill that was folded so many times that it looked like a little notebook.

"At first I emphatically refused this money which I had not asked for. But Villa soon convinced me with the following argument:

"'Take it, my boy. Take it and don't be foolish. I can do you a favor today. Who knows whether tomorrow things won't be the other way around. And you may be sure that if there's something you can do for me some day, I won't wait for you to offer it to me. I'll ask you for it myself.'

"That night, out in the street, I almost fainted under the first street light. For, as I unfolded the bill he had given me, I could scarcely believe my eyes. It was a hundred peso bill. I had never had one in my hands before. Against the red background there was a beautiful Mexican eagle with wide, outspread wings.

"The next day, though I didn't have anything to do there, I went to the courthouse after office hours. I felt a secret urge to talk with Villa, to express my gratitude and show him that I was happy. But, for reasons that I understood when I came to know him better, he did not appear at the grating that day. I was greatly put out by this, for I had nobody with whom I could share my feelings. Villa had warned me not to say a word, even at home, about the money, and I was determined to keep my promise. Finally we saw each other two days afterward.

"'How are things going, friend?' he asked me as soon as he came up. 'I think you look better than you did.'

"'I'm fine, General, and I'm certainly very grateful to you for the favor you insisted on doing me.'

"And we talked on like that. This time our conversation was longer and livelier. I certainly felt a deep gratitude to that rough man who had been so good to me, and I tried to make him feel my appreciation. When we said good-bye, he stretched out his arms through the bars to shake hands with me. I took his hand without suspecting anything, but as I noticed, when our fingers came together, that Villa was trying to slip something into mine, I tried to pull my hand back. But he clasped it still tighter and said:

"'This here is for you, too. When a fellow has been poor for a long time, a little money doesn't go very far. I'll bet you haven't got a cent left from the other day.'

"'Yes, I have, General. I've got nearly all of it.'

"'Well, if you have, you haven't done right. What you've been needing for a long time is some fun and a good time, and a good time runs into money, even when you don't have to buy it. Besides, isn't it queer! I was just thinking about a favor I was going to ask of you. A much bigger favor than these little ones I have been doing for you, and I'm sure you won't refuse me.'

"'What favor, General?' I asked him; and I was willing to lay down my life for that man, the first kindhearted person I had ever met.

"'I can't tell you today, my boy. Have a good time today and enjoy yourself. Tomorrow will be my turn.'

"I did not amuse myself that night. On the contrary, I suffered more than I ever had before. I couldn't close my eyes for a minute. Could I do what Villa wanted of me? The thought that he might ask something wrong never entered my mind. The only thing that worried me was that he might ask something beyond my strength and my ability. I was afraid I couldn't return the favor, and I felt very badly about it.

"Our next interview was brief. Villa began by saying, in a very persuasive tone, that if I was brave, I could do him a great favor, but that if I was a coward, it was better not to talk about the matter.

" 'I'm not afraid of anything, General,' I hastened to assure him.

" 'Not even of doing something bad, son?'

" 'Well . . .' I stammered.

" 'Of course you are, because you are a good lad. I only asked to see what you would say, for you may be sure I am not going to ask anything wrong of you.'

" 'I know that you are a good man, General.'

" 'Now that's just what I was going to talk to you about. You have been writing up the evidence in my trial; do you think it's right for the government to keep me a prisoner?'

" 'No, General, I don't.'

" 'Don't you think it's all a frame-up?'

" 'Yes, I do, General.'

" 'Then don't you think I ought to take things in my own hands, since the judges won't release me?'

" 'Yes, I do.'

" 'And don't you think it would be right for you to help me out of this hole?'

" 'Yes.'

" 'Well, sir, then you're going to help me. But remember: that's if you are brave. If you're afraid, it's no use.'

" 'I'm not afraid, General. I'll do whatever you tell me.'

"Villa's doubts about my bravery put me on my mettle, and my only thought was to attempt whatever he suggested, no matter what it might be.

" 'That's the kind of talk I like to hear,' he went on. 'We're all set. Now, first, take this package and lock it away in your desk where nobody can see it.'

"As he said this, he took from under his serape a little package, which he held out through the grating. I took it and put it in the drawer of my desk, under some papers. Villa went on:

"'In this package there is an iron saw, a handle, and a lump of black wax. Tomorrow when you come here, you fix up the saw—' as he said this he lowered his voice, and his tone became more impressive and confidential—'then you lock the door and begin to saw the bars of the grating. There's a little bottle of oil in the package to put on the saw so it won't get hot or squeak. Cut here first—' he pointed out one of the cross-bars—'and then here. After you have them sawed through, fasten the ends together with the wax, so nobody can tell they've been cut. Then day after tomorrow cut these other two bars here. Pay attention, buddy: here and here. When you finish, fasten them together with wax, like these others. Then in two more afternoons you saw these four places; but not quite all the way through, so the bars won't fall down. The last afternoon I'll come to see you, and if you've finished sawing the eight bars, I'll tell you what else you have to do. Well, so long! I'm going because I've been here talking a good while now. Oh, yes, be sure to gather up the filings from the floor. What you can't scrape up with your fingers, gather up with the wax. And now we'll find out if you really don't know what fear is.'

"As Villa was giving me these instructions, I could feel cold chills going over me, and I felt numb, though whether from fear or emotion I couldn't tell. The words of the *guerrillero*, which had such an effect on me that I have never forgotten them, whirled about in my mind grotesquely mixed with the figures of the eagle with its outspread wings that I had seen that first time on the hundred-peso bill by the street light.

"As he had said, Villa did not come back to see me again for four days. During this time I followed his instructions to the letter. My only trouble was that at first the saw teeth often broke. When Villa sauntered up to the grating at dusk the fourth day, he asked me in his usual easy manner:

"'Well, partner, how is everything going?'

"'O. K., General. I've done everything as you told me,' I

answered, deeply moved and lowering my voice till he could hardly hear me.

"'That's fine,' he said passing his fingers as though idly over the places where the bars were cut. Then he went on: 'Tomorrow I'll come round at the usual time. You saw through the places where the bars are still fast. But don't cut them all the way through. And only cut three. Leave the other one the way it is now, so the grating will stay in place. Then I'll come.'

"The next day Villa came a little while after I had finished sawing three of the spindles that were still holding the bars in place. He asked me if I had finished, and I told him I had. Then with one hand he pulled toward him the square of the grating that had been cut, which yielded without much effort, as it was barely held in place at one corner. Villa quickly handed me through the opening a bundle of clothing which he carried in his other hand, hidden under his serape. Then he glanced up and down the corridor, jumped lightly through the hole, pushed the piece of grating down into its place again, and in a corner of the office quickly changed his clothes. He put on a different hat, pulling it down low. In place of the serape he put on a cape and wrapped it around him, so as to conceal the lower part of his face.

"When he had finished, he said: 'Now let's get away from here quick, buddy. You walk ahead and I'll follow you. Don't be afraid of anything, and no matter what happens, don't stop.'

"I was so frightened that I don't know how I managed to put one foot before the other. Fortunately the corridors and the stairs were almost dark. As we were coming out into the hall that led to the door, I saw, a few steps away, a guard on duty who was coming toward us. My heart almost stopped beating, and, not knowing what to do, I stood still. But Villa walked right ahead; he passed me at the same time as the official and greeted him with perfect ease:

"'Good afternoon, chief,' he said in a hoarse, steady voice.

"When I saw that the guard walked on and paid no attention to us, I pulled myself together and followed a little behind Villa.

" 'Some friend!' said Villa as soon as we could talk. 'Didn't I tell you not to stop and not to be afraid no matter what happened?'

"We worked our way through the side streets until we came to the center of the city, and as we made our way there, Villa convinced me that I ought to escape with him.

" 'You don't want anything to happen to you, do you?' he asked.

" 'Well, naturally not, General.'

" 'Then you come with me. Otherwise tomorrow you'll be in jail. With me there's no danger of them catching you. Don't worry about your mother and your brothers and sisters. We'll let them know in time, and we'll send them anything they need.'

"In the Zócalo we took an automobile. Villa told the chauffeur to drive us to Tacubaya. There we got out and went up to a house as though we were going in. Then we came back to the car.

" 'The fellow we are looking for left for Toluca this morning. It's very important for us to see him. Can you drive us there? We'll pay you well, provided you don't ask too much.'

"The chauffeur agreed to make the trip, after Villa had driven a hard bargain about the price. And when we got to Toluca, Villa said to him as he paid him:

" 'Here's your money. But I'm going to give you ten pesos besides, so that you will come back for us day after tomorrow. We'll wait for you right here. If you don't come, it will be your loss, my boy. We'll pay you better on the trip home than we did coming here.'

" 'But are we going back to Mexico City, General?' I asked Villa as soon as we were alone.

" 'No, buddy. We're going to take the train now to Manzanillo. There we'll sail for Mazatlán, and from there we'll go by train to the United States. I gave that money to the chauffeur, telling him to come back, so that if the police get hold of him and question him, they won't suspect that it was us in his car. That's why I bargained with him about the price.' "

Some months afterward, when the Constitutionalist Revolution broke out, Villa said to Carlitos Jáuregui: "When I take Ciudad Juárez, buddy, I'm going to make you a present of the lottery houses in return for what you did for me." And the day after the brilliant maneuvers that gave the Division of the North the frontier city to have and to hold, Jáuregui received the monopoly of the famous kenos. These were the most innocent of the gambling establishments in Ciudad Juárez. The least innocent were the poker games, the roulette wheels, and the crap games. This concession Villa had given to his brother Hipólito.

2 THE CARNIVAL OF THE BULLETS

My interest in Villa and his activities often made me ask myself, while I was in Ciudad Juárez, which exploits would best paint the Division of the North: those supposed to be strictly historical or those rated as legendary; those related exactly as they had been seen, or those in which a touch of poetic fancy brought out their essence more clearly. These second always seemed to me truer, more worthy of being considered history.

For instance, where could one find a better painting of Rodolfo Fierro—and Fierro and Villa's movement were two facing mirrors that reflected each other endlessly—than in the account of how he carried out the terrible orders of his chief after one of the battles, revealing an imagination as cruel as it was fertile in death devices. This vision of him left in the soul the sensation of a reality so overwhelming that the memory of it lives forever.

That battle, which was successful in every way, had left not less than five hundred prisoners in Villa's hands. Villa ordered them to be divided into two groups: the Orozco volunteers, whom we called "Reds," in one, and the Federals in the other. And as he felt himself strong enough to take extreme measures, he decided to make an example of the first group and to act more generously toward the second. The "Reds" were to be executed before dark; the Federals were to be given their choice of joining the revolutionary troops or returning home, after promising not to take up arms again against the Constitutionalist cause.

Fierro, as might have been expected, was put in charge of the execution, and he displayed in it that efficiency which was already winning him great favor with Villa, his "chief," as he called him.

It was growing late in the afternoon. The revolutionary forces, off duty, were slowly gathering in the little village that had been the objective of their offensive. The cold, penetrating wind of the Chihuahuan plains began to blow up, and the groups of cavalry and infantry sought protection against the groups of buildings. But Fierro—whom nothing and nobody ever held back—was not to be put out by a cool breeze that at most meant frost that night. He cantered along on his horse, whose dark coat was still covered with the dust of battle. The wind was blowing in his face, but he neither buried his chin in his breast nor raised the folds of his blanket around his face. He carried his head high, his chest thrown out, his feet firm in the stirrups, and his legs gracefully flexed under the campaign equipment that hung from the saddle straps. The barren plain and an occasional soldier that passed at a distance were his only spectators. But he, perhaps without even thinking about it, reined his horse to make him show his gaits as though he were on parade. Fierro was happy; the satisfaction of victory filled his being; and to him victory was complete only when it meant the utter rout of the enemy; and in this frame of mind even the buffeting of the wind, and riding after fifteen hours in the saddle, were agreeable. The rays of the pale setting sun seemed to caress him as they fell.

He reached the stableyard where the condemned prisoners were shut up like a herd of cattle, and he reined in a moment to look at them over the fence rails. They were well-built men of the type of Chihuahua, tall, compact, with strong necks and well-set-up shoulders on vigorous, flexible backs. As Fierro looked over the little captive army and sized up its military value and prowess, a strange pulsation ran through him, a twitching that went from his heart or from his forehead out to the index finger of his right hand. Involuntarily the palm of this hand reached out to the butt of his pistol.

"Here's a battle for you," he thought.

The cavalrymen, bored with their task of guarding the prisoners, paid no attention to him. The only thing that mattered to them was the annoyance of mounting this tiresome guard, all the worse after the excitement of the battle. They had to have their rifles ready on their knees, and when an occasional soldier left the group, they aimed at him with an air that left no room for doubt as to their intentions, and, if necessary, fired. A wave would run over the formless surface of the mass of the prisoners, who huddled together to avoid the shot. The bullet either went wide or shot one of them down.

Fierro rode up to the gate of the stableyard. He called to a soldier, who let down the bars, and went in. Without taking off his serape he dismounted. His legs were numb with cold and weariness, and he stretched them. He settled his two pistols in their holsters. Next he began to look slowly over the pens, observing their layout and how they were divided up. He took several steps over to one of the fences, where he tied his horse to a fence board. He slipped something out of one of the pockets of his saddle into his coat pocket and crossed the yard, at a short distance from the prisoners.

There were three pens that opened into one another, with gates and a narrow passageway between. From the one where the prisoners were kept, Fierro went into the middle enclosure, slipping through the bars of the gate. He went straight

over to the next one. There he stopped. His tall, handsome
figure seemed to give off a strange radiance, something superior, awe-inspiring, and yet not out of keeping with the desolation of the barnyard. His serape had slipped down until
it barely hung from his shoulders; the tassels of the corners
dragged on the ground. His gray, broad-brimmed hat turned
rose-colored where the slanting rays of the setting sun fell
on it. Through the fences the prisoners could see him at a
distance, his back turned toward them. His legs formed a
pair of herculean, glistening compasses: it was the gleam of
his leather puttees in the light of the afternoon.

About a hundred yards away, outside the pens, was the
officer of the troop in charge of the prisoners. Fierro made
signs to him to come closer, and the officer rode over to the
fence beside Fierro. The two began to talk. In the course of
the conversation Fierro pointed out different spots in the
enclosure in which he was standing and in the one next to it.
Then he described with gestures of his hand a series of operations, which the officer repeated, as though to understand
them better. Fierro repeated two or three times what seemed
to be a very important operation, and the officer, now sure
about his orders, galloped off toward the prisoners.

Fierro turned back toward the center of the stableyard,
studying once more the layout of the fence, and other details. That pen was the largest of the three, and the first in
order, the nearest to the town. On two sides gates opened
into the fields; the bars of these, though more worn than
those of the farther pens, were of better wood. On the other
side there was a gate that opened into the adjoining pen,
and on the far side the fence was not of boards, but was an
adobe wall, not less than six feet high. The wall was about a
hundred and thirty feet long, and about forty feet of it
formed the back of a shed or stalls, the roof of which sloped
down from the wall and rested on the one side on the end
posts of the lateral fence, which had been left longer, and on
the other on a wall, also of adobes, which came out perpendicular from the wall and extended some twenty-five feet

into the barnyard. Thus, between the shed and the fence of
the adjoining lot, there was a space enclosed on two sides by
solid walls. In that corner the wind that afternoon was piling
up rubbish and clanging an iron bucket against the well-curb
with an arbitrary rhythm. From the well-curb there rose up
two rough forked posts, crossed by a third, from which a pul-
ley and chain hung, which also rattled in the wind. On the
tip-top of one of the forks sat a large whitish bird, hardly
distinguishable from the twisted points of the dry pole.

Fierro was standing about fifty steps from the well. He
rested his eye for a moment on the motionless bird, and as
though its presence fitted in perfectly with his thoughts, without a change of attitude or expression, he slowly pulled out
his pistol. The long, polished barrel of the gun turned into a
glowing finger in the light of the sun. Slowly it rose until it
pointed in the direction of the bird. A shot rang out—dry
and diminutive in the immensity of the afternoon—and the
bird dropped to the ground. Fierro returned his pistol to its
holster.

At that moment a soldier jumped over the fence into the
yard. It was Fierro's orderly. It had been such a high jump
that it took him several seconds to get to his feet. When he
finally did, he walked over to where his master was standing.

Without turning his head Fierro answered:

"What about them? If they don't come soon, we aren't going to have time."

"I think they're coming."

"Then you hurry up and get over there. Let's see, what
pistol have you got?"

"The one you gave me, chief. The Smith and Wesson."

"Hand it over here and take these boxes of bullets. How
many bullets have you got?"

"I gathered up about fifteen dozen today, chief. Some of
the others found lots of them, but I didn't."

"Fifteen dozen? I told you the other day that if you kept
on selling ammunition to buy booze, I'd put a bullet through
you."

"No, chief."

"What do you mean: 'No, chief'?"

"I do get drunk, chief, but I don't sell the ammunition."

"Well, you watch out, for you know me. And now you move lively so this stunt will be a success. I fire and you load the pistols. And mind what I tell you: if on your account a single one of the Reds gets away, I'll put you to sleep with them."

"Oh, chief!"

"You heard what I said."

The orderly spread his blanket on the ground and emptied onto it the boxes of cartridges that Fierro had just given him. Then he began to take out one by one the bullets in his cartridge belt. He was in such a hurry that it took him longer than it should have. He was so nervous that his fingers seemed all thumbs.

"What a chief!" he kept thinking to himself.

In the meantime, behind the fence of the adjoining barn lot, soldiers of the guard began to appear. They were on horseback, and their shoulders showed above the top fence rail. There were many others along the two other fences.

Fierro and his orderly were the only ones inside the barnyard; Fierro stood with a pistol in his hand, and his serape fallen at his feet. His orderly squatted beside him lining up the bullets in rows on his blanket.

The commander of the troop rode up through the gate that opened into the next lot, and said:

"I've got the first ten ready. Shall I let them out for you?"

"Yes," answered Fierro, "but first explain things to them. As soon as they come through the gate, I'll begin to shoot. Those that reach the wall and get over it are free. If any of them doesn't want to come through, you put a bullet into him."

The officer went back the same way, and Fierro, pistol in hand, stood attentive, his eyes riveted on the narrow space through which the soldiers had to come out. He stood close enough to the dividing fence so that, as he fired, the bullets would not hit the Reds who were still on the other side. He wanted to keep his promise faithfully. But he was not so close that the prisoners could not see, the minute they came through the gate, the pistol that was leveled at them twenty paces off. Behind Fierro the setting sun turned the sky into a fiery ball. The wind kept blowing.

In the barnyard where the prisoners were herded, the voices grew louder, but the howling of the wind made the shouts sound like herders rounding up cattle. It was a hard task to make the three hundred condemned men pass from the last to the middle lot. At the thought of the torture awaiting them, the whole group writhed with the convulsions of a person in the grip of hysteria. The soldiers of the guard shouted, and every minute the reports of the rifles seemed to emphasize the screams as with a whip crack.

Out of the first prisoners that reached the middle pen a group of soldiers separated ten. There were at least twenty-five soldiers. They spurred their horses on to the prisoners to make them move; they rested the muzzles of their rifles against their bodies.

"Traitors! Dirty bastards! Let's see you run and jump. Get a move on, you traitor!"

And in this way they made them advance to the gate where Fierro and his orderly were waiting. Here the resistance of the Reds grew stronger; but the horses' hoofs and the gun barrels persuaded them to choose the other danger, the danger of Fierro, which was not an inch away, but twenty paces.

As soon as they appeared within his range of vision, Fierro greeted them with a strange phrase, at once cruel and affectionate, half ironical and half encouraging.

"Come on, boys; I'm only going to shoot, and I'm a bad shot."

The prisoners jumped like goats. The first one tried to throw himself on Fierro, but he had not made three bounds before he fell, riddled by bullets from the soldiers stationed along the fence. The others ran as fast as they could toward the wall—a mad race that must have seemed to them like a dream. One tried to take refuge behind the well-curb: he was the target for Fierro's first bullet. The others fell as they ran, one by one; in less than ten seconds Fierro had fired eight times, and the last of the group dropped just as his fingers were touching the adobes that by the strange whim of the moment separated the zone of life from the zone of death. Some of the bodies showed signs of life; the soldiers finished them off from their horses.

And then came another group of ten, and then another, and another, and another. The three pistols of Fierro—his two and that of his orderly—alternated with precise rhythm in the homicidal hand. Six shots from each one, six shots fired without stopping to aim and without pause, and then the gun dropped on to the orderly's blanket, where he removed the exploded caps, and reloaded it. Then, without changing his position, he held out the pistol to Fierro, who took it as he let the other fall. Through the orderly's fingers passed the bullets that seconds later would leave the prisoners stretched lifeless, but he did not raise his eyes to see those that fell. His whole soul seemed concentrated on the pistol in his hand, and on the bullets, with their silver and burnished reflections, spread out on the ground before him. Just two sensations filled his whole being: the cold weight of the bullets that he was putting into the openings of the barrel, and the warm smoothness of the gun. Over his head one after another rang out the shots of his "chief," entertaining himself with his sharpshooting.

The panic-stricken flight of the prisoners toward the wall of salvation—a fugue of death in which the two themes of the passion to kill and the infinite desire to live were blended —lasted almost two hours.

Not for one minute did Fierro lose his precision of aim or his poise. He was firing at moving human targets, targets that jumped and slipped in pools of blood and amidst corpses stretched out in unbelievable postures, but he fired without other emotion than that of hitting or missing. He calculated the deflection caused by the wind, and corrected it with each shot.

Some of the prisoners, crazed by terror, fell to their knees as they came through the gate. There the bullet laid them low. Others danced about grotesquely behind the shelter of the well-curb until the bullet cured them of their frenzy or they dropped wounded into the well. But nearly all rushed toward the adobe wall and tried to climb it over the warm, damp, steaming heaps of piled-up bodies. Some managed to dig their nails into the earth coping, but their hands, so avid of life, soon fell lifeless.

There came a moment in which the mass execution became a noisy tumult, punctuated by the dry snap of the pistol shots, muted by the voice of the wind. On one side of the fence the shouts of those who fled from death only to die; on the other, those who resisted the pressure of the horsemen and tried to break through the wall that pushed them on toward that terrible gate. And to the shouts of one group and the other were added the voices of the soldiers stationed along the fences. The noise of the shooting, the marksmanship of Fierro, and the cries and frantic gestures of the condemned men had worked them up to a pitch of great excitement. The somersaults of the bodies as they fell in the death agony elicited loud exclamations of amusement from them, and they shouted, gesticulated, and gave peals of laughter as they fired into the mounds of bodies in which they saw the slightest evidence of life.

In the last squad of victims there were twelve instead of ten. The twelve piled out of the death pen, falling over one another, each trying to protect himself with the others, in his anxiety to win in the horrible race. To go forward they had to jump over the piled-up corpses, but not for this reason did the bullet err in its aim. With sinister precision it hit them one by one and left them on the way to the wall, arms and legs outstretched, embracing the mass of their motionless companions. But one of them, the only one left alive, managed to reach the coping and swing himself over. The firing

stopped and the troop of soldiers crowded into the corner of
the adjoining barn lot to see the fugitive.

It was beginning to get dark. It took the soldiers a little
while to focus their vision in the twilight. At first they could
see nothing. Finally, far off, in the vastness of the darkling
plain they managed to make out a moving spot. As it ran,
the body bent so far over that it almost seemed to crawl
along on the ground.

A soldier took aim. "It's hard to see," he said as he fired.

The report died away in the evening wind. The moving
spot fled on.

Fierro had not moved from his place. His arm was exhausted, and he let it hang limp against his side for a long
time. Then he became aware of a pain in his forefinger and
raised his hand to his face; he could see that the finger was
somewhat swollen. He rubbed it gently between the fingers
and the palm of his other hand and for a good space of time
kept up this gentle massage. Finally he stooped over and
picked up his serape, which he had taken off at the beginning of the executions. He threw it over his shoulders and
walked to the shelter of the stalls. But after a few steps he
turned to his orderly:

"When you're finished, bring up the horses."

And he went on his way.

The orderly was gathering up the exploded caps. In the
next pen the soldiers of the guard had dismounted and were
talking or singing softly. The orderly heard them in silence
and without raising his head. Finally he got slowly to his
feet. He gathered up the blanket by the four corners and
threw it over his shoulder. The empty caps rattled in it with a
dull tintinnabulation.

It was dark. A few stars glimmered, and on the other side
of the fence the cigarettes shone red. The orderly walked
heavily and slowly and, half feeling his way, went to the last
of the pens and in a little while returned leading his own

and his master's horses by the bridle; across one of his shoulders swung the haversack.

He made his way over to the stalls. Fierro was sitting on a rock, smoking. The wind whistled through the cracks in the boards.

"Unsaddle the horse and make up my bed," ordered Fierro. "I'm so tired I can't stand up."

"Here in this pen, chief? Here . . . ?"

"Sure. Why not?"

The orderly did as he was ordered. He unsaddled the horse and spread the blankets on the straw, making a kind of pillow out of the haversack and the saddle. Fierro stretched out and in a few minutes was asleep.

The orderly lighted his lantern and bedded the horses for the night. Then he blew out the light, wrapped himself in his blanket, and lay down at the feet of his master. But in a minute he was up again and knelt down and crossed himself. Then he stretched out on the straw again.

Six or seven hours went by. The wind had died down. The silence of the night was bathed in moonlight. Occasionally a horse snuffled. The radiance of the moon gleamed on the dented surface of the bucket that hung by the well and made clear shadows of all the objects in the yard except the mounds of corpses. These rose up, enormous in the stillness of the night, like fantastic hills, strange and confused in outline.

The blue silver of the night descended on the corpses in rays of purest light. But little by little that light turned into a voice, a voice that had the unreality of the night. It grew distinct; it was a voice that was barely audible, faint and tortured, but clear like the shadows cast by the moon. From the center of one of the mounds of corpses the voice seemed to whisper:

"Oh! Oh!"

The heaped-up bodies, stiff and cold for hours, lay motionless in the barnyard. The moonlight sank into them as into an inert mass. But the voice sounded again:

"Oh . . . Oh . . . Oh . . ."

And this last groan reached to the spot where Fierro's orderly lay sleeping and brought him out of sleep to the consciousness of hearing. The first thing that came to his mind was the memory of the execution of the three hundred prisoners; the mere thought of it kept him motionless in the straw, his eyes half open and his whole soul fixed on the lamentation of that voice:

"Oh . . . please . . ."

Fierro tossed on his bed.

"Please . . . water . . ."

Fierro awoke and listened attentively.

"Please . . . water . . ."

Fierro stretched out his foot until he touched his orderly.

"Hey, you. Don't you hear? One of those dead men is asking for water."

"Yes, chief."

"You get up and put a bullet through the sniveling son of a bitch. Let's see if he'll let me get some sleep then."

"A bullet through who, chief?"

"The one that's asking for water, you fool. Don't you understand?"

"Water, please," the voice kept on.

The orderly took his pistol from under the saddle and started out of the shed in search of the voice. He shivered with fear and cold. He felt sick to his soul.

He looked around in the light of the moon. Every body he touched was stiff. He hesitated without knowing what to do. Finally he fired in the direction from which the voice came. The voice kept on. The orderly fired again. The voice died away.

The moon floated through the limitless space of its blue light. Under the shelter of the shed Fierro slept.

Part Two

THE HOUR OF TRIUMPH

BOOK I

En Route to Mexico

---

1 VILLA OR CARRANZA?

The long months of my stay in Chihuahua brought about my gradual—gradual and voluntary—separation from the faction that had formed around Carranza and his unconditional adherents. The other faction—a rebellion within a rebellion —restless and impatient of restraint, represented an aspect of the Revolution with which I felt more in sympathy. This second group had already drawn together men like Maytorena, Cabral, Angeles, Escudero, Díaz Lombardo, Vasconcelos, Puente, Malváez—all those, in a word, who wanted to preserve the democratic and impersonal character of the Revolution, so that in the course of two or three years it should not have become the mere instrument of another oligarchy, perhaps more ignorant and selfish than that of Porfirio Díaz. To be sure, I didn't see how we were going to realize our ideals; it seemed to me enormously difficult, improbable— as improbable for a small group, however heroic its determination to fight to the last ditch against personal ambition and corruption, as it would have been easy if it had represented the unanimous undertaking of a well-directed, unified Revolution. But I had seen beyond evidence of doubt in Sonora that under Carranza's leadership the Revolution was headed for the most unbridled and unrestrained absolutism, and this was enough to turn me in any other direction in the hope of salvation.

The mere fact that all the group opposed to Carranza rallied around Villa as its military leader might have been taken, if not as a presage of our eventual defeat, as evidence of the internal conflict that thwarted the Revolution in its noblest objectives; because it was impossible to think of Villa as the standard-bearer of an elevated, reconstructive movement; and even as a mere brute force he had such serious limitations that dealing with him was like handling dynamite. But, in spite of this, the fact remained that the only military elements on which we could count for the support of our ideas were those commanded by him. The other important winner of battles, Obregón—Angeles, without any troops of his own, so to speak, had thrown in his lot with Villa—was following the lead of the new absolutism. So, for us, the future of the Constitutionalist movement was bound up in the following question: would it be possible to control Villa —Villa, who was too irresponsible and instinctive even to know how to be ambitious? Would he put his force at the service of principles that either did not exist for him or were incomprehensible to him?

This was the dilemma: either Villa would submit to the fundamental principles of the Revolution, and, if so, he and the Revolution would triumph; or Villa would follow nothing but his own blind impulses, and he and the Revolution would go down to defeat. And it was around this dilemma that the tempest of the Revolution was to revolve in the hour of triumph.

2 A Night in Coatzacoalcos

When Victoriano Huerta's fall was merely a matter of a short time, Villa ordered Colonel Carlos Domínguez and me to be in Mexico City during the entrance of the Constitutionalist forces and afterward to act as his representatives to the First Chief. The breaking-off of relations between Villa and Carranza gave the commission rather a perilous nature. But, notwithstanding, Domínguez and I accepted—as we had before accepted other things even more dangerous—and we set out from El Paso, Texas, for the capital by way of Cayo Hueso and Havana.

Ten days after we reached Cuba, we sailed for Veracruz on the *Maria Cristina*. There were several ticklish points about that trip, and one of them was the danger that we might be taken prisoner when the boat stopped at Puerto Méjico, which was still in the hands of Huerta's troops. But as it did not seem prudent to wait longer, for fear we might not be in the capital in time to carry out General Villa's orders, we decided to proceed on our way.

It was painful to break off our stay in Havana, so unexpected, so welcome, so agreeable had it been after the political agitations of the preceding months. Menocal, a brother of the President of Cuba, and Arturo Grande, an architect friend of Domínguez's, made of our stay in their lovely country an endless procession of pleasant hours. Even after we had left, on the ship, on the sea, I caressed the memory of many perfect days. The blue, the pearl gray, the gay houses of El Vedado; the shadowy halls with their mosaic floors and tiled wainscoting, opening at the opposite end into luminous patios that recalled those of Andalusia, with white rocking chairs and pots of blooming flowers; the splendid mornings at the Yacht Club, among beautiful bathers—the loveliest women of all America—under a sun that was life and fire; the evening strolls along the Malecón, with eyes fixed on the blue of the sea, vivid like no other. And so everything else, everything of the same superb, savory quality, even the commonplace, like the shrimps sold on the sidewalk in front of the Hotel Telégrafo, or the lowly, like the coconut milk and soursop juice drunk alongside the street stalls.

In spite of our fears nothing serious happened in Puerto Méjico, although we could not resist the temptation of going ashore on our native soil the night we landed.

To carry out this small adventure in patriotic enthusiasm —or sudden homesickness—Domínguez decided that we ought to disguise ourselves. How? As Spanish sailors. This was not difficult, thanks to the help of two officers with whom we had struck up an acquaintance on board, and who lent us part of their outfit. I do not recall with what naval rank I invested myself as I got into a handsome uniform trimmed with anchors and gold braid, but I had been metamorphosed into a figure that seemed to me fantastic as I stepped on to Mexican territory.

It was late as we strolled down the wharf, affecting a sailor's roll in our walk, and made our way into the town. The streets were deserted and dark. The feeble animation that existed near the wharf died away, like a flame that gutters out, in the faint flickers of a few thin scattered groups of people that sat and chatted beside their doorsteps.

Finally, in a little park we saw some booths that had managed to hold a few small clusters of men and women under the spell of their melancholy lights. We sauntered over toward them. There seemed to be a fair going on. There was a lottery stand, tastefully decorated with rows of pitchers, glasses, dishes, and other ornaments of pottery and glassware. There were two or three simple roulette wheels, three tables for cards and dice, a stand where rings were tossed on boards scattered over with coins, and a miserable eating place on wheels.

Domínguez and I stopped in front of the ring stand with the authentic curiosity of strangers. Ten or fifteen queer-looking fellows were throwing away their money, ballyhooed on by the proprietor of the stand and his wife. She seemed to be unusually clever at turning mere spectators into performers, because she was the one that extracted most of the copper coins from everyone's pocket. One of the players stood out among the rest. He was young and had on a yellow shirt, white trousers, black leggings, no coat, collar, or tie, a pistol on his hip, and a belt full of cartridges. He was playing with a furious determination to win, but he was so clumsy that

every time he tossed, the rings bounced as though made of
rubber off the red cloth where the coins were scattered.

The game, though extremely difficult, seemed at first
glance very easy. Two minutes after we came up, Domínguez
and I had a supply of rings in our hands. Domínguez was
eager to win something and he made his throws very carefully; he tried to work out a technique, using first one method
and then another. To me it seemed that it was next to impossible to throw the ring over a coin, and I threw just for
the fun of it. And it happened by the merest chance that
one of my shots fell over a ten-centavo piece. My skill caused
such surprise among the bystanders that they stopped playing for a few seconds. The woman of the booth came over
to me and, smiling, handed me the money I had won; and
while all this was going on, the fellow in the yellow shirt kept
watching first me and then Domínguez and then said something in a low voice to a friend who was standing near.

A few minutes later, playing in the same nonchalant fashion, I won again. But this time the ring fell over a twenty-
centavo piece instead of a ten. It caused a sensation. The
woman came over again to pay me, but this time she wasn't
smiling, and she was clearly put out. And the fellow with the
pistol, looking at me again, this time insolently, said to his
friend in a voice loud enough for us to hear: "You might have
known they would be *gachupines*. . . ."[1]

It wasn't hard to see what he meant. Partly because of the
Spanish uniforms we were wearing and partly because we had
won while the others lost, it was plain that we weren't very
popular with the crowd. So we decided it would be better
policy to move away from the ring stand, and we went over
to a nearby dice and card table.

There was nobody near the place except the old woman
in charge of it, who was half asleep beside the kerosene lamp.

"I'm very lucky at this," said Domínguez as he picked up
the shaker and the cubes.

[1] A disrespectful, insulting name applied to Spaniards in Mexico.

The old woman came to life when she saw us and became almost cheerful as Domínguez asked her: "How much a throw, señora . . . ?"

"Whatever you like, sir," she said, "but two reales is the limit."

Domínguez then gave himself over to losing. And he did it so conscientiously that the old lady began to cheer him on with loud cries, evidently intended to attract other clients to her booth:

"This time you're going to win. Just roll a seven, and the money's yours."

And her shouts attracted several of the players from the ring stand, among them the one in the yellow shirt, with the revolver.

Domínguez went on playing and losing. The fellow in the yellow shirt stood by, watching while Domínguez rolled the dice several times. He seemed to become convinced of Domínguez's bad luck and, thinking it would be easy enough to win merely by playing against him, buried his hand in his pocket. But it so happened—strange whims of chance— that he had no more than started betting his reales and pesetas when Domínguez's luck began to change. It seemed as though he could roll any number he wanted.

The man took the first three losses without blinking, hiding his real feelings behind a sarcastic little smile that made his dark oily skin seem still shinier. But as Domínguez went on steadily winning, he began to look lowering. At the end he began to play in such a hopelessly absurd manner that every time Domínguez tossed, the old woman simply gave him part of the money the other had bet, and kept part for herself.

There came a moment when the other could not stand the situation any longer, and he called from his end of the table to the other, where a friend of his was standing: "What a good thing it will be when we win the Revolution and settle the hash of all the *gachupines!* . . ."

As he said this, Domínguez very calmly set the shaker down

on the table, gathered up his money, and, looking straight at the fellow with the revolver for the first time, took him by the arm and made a gesture as though inviting him to step over to the other side of the square: "Excuse me, but I'd like to have a word with you."

"Wherever you like," said the other, walking along with him.

Everybody then—the fellow with the revolver, his friends, Domínguez, and I, started toward the darkest spot of the square. And there Domínguez, turning to face the man, spoke to him in the following terms, as befitted the occasion:

"Look here," he said; "in the first place, we're not *gachupines*, even though we look like it in these clothes. We're Mexicans and I want you to know that we belong to the forces of General Francisco Villa, for whom we are carrying out a secret mission in Mexico City. In the second place, the son of a bitch hasn't been born yet that can insult us and get away with it. So right now you're going to take back all your insolence or we'll settle the matter right here, with fists or pistols, whichever you like."

When the fellow in the yellow shirt heard the name of the Chief of the Division of the North, he was struck speechless. But he wasn't altogether a coward or a fool, for he answered Domínguez's attack, which had been extremely harsh, in a firm though conciliatory tone:

"All right, if you're not *gachupines*, I take back what I said. But if you are, everything I said goes, and we'll see about the consequences."

"Well, you heard me say that we weren't," answered Domínguez, calming down a little.

"Yes, but how do I know it?" insisted the other, who was trying to cover up his retreat. "Because if it's true you are with General Villa, it wouldn't be loyal to the cause to fight with you. But if it isn't true, my honor has to be avenged."

Here I interrupted: "Do you want to see our documents? Come with me to the ship and I'll show them to you. You can convince yourself that . . ."

"Papers? What do we need papers for? Anybody can see a mile off that you're telling the honest truth. I didn't mean any offense, and I want you to consider me a friend and fellow worker. I'm in the Revolution myself. I'm General Pérez. I came to this port incognito to carry out a commission of my own. . . . This is Colonel Caloca, my chief of staff, and this is Captain Moreno, my adjutant and a man in whom I repose the greatest confidence."

Once peace was established, General Pérez, who was delighted to have made the acquaintance of two of Villa's representatives, invited us to have something to eat with him at the lunch counter on wheels. The five of us sat down around a dirty table, like old friends, and we ate and drank everything the woman brought us. After the third bottle of beer General Pérez began relating his campaigns and something of his biography. Every now and then the sight of our Spanish merchant-marine uniforms: blue caps trimmed with gold braid, and displaying the emblem of the *Compañía Trasatlántica*, our white uniforms, with shining brass buttons and gold braid like that of the cap, at the cuffs, seemed to make him uneasy again. But finally, at about the sixth or seventh bottle of beer, the general became completely reconciled to the situation, thanks to one of those strange miracles of the language. He began to call both of us "chief" every time he spoke to us. And in this way he put his subconscious into a complacent mood with regard to a state of affairs that it would not tolerate so long as he treated us as equals. But by establishing us as superiors the instinct of submission in General Pérez, standard-bearer of liberty, became stronger than his instinct of hate.

3 A VISION OF VERACRUZ

At nine in the morning the *María Cristina* slipped between two Yankee dreadnoughts that were rocking at anchor before the bay of Veracruz. The passengers divided up into two groups, and some at starboard, some at larboard, we stood gazing in silence on those two floating steel castles, powerful, strange, fantastic. Under the August sun the sea lay pale blue, its broad waves smooth and calm. There was a moment when the warships were so close to us that the breeze brought us the sound of the foreign voices and we could see with absolute clarity—even the rakish grace of the white caps on the blond heads—the sailors gaily polishing the blue-gray barrels of the huge cannon.

But the sight was of brief duration, and an hour later the *María Cristina* disembarked us on one of the docks of the port, our souls torn between admiration, rage, and anxiety by what we had just seen.

That Veracruz was new to me. The old port of my childhood, filled until shortly before with wonderful memories of the past, was now going through one of those phases so typical of it, and which give it that outstanding and dramatic role in which history has cast it. It was a Veracruz of impotence, humiliation, tragedy. As they set foot on it once again, the North American troops tinged its atmosphere with an imponderable air of conflict. The heroic response floated anew over its blackened roofs, raising once more the cruel question of all heroisms that have gone down to defeat: why is it that a quality may be useless even when it is great?

Near the Naval Academy the children eagerly left their games to show the visitor the spot where Lieutenant Azueta fell. "Here," they said, touching the ground with their small caressing hands. And the visitor, especially if he was one like myself who had been born to emotional awareness of his native land beneath that light, seeing that blue marine expanse, caressed by that breeze, silently echoed the children's "Here," and then, raising his eyes from the ground, paused to contemplate the horizon. Down the street, in the distance, lay the quiet and glittering waters of the bay mirroring the gently swaying ships, the same waters destiny had once appointed for Cortés's arrival and the mighty epic of the conquest.

But at that moment Veracruz teemed not only with the
international conflict; it was bespattered by the internal as
well. That afternoon we saw Don Francisco Bulnes, Luna
Parra, and other eminences of the Huerta regime in Villa
del Mar. Bulnes had aged, and he seemed to me smaller than
I remembered him, as though he had shrunk in stature and
volume. I observed him for a long time without his seeing
me. It seemed to me that he was making an effort to con-
centrate, to meditate in time to the rhythm of the waves,
which broke at the foot of the terrace where we were sitting;
but his restless, questioning spirit was distracted against his
will by all the outward accidents that impinged upon it.
Above his Semitic nose his highly intelligent eyes gleamed,
missing nothing. Several times they came to rest on Domínguez and me, and on one of these occasions I noticed, despite
the reflections of sky and sea his glasses gave back, that he
was analyzing us piece by piece.

"He doesn't know us," I said to Domínguez; "but you may
be sure he has guessed who we are."

The day after our arrival we ran into Alfredo Breceda at
the door of La Parroquia. The meeting surprised us, and it
must have had the same effect on Breceda. He had firsthand knowledge of the fact that both Domínguez and I were,
so to speak, banned from all territory under Carranza's control. Then why, he must have asked himself, had we disembarked in Veracruz if it was not that we were en route to
the center of the Republic, which was held by Carranza?

As there was no reason to camouflage our plans, we told
him straight out what our political mission and program was:
we were on our way to Mexico City as envoys of Villa, and we
planned to continue our trip in two or three days. He, who
was devious on principle and by nature, did not tell us clearly
what he was up to. He spoke vaguely about "a very important
commission" entrusted to him by the First Chief; he mentioned a sum of money—two or three million pesos in paper
currency—that he was carrying with him to accomplish his
task efficiently, and assured us that he had been waiting

two or three days in Veracruz for the opportune moment
to leave for Mexico City. Before going, he added, it had
seemed to him the sensible thing to wait there for President
Carbajal to turn over the government of the Republic to the
revolutionary authorities.

As always when I went to Veracruz, my first visit was to
Don Delfino Valenzuela. Don Delfino Valenzuela, an illustrious son of Veracruz, who was not a general, nor did he
aspire to become the savior of his country through the presidency, but who, nevertheless, had done far more for his country than many generals and Presidents put together, for he
was a great teacher, a true educator. My former teacher no
longer directed the Cantonal School; he now had a private
school where he devoted himself to molding the soul of the
new generations, employing to this end the excellent methods
he had learned as a distinguished student of Rebsamén, and
his noble spirit unflaggingly at the service of cultural values.
I found him in his new school the first evening I set out to
look for him.

I should have liked to talk over with him my childhood
years; the pleasant memories of the school in Ciriaco Vázquez
Park, the bright classrooms with their high windows always
open to the sea breeze and the tropical perfumes of the
garden; those unforgettable afternoons, those privileged afternoons, when Don Delfino, the day's work done, gathered his
favorite pupils in his office to read to them, from a handsome
volume he took out of a handsome bookcase, the episodes of
the Reform campaign and the three heroic defenses of Veracruz. A multitude of images of those scenes, those readings,
those days surged through my mind. But the foreign bugle
calls the wind brought to us from time to time, and the outline of those strange warships, which neither Don Delfino
nor I could see at the moment, but which we divined beyond the Naval Academy, alight and vigilant at the mouth
of the bay, were too powerful and immediate an influence
for us to be able to disregard it.

When we had seated ourselves at the broad and project-
ing balcony (the typical balcony of Veracruz, oversized, with
a plain railing, so right for that climate), Don Delfino spoke
in a melancholy tone of the North American occupation. His
words as he uttered them seemed to be set like jewels in the
moonlight, and thus to duplicate the sadness of his purling
voice, a sadness which in some strange way became associated
in my mind with the feel of the wooden railing with its heavy
posts, half silvery green, half dark, rough to the touch and,
together with the moving blotch of our silhouettes, distorted
against the old blackened wall by the moonlight.

Don Delfino told me many things that night. But of them
all two stand out in my mind with absolute clarity, that absolute clarity peculiar to certain memories.

"The schools? First off, the Yankees turned them into
barracks. Then they remembered that there is such a thing
as public education, and they tried to get the teachers to
work under their orders. I, they said, was the obvious choice
to direct the educational service they planned to make us
carry on. The teachers, men and women, as you can imagine,
refused flatly, and to the last man. No, that's wrong; not to
the last man; there was one traitor . . . a traitor."

And that terrible epithet—traitor—fell from Don Delfino's
lips without a trace of hatred, or rancor, or anger. The only
touch of emotion as he spoke the word was a faint quaver
of his melancholy voice which, as it emitted the two syllables,
took on a muted timbre, a frozen tone. "Traitor!" The integrity of that flawless man suffered because of the faint-
heartedness of the weak, yet even as he despised them, he
excused them with a kind of pious generalization. In rounding out his thought, what he came to say was this: "We have
all the patriotism needed to save us someday, or perhaps to
disappear with honor; but mixed meanwhile with so much
weakness, so much pettiness."

For he felt that the North American occupation of Veracruz carried in its wake deep and troubling implications for
the future.

"This military occupation," he said, "is a preview of what may happen on a larger scale. From the material standpoint, the North Americans have made, or pretend to make, certain contributions, certain unimportant external improvements. For instance, they have screened the market place and meat market to do away with the flies. It is not much. But spiritually . . . To understand what this means spiritually—leaving out the basic factor of the humiliation—all you have to do is to observe what happens when one of the officers or soldiers of the invasion dismounts at the door of a store or bar; the bystanders fight for the honor of holding the horse's bridle, and for the tip. When the officer or soldier comes out, he gets on his horse and throws the lackey a coin."

Three days after our meeting Breceda we learned for a fact that Eduardo Iturbide had entered into negotiations with Carranza to hand Mexico City over to the revolutionary forces. At this Domínguez and I decided to leave immediately, for we felt that only by reaching the capital before Don Venustiano got there could we avoid being deported, a very real danger. In making our plans, we calculated that our friend Lucio Blanco would be arriving in Mexico City with the vanguard of the Constitutionalist troops, made up, for the most part, of the strong cavalry units which were under his direct command; and we were sure that Lucio, no matter what happened, would look after us.

Even in that we wanted to play square with Breceda, so we invited him to advance his trip and come with us. At first he raised certain difficulties because he did not see things too clearly; but when Domínguez informed him that we had friends we could count on in case we were discovered, who, we added, were powerful enough to save us from serious consequences if the arrangements between Iturbide and Carranza did not work out, he cheerfully accepted our offer and joined us in preparations for departure. I was of the opinion that the best thing to do would be to lose ourselves among the first- or second-class passengers; Breceda felt it would be safer to take a Pullman compartment and stay there, and in the end this was what we did.

The train left at seven in the morning. We traveled with the shades down; nevertheless, between the edge of the blinds and the windows, rays of light filtered through which filled the compartment with a pleasant half-light. Through them, too, we caught a view of the scenery along the route, and a glimpse of the next station.

Beyond Los Cocos we were out of the military jurisdiction of the foreign troops and among the outposts of the Federals.

"We are in enemy territory," said Breceda.

"True," answered Domínguez; "enemy, but free from invaders."

The train stopped. Outside there was the sound of voices and people moving about. We pulled one of the curtains aside a little, and peeped out. In front of our car stood a squad of soldiers. We saw the double row of dark, humble, sad faces under the ridiculous cloth caps. The bayonets gleamed in the sun. A sergeant, after parading several times in front of his small troop, stationed himself a couple of feet from our windows. It was a strange emotion, a mixture of uneasiness and joy, to see close at hand again those blue uniforms with their insignia and bright red piping.

4 THE RETURN OF A REBEL

As the train approached the capital of the Republic, the recollection of the afternoon of Huerta's treachery and of the hours that followed it came back to me vividly, and called up, as though it had only just happened, the spiritual effects those events aroused in me. A group of official thugs—I could see them now with the same emotion I had felt at the time— had gone to set fire to President Madero's house; another group was digging the hole in a park where they would throw poor Gustavo's body, still warm; and in the meantime, through the main streets of the city groups of students of the junior Military Academy drove about celebrating with frenzied shouts the triumph of the traitors. On Puente de Alvarado Avenue the young cadets drove past me, and, outraged by the crime that had just been committed, I could not restrain my indignation. Like a fool, I began screaming insults at them. Fortunately, Pedro Henríquez Ureña, a friend like a brother, a model of integrity of character, and a wise counselor, was with me, and he brought me to my senses with stern words of caution.

What was the point to breathing new life now into the images of that scene which, to tell the truth, I had never forgotten for a single one of my days as a revolutionist? Were those memories on the point, perhaps, of losing their quality of vengeful stimuli? Would they finally be blotted out by the downfall of the authors of Madero's death? What was clear was that eighteen months after the crime had been committed, the climate was ripe to call this by its rightful name: a crime, and so to call it in the very place where the betrayal and assassination had taken place. It was on this circumstance that I based the hope that my return would afford me a deep moral satisfaction, symbolically, at any rate. I felt that I was gradually arriving at the opposite pole of my earlier fury.

But there are states of mind that are unforeseeable; and this was what happened to the politician who left Mexico City to embark upon the Revolution in far-off lands, and who later, after years or months of struggle, returned to his prodigious valley on the crest of a militant and triumphant wave. For what one feels at such a moment is not the satisfaction of victory and triumph: a victory over brothers, an ephemeral triumph—selfishness, vanity. Nor is it the feeling of a duty fulfilled: always a somber and melancholy thing, on the verge of tears when feigning happiness. And even less the ignoble flattery of feeling that one's feet are on the path of success: a deceptive happiness, which deforms the soul and the truth. It is something basically disinterested and joyful—

the surprise, perhaps not translated into thought or words, of having recovered with longing, sacrifice, suffering the Valley of Mexico, a summit of natural beauty whose full savor one thus enjoys anew, and this time with the freshness of one's first impressions and the wisdom of earlier ones.

The subtile air of my great city, half of whose beauty consists in its transparence, an atmosphere which clarifies, purifies, and desiccates, revealed to me again (as though this time it were doing it only for the benefit of my senses) a world of serene happiness whose essential value resided in the invariable achievement of equilibrium: equilibrium between design and detail, line and color, surface and edge, mass and contour, the diaphanous and the opaque. The contrast between the damp shadows and the golden luminosity enveloped me in the supreme caress which is the play of light. The bodily sensation of feeling myself almost weightless, of recognizing in each movement of my limbs, each palpitation of my flesh, a winged, ethereal force filled my spirit with a secret assurance of being able to fly. True, my feet trod the ground, but only because I so willed it, for the pleasure of it, because this was the land I had been dreaming of, mine. A slight movement of the very foot on which I rested would have sufficed to launch me into the abyss of light of the uppermost regions and leave me there, endowed with the free, majestic motion of that which spurns the laws of gravity.

Drunk on clarity, but not a garish clarity, for some impalpable force managed to burnish even the faintest reflections, during the first moments of my return I did nothing but feast my eyes. Was there anything on heaven or earth comparable to the bliss of gazing once more on the white counterpoint of Popocatepetl and Iztaccíhuatl, whose magnificent beauty had been familiar to me from childhood? Mountains of mat white in the early hours of the morning; gigantic forms of gleaming quicksilver when the sun, at its zenith, gives free rein to the colors and nuances of color below; magic mountains, dream mountains, fairy-tale mountains when the afternoon covers them with the most gauzy and remote of their mantles, rose, violet, lilac, blue.

In their presence it seemed evident to me that the mountainous girdle of the valley must rise elsewhere, so as not to destroy the harmony, to grandiose proportions too. For this reason the source of natural beauty never wearies of producing there its supreme works: the immeasurably great in the immeasurably harmonious. From the two snow-capped volcanoes my eyes turned to Ajusco: a wave of rock, an overwhelming mass whose quietude—incomprehensible without the help of an entire system of mythology—is pure dynamics, force raised to the nth degree. In Ajusco I felt the pulsation of all the vigor of the valley.

At moments that huge divinity smiled, and when it did so, lingering over the less intense tones of its blue, it displayed with pride the Cyclopean ripple of its muscles: wide spaces of light filled its anfractuosities; its least furrow was covered with dense forests; the shadows of its waters hurtled down its crevasses and precipices. But the mountain did not always smile. Stern by nature, under the gaze of the glance that had seen it smile an instant earlier, it resumed its typical, storm-tossed expression. At such moments it was wrapped in the shades most characteristic of it: the dark, the gloomy, those which effaced every surface detail and made it grow, grow in the overwhelming unity of its volume. Above its towering peak the most menacing storm clouds gathered; out of them came the most deafening thunderclaps.

The mere sight of the mountains of the valley restored my spirit to its point of origin; as though there were an easier way of being which I had lost without being aware of it while I was away, and which I now suddenly recovered. It was as if the purity of my inner climate—spiritual and bodily—had been born anew by the contact with the purity of the outward climate. And this return to myself was strengthened by the ambience of the city, the effect of its perfectly aligned streets, the spaciousness of its great square, the flowered shade of its gardens, the mystery of its wood.

Everything had the same value as before, and yet everything impinged on me with new transcendence and glow, with the outpouring of the spirit that lies at the heart of all recognition. Infinite series of rediscovered sensations took possession of me, piling up in me, from the insignificant to the great, from the gentle to the intense, in arpeggios which ran through all my being at one and the same time. My body had recovered its perfect equation between the muscular and the tactile; its peripheral outlines coincided with the sense of its mass and weight; its volume displaced exactly the right space. The clothes I wore were the same, and yet they molded themselves to me more lightly and exactly, as though some invisible lining of dry, cool fluid were correcting the fit at every step. The mere tingling of the blood in the transition from the early morning hours to those in which the sun turns warm seemed to me something profoundly, secretly new. And in the same way the mere crossing from the shady to the sunny side of the street revealed to me a whole gamut of temperatures. There were infinite gradations of cool in the hallways set between two areas of sun: the street and the patio.

On the Paseo de la Reforma our car was moving in the direction opposite to the wood. At the end of the avenue, closing the double row of trunks and foliage, the wooded curtain of the hill dropped plumb. Its green velvet stretched from cloud to cloud. And higher still, in the refuge of its years, stood the castle with its unassuming contours, a castle sober in line and quality, striking in its fixity above the sea of gigantic branches. The car moved on swiftly; it entered easily, lightly as the air, into the spaces between the verdure. Farther on, the perfume of the ancient foliage—are these not the oldest trees in the valley?—added another dimension to the stillness. The huge red trunks, the regal tops of copper filigree in gigantic, disheveled locks nourish themselves on quiet, drink up quiet in the sap their millenary roots draw from the earth. The air, warm at first, suddenly grew chilly halfway down the Gran Avenida, as it became perpetual shade. The car's route took it through the place where the branches, high above the ground, are forever interlaced. Rey Avenue welcomed us to its aloof intimacy.

The mystery of the wood communicated to me one of the most authentic vibrations of the soul of my city; another was awakened as we drove slowly through the most traditional or most modern Mexican streets: from Don Juan Manuel, from San Ildefonso to San Cosme or Versailles. Most of all I felt it at the sight of the Zócalo. The Zócalo! The memory of the beauty of that great square had suffered greatly by comparison with squares of other lands. But lo, seeing it anew, it instantly regained its supremacy; its presence wiped out the impression of all the others. What was it I found again in its simplicity—horizontal and austere—of an old colonial palace? Or in the baroque and violent profile (and its grandiose and smooth surfaces) of its juxtaposition with the Cathedral and the Sagrario? The arcades again seemed to me to evoke a long history, as though they had witnessed the prowesses of a race. And this was the throb that aroused the deepest reverberation in the heart of the rebel returning to his home, to his city. That square was in keeping, like the mind of him who conceived it the day after overthrowing an entire civilization, with the grandeur of the surrounding valley; it was expansive, like the gesture of the nation that should have developed there, like its ambitions, its achievements. Would that nation one day come to be? Would it be the same which we—out of duty or passion—were now staining with blood in an interminable struggle whose reasons we hardly knew?

BOOK II

Revolutionary Justice

---

1 A POLICE INSPECTOR

Two days after my arrival in Mexico City I met General
Cosío Robelo in the Café Colón. He had just come from
Teoloyucán, where Carranza still was, and he had just been
appointed Chief of Police. We congratulated each other,
though without knowing or saying clearly what about, and
we felt it fitting to crown the expression of our rejoicing as
triumphant revolutionists with great muscular demonstra-
tions: my poor bones cracked in the general's bearlike arms,
and my breast was almost crushed against his, which was
like that of a gorilla.

A great friend was Cosío Robelo, and a man of discern-
ment. At that time his conversation was still abundant. He
had not yet reached that other stage—so characteristic of him
and so wise—in which he more and more abandoned words
as an adequate vehicle of expression and limited himself to
the eloquence of the smile. This he already employed to
give outward expression to indeterminate states of beatitude,
beatitude in which the bodily and the mental made no attempt to stake out their respective frontiers. But, in contrast to what would develop later, after each of those all-
embracing smiles, he would break out in phrases which
were obedient to the ideas. Alongside the almost indeci-
pherable text, the expression of his face, he supplied the

verbal exegesis which threw a certain amount of light on the problem. And as he talked his eyes, which in the set expression of the smile had been shrinking in size until they became mere slits, suddenly regained their normal proportions and animation, as though his voice had brought them back from some infinitely remote spot.

On this occasion he entered more determinedly than usual into the realm of loquaciousness and finally took me aside to propose that I should help him to organize the metropolitan police force.

"I have special reasons for asking you to do this," he said. "Someday you'll know why."

I a chief of police! A detective! The proposal was so strange that if it had not been part of the whirlwind of the Revolution, I should have laughed at it. But Cosío Robelo was so determined that I not only had to accept, at least for the time being—hoping that later on he would get over the notion—but I agreed, for there was nothing else to do about it, to go with him to headquarters immediately so as to enter upon my duties as reorganizer of the police force of the Republic's capital without delay. And indeed I entered upon them. Cosío Robelo had another desk put directly across from his and he at once turned it over to me, giving the operation almost the air of an official act. Then embracing me again, he said: "This is your place. This way we'll be near each other and we can work together on everything."

The truth is, there was something about the whole affair that couldn't be explained by the mere fact that Cosío Robelo and I had happened to meet in the Café Colón. Everybody knew that I didn't know the first thing about police service, and there was no reason why I should. There was something hidden, something that I couldn't figure out. And this doubt, which took hold of me at once, bothered me for several days; it would still puzzle me if several weeks later Cosío Robelo himself, loyal friend that he was, had not cleared things up for me.

But in spite of my uneasiness I began my duties as a reorganizer, or, rather, what I imagined these duties to be.
Months before, in Sinaloa, the haphazards of the Revolution
had made a reformer of hospitals out of me; now the same
blind and invisible force hurled me almost to the other extreme. Before, my duty had been one of mercy; now it was
one of vengeance; before, consolation; now punishment. But
I didn't want to make mistakes that I could avoid, if possible, so I began looking around for the classic authorities, in
order to instruct myself on the subject. I discovered that
there is a very copious bibliography on police questions, and
I read the first two or three books I got hold of: *Justice and
Police*, by Maitland, and *Mysteries of Police and Crime*, by
Griffiths.

The frame of mind my new duties aroused in me was to
be reflected in one of the many incidents that took place
during those days.

When the Constitutionalist troops entered Mexico City,
Obregón issued a terrible proclamation against all distrubers
of the public order. All thefts, assaults, or other acts of de-
linquency, the proclamation ran, would be punishable by
death, without any legal procedure beyond establishing the
identity of the criminal. The order also provided the same
punishment for the military authorities who permitted such
crimes or allowed them to go unpunished. And Cosío Robelo
had orders to carry out this martial law without considerations of any sort. The orders were the kind usual in such circumstances, based not so much on actual needs as on the
psychological effect they produced. It is a known fact that
at every decisive hour in the life of a nation there is a tendency to exaggerate human values by the simple procedure of
distorting them, turning them inside out. It is an effort to
translate the extraordinary inner event into some visible
counterpart, and one resorts, as to the most sonorous of
solemn instruments, to "emergency measures"—the more arbitrary, the more fitting the "emergency"; and the more arbi-

trary, the more drastic and irreparable their consequences. And as there is nothing more definitively irreparable, or more subversive of the essentially human than to kill, as soon as men turn solemn, as soon as they begin to talk of saving the country, of saving society, or simply of saving other men, the first thing that occurs to them is to devote themselves conscientiously to killing their fellow men. Take those two lines of our national anthem which go: "War, War! The nation's banners, Soak in waves of blood". It is one of the most horrendous things any nation has ever sung.

Now, one afternoon the police caught two poor devils in the act of robbing a warehouse or a small general store, I don't recall which. They were taken red-handed, and that same night they were brought to the Sixth Precinct station and given what was known as a summary hearing, which was nothing more or less than a simple method of legalizing and justifying plain murder. The simplicity of the proceeding was marvelous: any sergeant, any court clerk, could apply it without the slightest difficulty. The policeman or policemen would set forth the nature of the crime committed by the prisoner, who in his turn gave his side of the case. It amounted to two or three declarations and a preliminary questioning before the officer in charge. When this had been done, the findings were laid before the Chief of Police, who, under penalty of suffering himself the punishment provided for the others, was obliged to order immediate execution.

That night in less than two hours the documents of the case had been drawn up, and ten minutes later they had gone from Revillagigedo to Humboldt Street. Cosío Robelo received them, read them, but did not want to decide anything right away. I remember his words perfectly as he laid the slender sheaf of papers on the table. The clock was just striking the hour. "Ten o'clock. It's too late to order them shot. We'll wait till tomorrow to decide the matter."

But the next day there was no pretext for postponing the case. As soon as we reached the office, there lay the papers in the middle of the table, demanding examination and a decision.

Cosío Robelo went through them again. Then he said to me:

"There's no question about the facts."

I kept quiet. Cosío Robelo began to stare at me. I noticed that his complexion was even ruddier than usual, and the very whites of his eyes were bloodshot. The struggle between his head and his heart was making itself manifest.

"And there's no doubt either," he went on, "about what was ordered by the Military Council."

I didn't say a word.

Several minutes went by like this. Then Cosío Robelo, who had been pacing the room, stopped, and asked me with the air of a person seeking help:

"What would you advise me to do?"

"I don't advise anything."

"Oh, come!"

"Remember that I'm a civilian."

"That doesn't make any difference in this case."

"Yes, it does," I replied. "Your duty is to behave in accordance with the military code, which you have accepted as the norm of your conduct, whereas mine is to behave in accordance with my status as a civilian."

"Well, as a civilian, what would you do?"

"I wouldn't assume or share the responsibility of any execution."

"And as a soldier?"

"That's why I'm not a soldier."

"That means that you would shoot them?"

"I would obey orders or I would resign. The military career separates the range of human actions into two areas that cannot always be reconciled, and there are occasions on which a choice is required, even within strict military legality. Then it's a question of being a good man or a good soldier. Now, to decide this is a question of conscience—one could almost say, of religion."

As might have been expected, my words neither calmed nor fortified Cosío Robelo. On the contrary, they made him more uneasy and perplexed than before. They were less the expression of the will than of dialectics, and, as such, useless as a guide to conduct. But after struggling with himself for two hours—the struggle between the small but urgent legal duty and the larger, but more remote—he did what anyone else would have done in his place: he signed the order to apply martial law in the case, the law which takes no account of guarantees or sentimentalisms, which knows no duty beyond that of obedience and victory.

But his decision did not make him any easier. After he had issued the order, he grew more nervous, more excited, and more dissatisfied with the sense of his responsibility. At that moment he was a good man who had been hemmed in between the sword and the wall and had chosen the wall, but for whom the wall had become as sharp and piercing as the sword.

A few moments after he had issued the order, he called in the Assistant Chief and ordered him to be present in person at the executions to see that everything was carried out in accordance with all the legal prescriptions for such cases. And a little while after the Assistant Chief had left, he said to me:

"I'd appreciate it very much if you would go and see how *that* is coming along, and if you find the slightest irregularity, come and notify me at once."

I set out.

2 IN THE SIXTH PRECINCT STATION

On the way I kept thinking about what Cosío Robelo had said and wondering what he understood by irregularities in an execution that had been ordered without due process of law or guarantees of any kind for the accused. And the more I thought about it, the greater became my doubts. Because, once the supreme irregularity of ordering a group of men to stand another man before a wall with his hands tied behind his back and kill him is admitted, none of the other details seem important. Perhaps the rules of a proper shooting demand that the homicidal fusillade be fired by expert marksmen; in this way the cruelty of death is attenuated. Possibly the criminal is not supposed to be dragged to the spot of execution; this keeps the executioner from being too conspicuous. No doubt it is provided that if the condemned person offers resistance, he is not to be riddled with bullets, or thrust through with bayonets, or have his skull smashed in with gunstocks. But in the last analysis what difference did these hypocritical and incidental details make beside the undeniable fact than an execution had been ordered without legal or moral considerations?

As the distance was short, I didn't get far with my ideas. All the police stations in Mexico are sinister-looking places, but, above all, that of the Sixth Precinct. At the doors there was a crowd of curious spectators composed of the public and the police, and these two elements—at swords' points when it comes to respecting the law—were joined in a single morbid interest: hearing and seeing what was going on inside.

I went in. The filthy routine of that prison antechamber was in a state of suspense. There was a kind of cold, unfeeling expectation, something out of the ordinary in the air, which transformed the daily prison atmosphere, making it perhaps worse than usual.

As I crossed the courtyard, the eyes of the employees and prisoners who were watching from the doors of the different sections followed me. Then they turned back to the hall that communicated with the adjoining courtyard. There were four or five policemen waiting there, standing in single file and armed with Mausers. Their belts and puttees of yellow leather were in vivid contrast with the blue of the uniforms. They were standing with their backs to the first courtyard and facing the second. Their rifles were new or had seen little use, and between every two ankles appeared the rear angle of a gunstock. Near the policemen and the official in charge stood the assistant chief of police, the captain of the precinct, the clerks, a doctor, and two men of the lower classes. It was evident at first glance that these two—blue pants, coarse cotton shirts, bronzed faces, palm-leaf hats, narrow-brimmed and of various colors—were the leading characters in the execution. The taller of the two was barefooted.

I did not join the group. I stood watching them some six or seven feet off, through the grille that separated the corridor from the office next to it. The tall, barefooted prisoner was talking. The other nodded his approval of what his companion was saying.

"But how can I be resigned, Chief? Does that seem like justice to you?"

He was addressing himself to the assistant chief of police, whose face I could not see, as it was hidden under the brim of his wide hat. He must have seemed unmoved, to judge by the rising emphasis that the condemned man put into each new phrase. But if his face was impassive, his hands revealed his nervousness. They were clasped behind his back, and his fingers kept continually twisting and working.

Meanwhile the condemned man went on: "I'm not saying anything against the orders, Chief, or what you say about when the troops enter large cities. But, honest to God, it isn't justice to shoot a man for such a little thing. Just think of it—shooting! This gentleman here who knows all about it"—pointing to one of the clerks (dirty, unkempt, with a greasy skullcap pulled down almost to his eyes)—"can tell you, sir, that things are not done like that."

The clerk cut in: "I'm not saying anything; don't talk about what you don't know."

"About what I don't know, my Chief, and they're going to kill us? Well, then, let them fetch a lawyer and he'll tell them, because it's written in his books."

Here the assistant chief of police interrupted: "I told you before that this was no time for lawyers."

"Then when is the time, Chief?"

"During the trial."

"But there hasn't been any trial. You know that."

"Yes, there was. That was the trial last night."

"I swear to you it wasn't, and if they say so, it isn't true. Trials, God help me, are very different. There are judges and witnesses and lawyers and people, and they last a long time. The papers tell about it and even print the pictures, especially if you're sentenced to death. They don't send a person to the grave like this."

The other prisoner had begun to cry, listening to his companion. His appearance was one of complete submissiveness, and he was inferior in intelligence and ability to the other, in spite of the fact that he wore shoes and was better dressed. Something in his attitude denoted astonishment at the tenacity with which his companion defended the lives of both of them, but at the same time he seemed resigned to the inevitable. This showed even in the slow trickle of his tears. Each time the assistant chief or the captain of the precinct indicated that there was nothing to do but yield, he looked up inquiringly at his companion and seemed ready to walk over to the wall and wait for the bullets. But afterward, seeing that the other continued unshaken, he settled down again during the respite. The gentleness of the assistant chief was largely responsible for the delay. He was so determined that the rules for an execution should not be violated that he hardly made use of his authority. He talked in a persuasive, almost kindly tone. However, his eloquence, like the captain's, was as nothing compared with that of the prisoner, whose arguments received hardly any reply. The truth was that at heart nobody believed that there was any need, much less justification, for shooting those two unhappy wretches. Only the dirty clerk kept repeating over and over with a hateful smile:

"Nothing can be done about it. Nothing can be done about it."

The prisoners kept turning toward him; the one in tears, in silent contemplation; the other to say, as in parentheses: "No, sir. Why can nothing be done? You know it can better than anybody else, for you wrote out the declarations."

And immediately the prisoner resumed his defense before the assistant chief and the captain.

"If it is true that General Obregón has ordered us to be shot—and it isn't that I doubt your word, Chief; it's that I can't believe it—at least let the general hear us. And I know that if he hears us, he won't have us shot even if I tell him the honest truth, Chief, just as I've told it. Because I don't want to deny that we did go into the place to see what we could pick up, but we didn't have any bad intentions; I mean, we didn't intend to kill or hurt anybody, and we didn't have anything to do it with. It's just being so poor that makes a fellow think about robbing, but that was all. . . . No knife or any kind of weapon. . . . The police testified to it, and it's all down in the papers. Now, Chief, how can you believe that if General Obregón knows all this, he is going to have us shot? That's all I want you to do, please—there's plenty of time afterward to kill us—only that, to take us where General Obregón is and have him hear us. . . ."

The assistant chief began to show signs of pity and impatience, the latter for the very reason that he could not say anything that would carry weight against the eloquent, desperate obstinacy with which the prisoner pleaded his case. Suddenly he broke out, in a harsher tone than he had used before:

"Well, brother, it seems to me we've had enough arguing. Will you obey or won't you?"

"But, Chief (please God you never find yourself in a fix like this!), how can I obey when they're going to shoot me? Just put yourself in my shoes, have a little pity. Besides, I've got a little girl, Chief, a little girl four years old. What's going to become of her if they kill me? Why must she suffer for what I've done, and, besides, it doesn't deserve a punishment like this. I was only going to rob—yes, I admit I was

going to rob—but do you think it's justice to punish me as if
I were a murderer, and one of the very worst? If you could
only see my little girl you'd realize that I don't deserve this.
She's not like me; I'm bringing her up and educating her
right. She goes to school already. The things I was going to
steal were for her. Why, yesterday at this time I was with
her, all my troubles forgotten, never doubting that I'd live
to see her a woman; and now they want to kill me just because I had a wicked temptation and the Devil took advantage
of me. No, Chief, don't shoot me, for your sweet mother's
sake. The Holy Virgin will reward you, unless some day I myself find a way to repay you for such a great favor as saving
the lives of the two of us—"

"That will do," shouted the assistant chief. "I have to obey
orders. If you won't go to the wall of your own accord, we'll
have to take you there. Officer!"

"At your orders, Colonel."

The prisoner: "No, Chief, don't get angry. Not by force.
It isn't necessary. I defended myself because I think it's jus-
tice. But I'm not afraid, and I don't want them to say I am.
When the time comes, I know how to die like anybody else.
But I want to ask one favor: let them bring my little girl so
I can tell her good-bye, and if it isn't too much trouble, I'd
like to have a priest come. If they have to shoot me, I'd like
to die with an easy conscience."

The assistant chief looked at his watch. Then he said something in a low voice to the captain. Meanwhile the two condemned men talked to each other, or, rather, the taller one
spoke a few words to the other, who answered with several
nods of the head.

"See here," the assistant chief ordered a policeman, "have
this man explain where his daughter lives and have them
bring her at once. We can't do anything about the priest.
And you," he went on, turning to the other prisoner, "is
there anything you want? What can we do for you?"

"Nothing for me, Chief. If they're bound to shoot us, what
difference does it make if we die with consolation or without

it? I see that they're making an example of us. Someday their conscience will accuse them."

I took advantage of this respite to go out to find Cosío Robelo. I wanted to let him know that the execution was being carried out with all regard for the rules, but that, notwithstanding, it seemed to me an abominable, gruesome action. The preserving of order in the city did not justify such measures against two poor devils who were no guiltier than half of the Constitutionalist army. But at headquarters I found that Cosío Robelo had left. And though I looked everywhere for him, I couldn't get hold of him until two hours after the sentence had been carried out.

That same afternoon I passed by the Sixth Precinct station again. In front of one of the sheds used for the fire engines a group of people was gathered. I drew near. There were the two corpses on public view. The face of the taller one still seemed to have a trace of the persuasive power with which he had tried to save himself. His bare feet—young, strong feet—were stained with trickles of dried blood. The other corpse lay not so much on the dirty canvas of the stretcher as in the bosom of his utter resignation.

3 Pancho Villa's Pistol

Revolutionary justice as meted out by the police was so repugnant to me that I immediately decided to dissociate myself from the organization in charge of its administration. Only one thing detained me: I was afraid of hurting Cosío Robelo's feelings, and since all laws and personal guarantees had been suspended, he could not be held—nor did I hold him—personally responsible for these summary executions. But I soon saw that my fears were ungrounded. At my first words the chief of police admitted that I was right, and he even hinted that he would gladly imitate me if his military obligations permitted.

And Cosío Robelo took advantage of the occasion to reveal to me the real reason for his insisting on my joining the force. With stupefaction I heard him say: "You know why I insisted as I did? Because that was the only way I could keep from arresting you, as Carranza had ordered me to do when he appointed me chief. Fortunately, things have changed now; thanks to the efforts of Eduardo Hay, who seems to be very fond of you, the First Chief has countermanded the order."

Soon afterward other events, bearing more on the future developments of the Revolution than on its immediate problems, came to occupy my mind. What especially interested me was to see how events were slowly drawing together different leaders of the forces in Sonora and Sinaloa into an anti-Carranza faction.

The situation in this respect was so far advanced that I had set my heart on having Villa and Lucio Blanco join forces and purposes, even without their knowing each other. The opposition of both to Carranza's autocracy, clear and open in Villa, tacit as yet in Blanco, but determined, would bring them together, without a doubt, for the action that would very shortly get under way. But a common objective, born of similar, or outwardly similar, motives, did not satisfy me. It seemed to me that a sentimental bond of some sort was necessary, even if it did not outlive the moment of its usefulness.

The thing was not easy in spite of the favorable circumstances that Villa and Blanco had never met. In the realm of sentiment, how could one establish a sincere point of contact between Lucio, all bravery, generosity, and idealism, and Villa, uncontrolled blind force that stopped at nothing, illuminated only by the feeblest ray of moral light, which filtered into his soul through some almost imperceptible crevice? Blanco was so noble that he disdained even glory—this was his weakness; so human that the horror of killing practically paralyzed his activity after the first revolutionary impulse. Villa, on the contrary, could see only one clear guiding

principle through the shadows that surrounded him: to accumulate power at any price, to get rid of obstacles by any
means whatsoever. The only way to carry out my desire would
be by a well-staged surprise, and the first move must come
from Villa. It could not come from Blanco, for he was too
proud. And Villa was an ex-deserter who trusted nobody.

Back in Chihuahua again, the opportunity presented itself. Domínguez and I had returned to inform Villa as to the
result of our trip to Mexico City when the Constitutionalist
troops had marched into the capital. And we were also carrying a letter from Blanco to the Chief of the Division of the
North saying that he had talked with us and had completely
outlined to us his ideas about Carranza and his adherents.

As we were waiting to be received, Villa suddenly appeared
in the doorway to say something to his secretary, Luis Aguirre
Benavides, who had been talking with us while we waited. It
was early in September and the weather was warm. Villa
came out in his shirt sleeves. He had on his hat, his usual
custom when he was in his office or in the house. As he talked
with Aguirre Benavides, his robust, khaki-clad figure stood
out sharply against the white painted door. From under his
hat a number of saffron-colored curly locks of hair clustered
around his forehead, matching the thick, untidy mustache.
But as he turned around nothing about the man drew one's
attention like the enormous pistol that hung from his hip
in a huge holster. The butt of it shone with the gleam of a
thing that is in constant use, not with the effeminate polish of something meant for show. The handle described a
broad prolonged curve against his side, like the tail of those
fantastic kites in children's books. Around both sides of his
waist ran a thick row of shells, whose size made one think of
torpedoes. They looked like a row of copper columns without
capitals, cut in two by the dark strip that held them in place
on the belt. The steel bullets, huge and polished to a high
luster, gave back the light from the windows in dull gleams.
At the sight of them it was inevitable that one's imagination

should begin to calculate the density, shape, the lethal inertia of those bullets as smooth as a caress.

"This man wouldn't exist if his pistol didn't exist," I thought to myself. "It isn't merely an instrument of action with him; it's a fundamental part of his being, the axis of his work and his amusement, the constant expression of his most intimate self, his soul given outward form. Between the fleshy curve of his index finger and the rigid curve of the trigger there exists the relation that comes from the contact of one being with another. When he fires, it isn't the pistol that shoots, it's the man himself. Out of his very heart comes the ball as it leaves the sinister barrel. The man and the pistol are the same thing. Whoever counts on the one can count on the other. Out of his pistol have come and will come his friends and his enemies."

And then the idea I had been looking for came to me.

"To bring Villa and Blanco together," I said to Colonel Domínguez, "we ought to have Blanco receive, as a present, Villa's pistol. If Villa offers it, there'll be no mistaking his attitude. And Blanco, when he accepts it, will understand what this means. You leave it to me."

Villa's great problem in those days was the question of who should be appointed President *pro tem.* At first glance it seemed as though he was willing to support anybody as long as it wasn't Carranza. But on closer investigation it was evident that he was interested in having a man he could count on. His candidate then was General Angeles, and it was with him that our conversation dealt. A strange combination, that of an illiterate guerrilla leader and our master technician of the war! Villa, the irresponsible, found in Angeles, a man tormented by the sense of his obligations as a revolutionist, a complement he could understand. In this—as in many other things—he showed his superiority over the half-educated leaders of Sonora—with the exception of Maytorena—and Coahuila, who hated and maligned Angeles from the start simply because they weren't fit to tie his shoes when it came to ques-

tions of culture or military strategy. It was natural that Sonora should have engendered the school that won its battles
by bribing traitors among the enemy; and Angeles would have
let himself be torn limb from limb before going to a framed-
up victory. Angeles had been an honor cadet at Chapultepec
and had assimilated a tradition of honor there that is worth
more than many revolutions put together. His attitude was
radically opposed to the corruptness of Carranza's party and
to that part of the Sonora group which for the time being was
booming Carranza while waiting for a chance to betray him
and assassinate him. But Villa did not see this diametrical
opposition between Angeles and the Carranza group, or pretended not to see it.

"Angeles," I said, "is a splendid man, who deserves a lot,
but as a coalition candidate he won't do."

At this Villa got excited. He broke off the mysterious form
of secret conclave that our conversation had taken—he sitting
very close to us, his elbows on his knees, and his face in his
hands—and stood up. Still talking, he moved over to the
door, and we after him. And the three of us went out into the
anteroom without having really finished our parley. A number of his subordinates and close friends were in the room,
and they came over and began talking to him as soon as they
saw him. Was he angry? I had a feeling that our plans had
gone on the rocks that last minute because I had been too
sincere. Yet I hated to admit defeat and decided to make a
final test of the situation.

"Now, the matter of Lucio Blanco," I said to Villa, without
any preliminaries, point-blank, "could be completely fixed up
by a friendly gesture on your part. For instance, if you would
send him your pistol with your compliments."

Villa looked at me, looked at Domínguez, and answered
after a moment's pause, as he unfastened his belt:

"That's not such a bad idea."

Then, while all looked on in silence, he handed me his
pistol, with cartridge belt and everything. A shiver ran
through me as I felt it in my hands, still warm, and I passed

it on to Domínguez *in continenti*. It seemed to me that it
burned me just to touch it.

And meanwhile Villa added: "Just tell General Blanco to
be careful with it, as it's a very fluky pistol."

But before he had finished the phrase, he went pale. With
a quick movement he felt both his hips and whirled around,
looking at us all. And as though moved by instinct, he backed
up against the wall.

"Say," he said excitedly, "somebody give me a pistol, I'm
unarmed."

And he was so wrought up as he pronounced these words
that I thought he was going to jump on Domínguez and take
away the pistol he had given him a few minutes before. Without knowing it I had just done something nobody had ever
tried with Pancho Villa. I had disarmed him. Disarmed him!

He realized the imprudence he had committed and reacted
immediately with all the brutality that comes from long years
of living like a hunted animal, pursued by the mounted police. How long since Villa had found himself in a situation
of this sort, defenseless in a group of armed men, several of
whom had different ideas and interests from his? He, who
never drew his pistol without having settled the matter in
question before he returned it to its holster, had fallen by
surprise into the thoughtless mistake of handing over his arms
to a man he hardly knew, the very one who only two minutes
before had aroused his anger by disagreeing with him.

As they heard Villa's alarmed request, several of those
present held out their pistols to him. Luis Aguirre Benavides
said, offering him his:

"I'd give you this one, General, but it's very small and besides it's an automatic, and you don't know that kind very
well."

"Bah, what kind don't I know well?" said Villa, taking it.

It was a little .32. Villa gripped it with a smile—it seemed
that his annoyance at finding himself without arms had disappeared—and broke it, letting the bullets fall out one by one.
As they dropped to the floor, Aguirre Benavides gathered

them up and then handed them all back to Villa. He reloaded quickly; then he pulled back the trigger and, aiming at my forehead, said:

"Now say something to me."

The mouth of the barrel was about two feet from my face. Above the sights I could see the feline glitter of Villa's eyes. The iris was like an agate: full of infinite minute dots of fire. Tiny golden lines radiated out from the pupil and on reaching the white turned into fine reddish filaments that disappeared under the lids. The vision of death seemed to come from that eye more than from the dark little orifice of the barrel. Neither the one nor the other moved the least bit; they were fixed; they were of one piece. Did the barrel aim so that the eye could fire? Did the eye aim so that the barrel could fire? Without looking away from the pistol I could see that Aguirre Benavides was calmly smiling, that the officers were watching us, curious and unmoved, and that Domínguez, at my side, was hardly breathing.

I cannot say which was greater in me at the moment, fear or indignation. Nevertheless I controlled both feelings—successfully, I think—and answered Villa:

"What do you want me to say? Something good or bad?"

"Whatever comes out of your heart."

"Well, I hope this isn't going to be a fluky pistol, too," I said.

But Villa wasn't listening to me. He looked at Domínguez and slowly let his arm fall as he asked:

"Now, which of you two is the braver?"

As I had just had a horrible fright, I answered without a moment's hesitation: "Domíngucz."

And Domínguez, who rightfully had a good opinion of his own bravery, said: "Neither one."

"Well, it's my opinion," Villa answered, "that the civilian is braver than the soldier."

For that unjust and inexplicable remark Domínguez never forgave Villa, nor, do I think, me either.

4 A Forced Loan

On our way to Mexico City Domínguez and I made the acquaintance of Colonel Ornelas, chief of staff of one of the generals who was operating in the interior of the Republic. He was young, intelligent, outspoken, and a great talker. All the time we were together he narrated to us episodes of his life in the service, and on one occasion, when we had a long wait on account of locomotive trouble, he entertained us with a full-length portrait of his general.

We were sitting along the railroad track with some other revolutionists—colonels and rifle and pistol officers—who were on the same train. The autumn afternoon was fading beautifully into twilight. The nearby mountains seemed slowly to wrap themselves in the violet vapors that rose out of the bottom of the valley, which was already half dark.

"This time," said Ornelas, "we were confronted with the problem of paying the troops as soon as we took the town. The general sent for me and said:

" 'Do you know that there's not a cent in this brigade's treasury?'

" 'That's what I've been told.'

" 'Well, no need to get downcast about such a trifle. This little town will give us a lift for a few days. We're going to try out a plan which is infallible for getting loans on a big scale; it's a plan that tames the strongest wills.'

"And then, after spouting along some more in the same pedantic fashion—which in no wise detracted from his shrewd, cool, efficient manner of going straight after what he wanted, and getting it at any cost—he held out to me a paper with several names in his own handwriting and said:

" 'Here are the names of the five richest men in the town. Some have land, some land and a store, but they are all stuck-up reactionaries, and supporters of Huerta. They are to report at headquarters immediately if they do not want to be shot for giving aid and comfort to the enemy.'

"The general and I were in a room of the house that had been selected for the brigade offices. Through the wide, open window we could see on the far horizon the ruddy sea into which the sun was sinking. All along the street groups of soldiers were unsaddling the mules. As we talked, orderlies came in and out of the room loaded with luggage and other equipment.

" 'About this order,' I said, after reading the five names on the list, 'shall I have it delivered or shall I carry it out myself?'

"The general reflected for barely a second and then answered quickly:

" 'That's right; you attend to it yourself.'

"I took ten soldiers of the guard and started off, though as soon as I got outside the door, I hesitated, for I did not know which way to go. Left? Right? The town was strange to me. Where did they live and who were Don Carlos Valdés and Don Ciriaco Díaz González, who headed the list of the victims selected for the loan? But an obvious idea occurred to me and I headed for the little public square where on subsequent afternoons I would while away my hours watching the flight of the magpies among its venerable leafy trees.

"In the square I soon obtained the information I needed. But as I had to traverse several streets and stop at various houses in the company of my detachment of soldiers, alarm began to spread through the town. The sinister air of my men and the uneasy look of those who followed us revived the fright produced by the morning's skirmish.

"Fortunately it didn't take long to find four of the prominent citizens chosen by the general. Everybody in town knew them and their families, their homes and their places of business. But there was one exception, the first man on the list, Don Carlos Valdés. At first nobody knew who he was.

" 'Carlos Valdés? Which Carlos Valdés?'

"Finally I managed to find out that there was a Carlos Valdés in the town; but I was told that this couldn't be the Valdés on my list; that I must mean Don Vicente Valdés.

" 'But why can't Don Carlos Valdés be the one I'm looking for?'

" 'Because Carlos Valdés,' I was informed, 'isn't one of the leading people in this town, like the others you are after, and Don Vicente is. He's not one of the richest, but he's not one of the poorest, either.'

"But as my orders called for Don Carlos Valdés and not Don Vicente, I asked to be shown where he lived, and when I had located him, I brought him in with the other four authentic, or at least undisputed, magnates.

"My general received the candidates for the forced loan with all the protocol and paraphernalia prescribed for such cases. He was standing behind his campaign table, his jacket buttoned to the throat, his chest thrown out, freshly shaven, and the ends of his mustache waxed to a point like those of the Kaiser. At each end of his table, on stools, were the cash boxes of the brigade, open to reveal their emptiness.

"He allowed several minutes to elapse in silence, the better to intimidate his victims, and then began:

" 'I greet you, gentlemen, though I cannot bring myself to shake your hands; for you are traitors, cowards, disloyal citizens, enemies of your country and its free institutions, while I . . . I am a worthy representative of the brave revolutionary army—'

" 'General!' one of the five tried to interrupt.

"But the general, it goes without saying, pulled him up short.

" 'Oh, no,' he said, 'under no circumstances. Under no circumstances am I to be interrupted.'

"And to leave no doubt as to the meaning of his remark he turned to me and repeated emphatically:

" 'Under no circumstances am I to be interrupted!'

"I still had the guard of ten soldiers with me, and I ordered them to present arms and stationed them behind and along-side the prisoners.

"Meanwhile the general had taken from his pocket a copy of the list he had given me a little while before and read it over to himself. Then without raising his eyes, but addressing the prisoners, he went on:

" 'Don Carlos Valdés. Which of you is Don Carlos Valdés?'

" 'I am, sir,' said the one in question.

" 'Don Ciriaco Díaz González. Which one is Mr. Díaz González?'

" 'I,' answered a sharp, dry voice.

" 'Oho! So you are! Pleased to meet you. . . .'

"And then: 'Don Pedro Salas Duarte. Which one is Don Pedro Salas Duarte?'

" 'Your humble servant, General.'

" 'All right, we'll soon see about that. And Don Marciano de la Garza?'

" 'At your orders, General.'

" 'Then you, I suppose,' said my general turning to the only prisoner whose name he had not yet pronounced, 'are Don Ignacio Muriedas.'

" 'I am,' agreed the other, with an air and accent that marked him as a Spaniard.

" 'Very good, gentlemen,' the general went on in his ora-torical tone; 'now, the Revolution requires funds which we, her noble, her pure, her unsullied servants cannot call up out of the thin air. And it is only fair that you—the classes and the individuals responsible for the present state of af-fairs—should defray the expenses of the war which you alone have caused. You are in duty bound to fill the empty coffers so my troops can be paid, and that is the reason for this inter-view which you have so graciously honored with your pres-ence. The forces it is my privilege to command, which this morning freed this town from the ignominy of continuing under the sway of the reactionary troops, expect you to supply, without pretexts or delays of any sort, the modest sum of thirty-five thousand pesos in cash. In spite of everything, I don't want to be unfair; we will not consider the advance of the thirty-five thousand pesos as punishment for helping the enemies of the liberty and laws of the Republic— I don't want to set myself up as judge—; we will simply consider it as an obligatory loan, for which you will be given a receipt, and reimbursed when the cause triumphs. But there are two points on which I must be inflexible: the first is that the quota assigned to each of you will not be lowered by a single cent; and the second, that the time allotted for each one to make his payment cannot be extended one second.'

"The five men condemned to the loan must have been feeling an acceleration in their heartbeats as the general proceeded with his speech. They kept swallowing; the veins on their foreheads bulged; they stood as though rooted to the spot, but their hands kept working nervously in their pockets. Only one of them, Don Carlos Valdés, seemed to take the situation with relative calm. He kept looking at the general, and an almost imperceptible smile, half ironical and half melancholy, played around his lips.

"The general made a slight pause and then went on, looking at his list:

" 'Mr. Carlos Valdés: the forces I command grant you a period of twelve hours, beginning this minute (it is now'— looking at his wrist watch—'7:47 P.M.), to supply the brigade's treasury with the sum of five thousand pesos. If you do not comply with this demand, you will be hanged, without further preliminaries, tomorrow at 7:47 A.M.'

"The row of the five rich men stopped breathing as they listened. From red, they turned white. Valdés tried to talk and opened his mouth, but before he could emit a sound, the general was saying:

" 'Mr. Ciriaco Díaz González: you have been granted a period of fifteen hours, beginning this minute (it is now 7:49 P.M.), to supply the treasury of my troops with the sum of six thousand pesos. If this demand has not been complied with, you will be hanged at 10:49 tomorrow morning, without further proceedings. Mr. Pedro Salas Duarte: you have been granted a period of eighteen hours to furnish our treasury with the sum of seven thousand pesos. It is now 7:51 P.M. If you do not comply with the orders just received, you will be hanged tomorrow, without further formalities of any sort, at 1:51 P.M. Mr. Marciano de la Garza: you have been granted a period of twenty-one hours (it is just 7:53 P.M.) to supply our treasury with the sum of eight thousand pesos. If you do not comply with the order, you will be hanged, without further formalities than making sure that the clock is right, tomorrow at 4:53 P.M. Mr. Ignacio Muriedas, you have been granted twenty-four hours to supply the treasury of my brigade with nine thousand pesos. It is now 7:55 P.M. If you do not obey this order, tomorrow you will be hanged, without further preliminaries, at this same hour and minute. Just one more word. While the orders you have just heard are being carried out either one way—as I hope—or another—as I should lament—you will be prisoners here at headquarters, under my surveillance. Nevertheless, you will be given every opportunity to communicate with your friends and relatives.'

"My general, having finished, twirled the points of his mustache, drew over a chair, and called me to him to give me instructions about putting up the prisoners.

"They had not yet recovered from their astonishment and stupefaction. Don Carlos Valdés, who had seemed so courageous a few minutes before, made vain efforts to regain his poise. Finally they all tried to talk at the same time, but the general, who had been keeping an eye on them, brusquely cut them short:

"'It's quite useless, gentlemen; you're wasting your time trying to tell me anything. Orders have been issued, and time moves fast. You either hand over the money or you hang. You couldn't have a clearer-cut choice. At any rate, I can permit no arguments.'

"There followed a long, painful silence. Valdés began to breathe deeply, and suddenly, spurred on by his imminent peril, he broke out, in spite of the stern gesture with which my general endeavored to silence him.

" 'I shall be quiet in a moment, General, but first I must tell you what perhaps you do not know, and what my health and my duties demand that I inform you of. As the honorable gentlemen here with me can testify—and I deplore their fate as much as my own—I am very poor; poor myself, poor in relatives, and poor in friends. I am not lying to you. I am telling you the truth. I have no houses, no land, no money, no store, no bonds, no bank accounts. Twelve hours to bring together five thousand pesos! I can't help thinking I must be dreaming. A year would be too little, I assure you. So, as far as I am concerned, you don't need to make your executioners wait. You might just as well hang me now as tomorrow at 7:47.'

" 'The Revolution, Mr. Carlos Valdés, has no executioners, nor does it need them,' replied the general, and added: 'You will regret those words.'

"Everybody kept silence."

5   THE HANGMAN'S NOOSE

We lighted a bonfire, for the sierra was sending its cold night breath down on us, and gathered around it. The flames threw a ruddy glow on our faces, and cascades of burnished gold over our serapes. Behind us the shadows grew thicker, forming a dense hostile mass at our back; around the blaze of light in front ran a circle made up of pairs of gleaming eyes and tightly wedged bodies, which were toasted on one side and half frozen on the other.

By the light of the fire the story extended the scope of its interest. Colonel Ornelas paused a few moments to relight a cigarette and then went on in the same tone of voice as before—dry, outwardly indifferent, but tinged with an emotion that he hated to reveal.

"I told the general what was being said about town. To judge by the most reliable opinions, Don Carlos Valdés couldn't scrape up five hundred, one hundred pesos, let alone five thousand.

"'You're new to this work,' said the general, 'and anybody can fool you. Take my word for it, of the five prisoners we have here, the most valuable from our point of view is Don Carlos Valdés. Wait and see.'

"Meanwhile the news had run like wildfire through the town. People talked of nothing but the forced loan that had been demanded by us, and of the critical situation of the five men picked to furnish the money or die on the gallows. A host of relatives and friends of the prisoners came to headquarters to bring them help, sympathy, and advice. Several delegations from the poorer classes managed to get in to see the general and tried to convince him that Carlos Valdés was not and never had been a man of means. But the general became furious; he said that neither he nor the Revolution ever made a mistake, and that he would make an example of those who deceived him or were a party to concealing the true state of affairs. Nor did he show himself any more tolerant with those who came to plead for an extension of time.

"'You must remember, General,' they said, 'that this is a little town and it has been ruined by the war. Only yesterday, before you entered, the Federals carried off everything they could lay their hands on. Just stop and think, it is beyond our powers to raise a sum like thirty-five thousand pesos. We haven't got it and we can't raise it in a few hours. Give us at least time to get in touch with people we know around here, four days, or three, or two. Accept our word of honor that we will pay. We are honorable men, who are in the habit of keeping our word. That's why we are called supporters of Huerta and foes of liberty. . . .'

"But my general, brisk and to the point, twisting the ends of his mustache, merely replied:

"'Our orders have been given and the time limits are set. You people who are cowards and traitors are going to find out that you can't fool with the Revolution or with me, who represent it with a dignity in keeping with its glorious ideals, its heroic and just ambitions. If Don Carlos Valdés has not handed over his five thousand pesos before the hour that has been set for him, tomorrow morning at 7:47 you will see him swinging from the end of a rope. Gentlemen, you are wasting your time.'

"My general retired at ten that night, leaving orders that he was not to be called until seven the next morning. Quiet settled down over headquarters, except in the rooms occupied by the prisoners, where a muted agitation kept up. Friends went in and out of the rooms; messages were sent; letters were written. The prisoners were horribly nervous; every five minutes they looked at their watches. Only Don Carlos Valdés seemed oblivious to all these anxious efforts. Calmly he sat talking to a group of women that had gathered around him:

" 'I haven't got five thousand pesos, and I never will. If I should try to borrow this amount, everybody knows I could never pay it back. I know that if the town could, it would try to save me. But how can I expect it to save me when it isn't going to be able to find the money to save my four companions from the noose, and they're really rich and can pay back with interest later on whatever is done for them now? Let's hope that this general who talks so much about bravery, justice, and heroism will come to his senses and realize that I am a poor devil. In that case he won't carry out his threats. And if he does, well, his crime be on his head. . . .'

"All night long, efforts were made in the town and in the vicinity, for messengers were sent out in different directions, to save the five men selected as victims by the general from their terrible situation. But in spite of all these attempts it struck seven the next morning and not a cent had been turned in. My general called me as soon as he woke up:

" 'Has Don Carlos Valdés got his money here?'

" 'No, General. His isn't here, nor anybody else's. And as far as Don Carlos Valdés is concerned—'

" 'Very well,' he cut in. 'We have to hurry and get things ready.'

"After reflecting for a few minutes he went on:

" 'Look here. Out in the yard there's a spindly ash. For lack of anything better we can use that for a gallows. Have them tie a stout rope to the strongest branch of the tree, with a slip noose at the end, and get ready whatever else may be needed. Not an ordinary knot, you know; a regular hangman's noose. You'll have to attend to everything quickly because it's after seven already and we've got just a little more than half an hour. Oh, as you go out, would you mind telling Juan to bring in my breakfast, please.'

"I immediately left to carry out my orders, though it wasn't so easy as might have been expected. For the only strong branch on the tree was a very low one. We had to measure Don Carlos Valdés's height to make sure that if he were put on a chair, which was to be taken away when the time came, there would be enough room between his neck and the bough for the rope and the noose. In this way, when the chair was jerked away, the body of the condemned man would swing clear of the ground, and his own weight would hang him.

"The general finished dressing at 7:30, and came out in the yard to see what I had done. He stood up on the chair that was under the tree. He hung on to the rope with both hands to make sure the branch would hold. He observed the distance from the ground, and finally he picked up the noose and examined it very carefully.

" 'This knot,' he finally exclaimed, 'is no good at all. I told you it was to be a regular hangman's noose, the kind meant specially for this purpose, which never fails. Why didn't you obey me?'

"I answered him: 'General, this is the best kind of noose I could manage. I don't know how to tie the special kind for hanging, and none of the officers or soldiers here knew how either. I sent for two soldiers who have been in jail, and they couldn't give me any information about it.'

" 'Well, none of you knows very much,' he answered, 'and you don't deserve the confidence I repose in you. Give me that rope, and I'll teach you how to tie the knot.'

"One of the soldiers climbed into the tree and untied the rope and threw it to me; but the general, agilely stepping ahead of me, caught it in the air. He tucked his riding crop, which he was carrying in his right hand, under his arm and put his cigarette in one corner of his mouth so it would not be in his way; the thread of smoke rose parallel to his mustache, making him half close one hard eye. And there in the middle of the yard, under the curious gaze of officers and soldiers, he set dexterously about tying the sinister, complicated death noose. The smoke of his cigarette annoyed him and gave his face, contorted to strange angles, a satanic, Mephistophelian expression revealing a foretaste of his pleasure at the prospect of upsetting the established order of things. With rapid, skillful movements of his fingers he brought one end of the rope over the rope itself, twisting it so as to form at the end the strangling noose. It was a long, closely wound cylinder, on the inside of which the rope ran freely, and which was as stiff as iron, so as to break the prisoner's neck at the vertebræ below the head, when the chair was jerked away.

" 'There you are,' he said, handing me the noose. I took it, looked it over, and threw it to the soldier in the tree, who caught it and tied it to the bough again.

"At 7:40 the general sent to ask Don Carlos Valdés if he was ready to hand over his share of the loan. Valdés answered that he was ready enough, but that he didn't have the money or any hope of getting it. Thereupon the general ordered a squad of twenty men to bring the prisoners into the yard. Then he said to me:

" 'Order all the officers in the building to report here at once.'

"When I returned, profound silence reigned in the yard. Fifteen feet from the ash tree stood the rich men sentenced to the loan or the noose, forming a parallel line with the branch from which dangled the rope swollen with its monstrous knot. To the right, at a right angle to them, stood the twenty soldiers in double column. To the left the officers formed a semicircle around the general in the order of their rank. The general was giving orders in a low voice to the sergeant and corporal of the squad.

"The sergeant immediately went over to his company; the corporal walked over to a chair that had been placed beside the one exactly below the noose.

"It was 7:45. The prisoners were deathly pale; they tried to avoid seeing anything, but they saw everything. Valdés was the calmest of them all. But he was not wholly serene. One touch revealed his subconscious anxiety: the way he kept rubbing his dry lower lip with his left hand.

"The general drew from his pocket the list he had made up the previous evening, and read in a voice that reverberated solemnly:

" 'Don Carlos Valdés.'

" 'Present,' answered Valdés.

" 'Are you willing to obey the orders the Revolution has dictated to you through me?'

" 'As I told you, General, and I don't see how you can have any doubts about the matter, I am perfectly willing to obey, but I have no money, nor any way of getting it.'

" 'Very well, Mr. Valdés. You will have only your own stubborn refusal to obey legitimate orders to blame for the consequences. You have two minutes in which to make up your mind. As the Revolution must be prepared to carry out its orders, we will proceed with certain preparations. . . . Sergeant, you have your orders!'

"The sergeant took two soldiers and went over to Valdés. He tied his hands behind his back and then, taking him by the arms, led him over to the chairs and made him climb up on one of them. Then, leaving the two soldiers with the condemned man, he stepped back to his place with his squad.

"In the meantime the corporal had climbed on to the other

chair and, raising his arms, brought the noose around Don
Carlos Valdés's neck.

"The sergeant called out: 'Present—arms!'

"The fellow prisoners of Valdés were in a state of mortal
terror. Their legs shook, and their eyes, almost popping out
of their sockets, were glued to the rope. Valdés was very
pale, but very quiet, and he kept his eyes fixed on the general, who in turn had his fixed on his wrist watch.

"Several seconds went by. Suddenly the general raised his
head to look at Valdés and said:

"'Don Carlos Valdés: it is now 7:47. Your time is up.
Are you ready to hand over the five thousand pesos, yes or
no?'

"Valdés kept looking at the general without answering a
word. The general then turned to the corporal.

"'Carry out your orders!' he said.

"The corporal jerked away the chair on which Valdés was
standing and left him hanging from the rope.

"The noose instantaneously closed up, and the knot held
tight. Don Carlos Valdés threshed about in the air with
frightful contortions and a horrible fluttering of his tied
hands.

"The other four prisoners gave a scream of terror and,
clinging to each other, turned toward the wall.

"The officers shuddered.

"The general did not move an eyelash.

"At nine o'clock that morning Don Ciriaco Díaz González
handed over his six thousand pesos. Don Pedro Salas Duarte
paid his seven thousand before eleven. And the two other
leading citizens paid their quotas before noon.

"A little while later the general, looking at the money
stacked up in orderly heaps on his campaign table said to me:

"'See how this system never fails to bring results? They
all paid up.'

"'All except Valdés,' I answered.

" 'Valdés? Of course. But I knew he wouldn't pay. He didn't have a cent to his name.'

" 'But then . . . why did we hang him?'

" 'Why? God, you're green. Because if we hanged him, there was no doubt that the rest would pay.' "

BOOK III

Political Prisoners

1 SHADES OF THE PRISON CELL

Back in Mexico City again, I threw myself wholeheartedly into the anti-Carranza movement.

Luis Cabrera used to come almost every day to the house where Lucio Blanco lived in Héroes Street—the beautiful mansion that had belonged to Don Joaquín D. Casasús. He often lunched or dined there, and afterward he used to embark on long discussions with Lucio, which we, the latter's friends, avoided interrupting even by our presence.

One morning shortly after Cabrera's arrival, Lucio took me aside and said:

"I think it's time to come out in the open with Cabrera. Nevertheless, we can't take too much of a risk, so I think it would be better if you spoke to him in my name. Be as clear as you can without going into details—above all, don't mention any name but mine—and ask him, for me, to say where he stands."

So I went over to Cabrera and, taking him by the arm, led him into one of the rooms at the rear of the house where we could talk without anybody's interrupting or overhearing us.

There was a little corner sofa in the room, and we sat down there and began to talk. Our conversation flitted from one topic to another, and when finally a favorable opportunity presented itself, I entered on the subject without any hedging.

"Carranza," I said, "is nothing but a self-seeking politician who is devilishly shrewd at turning to his own advantage his training in the old school of Mexican politics. There is no real sense of civic duty or ideals of any kind in the man. Nobody who is not a flatterer and bootlicker, or that doesn't pretend to be to further his personal ambitions with Carranza's help, can work with him. He systematically corrupts people; he fans the evil passions, the petty intrigues, even dishonesty, in those who surround him, so he can better manage and hold the whip hand over them. There is not a revolutionist with any personality, or even sincerely devoted to the cause, who, unless he has been willing to let himself be used as a tool, has not been obliged to break with him or accept an insignificant, humiliating role. And those who have not yet openly broken with him are on tenterhooks and don't know what attitude to take. You know as well as I do that many of our friends are in one of these two situations. This is what has happened or is happening with Maytorena, with Angeles, with Villarreal, with Blanco, with Vasconcelos, with Bonilla, and even with you. You remember the rebuffs and secret hostility with which he treated you when we were in Nogales. The truth is that Carranza dreams of the possibility of becoming another Porfirio Díaz, a bigger and better Porfirio Díaz, for at heart he admires and venerates his memory. Isn't it apparent that Carranza is trying to turn everything to this one end, and that he doesn't care a rap about the good the Revolution might bring to Mexico? You know perfectly well that from the first moment Carranza has systematically kept the Revolution divided against itself. When he came to Sonora, he was defeated, helpless, without resources of any kind. He knew what a poor military leader he had in Pablo González, and he wanted to take refuge in a remote corner of the country where nobody would dispute his command. Nobody else would have behaved so nobly with him as Maytorena did. He put himself at his service and recognized him as leader,

because he thought his first duty was to preserve the unity of
the Revolution. But as Carranza knew that the only person
who would have the right to dispute his leadership when
they triumphed was Maytorena, the minute he felt himself
strong again, he set about widening the breach between the
two Sonora groups, those of Maytorena and Pesqueira, and
paid him back with treachery for saving him from failure and
ridicule. As soon as he saw that Felipe Angeles was a good
and able man, all uprightness and unselfishness, made for big
things, not for the mean tricks nor the underhanded wire-
pulling of selfish, ambitious fakers, he shoved him to one
side, tormented him until he made him lose his head. Finally, when he realized that Villa was responsible for the
Revolution's military victories, he hampered him in every
way he could. Carranza and his followers cannot forgive Villa
for the big victories from Ciudad Juárez to Zacatecas, for they
all know that they owe their success to those victories. As
long as Carranza is in control, the Revolution will never have
the ambition nor the vision nor the ability to carry out a
program that would justify it. Carranza's only idea is to
get rid of all those who do not accept and submit to his dictatorship, and once he has done this, you may be sure that
he'll let those who back him up do whatever they please.
With Carranza the country and the Revolution are headed
straight for destruction: it will become a series of personal
struggles, disguised as the conflict of principles; it will become a state of anarchy in which scoundrels will stop at
nothing to get power and riches, and will not feel the least
scruple at plunging Mexico into a situation still worse than
under Victoriano Huerta. For this reason we believe that if
Carranza doesn't go, we'll have to give up hope of any good
coming out of the Revolution. General Blanco knows that
you do not belong to the servile group of Carranza followers,
and so he has asked me to lay these ideas before you in his
name and tell you about our plans. We are determined to
oppose Carranza's selfish and unprincipled domination. Do
you want to join us?"

Cabrera had interrupted me several times in the course of my talk, either to make sure of my meaning or to approve and assent to what I was saying. When I had finished, he said that, in principle, he agreed with what I proposed to him; but, still, he wanted time to think things over before he definitely said yes or no. So we agreed to take up the matter again two or three days later.

Cabrera's answer did not please Lucio Blanco.

"I'm very much surprised," he said; "for, from what I had talked with him, I imagined he would accept at once without hesitation. I regret now that we took this chance."

I did not feel the same way. Cabrera might or might not be on our side; but, in any event, the matter was a serious one and he couldn't be expected to plunge into it head first, without thinking. Besides, looking at things *a posteriori*, from the point of view of his personal success, Cabrera would seem to have been right. At that time, when he said he agreed with me, if he had also said that he would join us, afterward he might not have been able to go back on his word when he changed his mind, and he would have suffered the same fate as all the other opponents of Carranza at the time: death or exile after the failure of the Convention. The other way he did achieve his personal ambitions; he won back consideration and power, he became influential, was made minister. Of course, one could say that if at the time all the revolutionists of Cabrera's standing and ability had stood out against Carranza, he couldn't have done what he did and Mexico would have been spared this visitation and all its demoralizing consequences. But that raises another question: if it had not been Carranza, could we be sure things would have been any better? This becomes a matter of opinion. Some of us say yes, and some no, but neither side can prove its point. The only thing is that we who said yes have the satisfaction of not having taken part in the work of destruction.

And I did not feel with Lucio that we had exposed ourselves by talking with Cabrera. I had then—and will always have—a very good opinion of Cabrera. My dealings with him, which were not only of a political nature, had given me reason to believe in his loyalty, or that he would at least keep quiet like a gentleman. Even now I do not think I was mistaken.

Nevertheless, subsequent events took the course that might have been expected. Two or three days after my conversation with Cabrera, Colonel Domínguez and I met Alfredo Breceda at Blanco's house.

"Well, well," he said, "I'm certainly glad to see you, and especially the two of you together. I was looking for both of you. The Chief wants to have a conference by telegraph with Villa, and he wanted you to be there, and help him to reach an understanding with the leader of the Division of the North, since you are acting as his agents here. Don't you feel that we all ought to make an effort to smooth out these petty quarrels that are dividing us?"

Domínguez, always uncalculating and impulsive, immediately accepted Breceda's proposal. And he did it in such a way that when I tried to interfere, it was too late. Breceda had already affectionately linked arms with both of us and was leading us toward the door, bubbling over with flattery and pleasantries.

We all got into the automobile that had brought Breceda, and started toward the palace. On the way I kept thinking what an idiotic thing we had done. That morning Breceda oozed treachery from every pore. One had only to look at him to see it: his face was greener than ever; his lips, more livid and shapeless than usual, and his eyelids, half smooth and half lined, like a bat's wing, drooped still farther over his dull eyes to conceal their expression. And how could anybody that knew Carranza at all believe Breceda's lies about the conference with Villa by wire, and all the other nonsense he chattered on the way? Carranza would tolerate and forgive anything except not bowing down to him completely and not looking on him as the very embodiment of divine inspiration.

It was ridiculous to think that he was suddenly going to accept Domínguez and me, who took no pains to hide our lack of respect for him, as Villa's representatives, and want us to help him placate the warrior's anger.

When we got to the palace, Breceda led us into a waiting room in the private offices. There was nobody there.

"Please wait for me a minute here," he said. "I'm going to let the Chief know you're here, and then I'll come back for you." And he went out.

"You're not dry behind the ears yet," I said to Domínguez as soon as we were alone. "Breceda will soon be back for us, but he won't be alone. Get ready to see a squad of soldiers come through that door. I don't say we should have refused to come, but we shouldn't have come like this."

Domínguez didn't say anything at first. On the way from Lucio's house to the palace he had had plenty of time to see how I felt about the situation.

Then he said: "You're too suspicious." And he began to pace up and down the room.

I opened one of the French windows that overlooked the street and leaned over the balustrade. Acequia Street, bustling with crowds at that hour of the day, was a sight to behold. The most typical aspects of Mexican life eddied around both sides of the Volador Gate, then became woven with invisible strands into the fabric of the city. Ten, fifteen, twenty-five minutes went by like this.

"One of two things," I thought as I stood there: "either Alfredo Breceda hasn't been able to get in to see Carranza, and that's detaining him, or he is having difficulties managing the details of our arrest without any fuss."

I tried to take my mind off our plight by watching the sights in the street, which afforded a continuous panorama of bright, unexpected, amusing scenes of local color, all radiating from the Volador Gate. Little by little, however, this very spectacle, a dazzling blend of light and sound, made the image of freedom seem more beautiful and desirable than ever to me. The most trivial of the incidents taking place in the street and the gutter awakened in me the horrible sense of oppression that the lack of liberty produces. It was as though the noise from the sidewalk and the shouts of the fruit vendors were tearing from my soul the apathy that had settled over it half an hour before at the stupid idea of the inevitable.

"Why let oneself be caught like this?" I thought. The idea, vague at first, and somehow mixed with the sight of piles of bright oranges for sale and the pushcarts of the pastry peddlers with their heaps of cakes, glossy as sugared patent leather, suddenly grew clear. And once clear, it immediately transformed itself into action. I left the balcony and went quickly into the room where Domínguez was pacing like a caged animal, for he already felt himself a prisoner. He looked at me inquiringly.

"Let's go," I said, lowering my voice which echoed through the empty room. "It's foolish to stay on here. If Carranza really wanted to talk to us, I wouldn't care how long we had to wait. But they're making us wait too long to catch us. Anyway, I'm going, if you don't want to."

Domínguez agreed with me, and we began to consider the best way to get out of there. First of all, we had to keep from being seen by the members of the secretarial staff, and not go through the waiting room. So we opened one of the doors leading to the corridor that encircled the inner patio, and slipped through it. Then we walked calmly down the stairs to the other courtyard and out of the front door. Then, free in the Zócalo, in a minute we were lost in the crowds crossing it in every direction.

How bright the sun seems when one has felt himself on the point of losing it!

We went back to Lucio Blanco's house and told him what had happened. He absolutely agreed with me that Breceda had laid a trap for us.

"I'd advise you not to leave here," he said, "until I can

find out how things stand. I'm going to sound Carranza out. We'll see if this comes directly from him, or if it is one of that busybody Breceda's machinations. Anyway, it's a good thing to get to the bottom of it if we can. After Guzmán's talk with Cabrera, this looks very bad to me."

2 REQUISITIONED FOR THE SERVICE

Domínguez and I stayed and had dinner with Lucio Blanco that day. The servants of the Casasús family, whom Lucio had kept on, served us. The dining-room furniture, naturally, belonged to the Casasúses; likewise the dishes and the silver. And if I am not mistaken, we even saw a bottle or two on this occasion from Don Joaquín Casasús's cellar, which had been abundantly stocked when Blanco billeted himself in that magnificent house.

The cellar, as well as everything else in the house, was a constant source of worry and annoyance to Lucio Blanco rather than of sybaritic satisfaction. At first, so nobody would touch the wine, he had the cellar padlocked. And with the same idea in mind he got hold of good grooms to take care of the splendid horses in the stables. He had a scrupulous respect for the belongings of others—in so far as respect was possible under the circumstances. For this same reason he raised the housekeeper's salary, putting her in charge of the house and everything in it and making her personally responsible for its care. But as he heard afterward that in spite of all the precautions and all the locks the precious liquor was disappearing from the cellar without anybody's knowing how, he decided to use it himself for the table.

"I'll have to choose the lesser of two evils. If the wines are going to be stolen, it's better for me to take them and use them for my guests. In this way I'll be openly responsible and will have to pay for them, and nobody can say I sneaked them out to send to my relatives. We might as well face the facts. The Revolution is not all idealism; we have our blackguards, too, and unfortunately they are the ones who set the tone here. To these rascals the Revolution means a chance to steal and destroy everything they can lay their hands on."

It was the same with everything else in the house. Blanco had the worst kind of a time to keep the library of the translator of *Evangeline* from being sacked to the last volume. The half-educated Coahuilans who accompanied Don Venustiano were such fast workers that two or three days after the troops entered Mexico City, they had secured an order from General Headquarters to take to Saltillo whatever volumes they wished from Don Joaquín's superb library. A more predatory order was rarely issued, and if it was not carried out—or at least not while Blanco was living in the house—it was thanks to the efforts of this revolutionary general, who stood out against robbery when freebooting was the law of the day.

For the explanation of what took place while Carranza was in power is to be found, better than in anything else, in the voluntary confusion that sprang up between *meum* and *tuum*, the confusion having to do with taking, not giving. Without this peculiarly characteristic detail his rule becomes an almost unintelligible political phenomenon. One cannot otherwise understand the historical significance—as apart from the merely individual—of the private acts of many of Carranza's close followers, nor the culminating moments in the political events of these days and shortly afterward: the official looting of the banks, the paper-money scandal in Veracruz, and the standardization of the currency.

It is curious how the public, so prone to make mistakes—notwithstanding what is said to the contrary—and so inclined to attribute heroism and grandeur to clay-footed gods, hit the nail on the head in this case from the very first. From Carranza the popular fancy coined *carrancear*, and "to carranzaize" and "to steal" became synonymous. Stealing became a categorical imperative among the adherents of Carranza, in part because it was a safe, quick way of getting what they wanted, and in part a sport and amusement. Besides, it was an arm against their enemies, or those they considered their enemies, and friends and relatives of these. It became the norm to wipe out opposition by kleptomaniac methods. This was what unprincipled leaders had made of a popular uprising that at first had wanted only to restore the political and moral balance which had been destroyed by the betrayal and assassination of Madero. This systematic thieving explains what happened in the wealthy homes that had been taken over in Mexico City. It also throws light on certain seeming contradictions. For instance, the actual occupants of the house did not, as a rule, take anything for themselves, or very little. But at the same time it was almost incredible how they tolerated, or even encouraged, the slow looting of property that was not theirs, furniture, bric-à-brac, even clothes. There were many cases of this, like that of the young officer who was quartered in a beautiful mansion in Tacubaya. The fancy girls that used to call on him almost never left with empty hands. The dialogue that preceded the thieving always ran something like this:

"Oh, boy, what a stunning lamp!"

"Do you like it, sugar?"

"Do I like it! I'll tell the world! Aren't those three girls the best-looking things?" (It was a beautiful alabaster lamp, with the three Graces for a base.) Just look at their arms and their legs! And what a precious shade! Honestly, I don't know which I like better, the lamp or the shade."

"You know," answered the officer, thus made aware of the beauties of the lamp, "it is a pretty lamp."

"Listen, honey, why don't you give it to me? Come on, give it to me!"

"Why, chicken, you must be crazy. How'm I going to give away a lamp that isn't mine?"

"Well, then, don't give it to me; let me take it."

"That's a different matter. Take it if you want to. But I don't promise that they won't come and take it away from you afterward."

And "Chicken" or "Baby" or whoever it might be would leave the house carrying off in her car whatever she liked best.

Things of this sort did not happen in the house in Héroes Street. There Lucio Blanco, out of a sense of honesty and fair play, tried to act as a faithful custodian of the beautiful furnishings and fittings that chance had put in his hands. But it must be admitted that he was only partly successful. There was such a spirit of rapacity in the air that it affected the very ones detailed to combat it. Did not the woman who had been recommended to Blanco as scrupulously honest and reliable, whose one duty was to see that nothing was stolen, force the locks on the closets to make it seem that certain things she had taken had been stolen? That day Lucio forgot his gallantry, and the lady, who had entered the house a few weeks before wearing a halo of uprightness, was literally kicked into the street.

But the poor house could not be saved. Blanco's efforts fell helpless before the very nature of things. The only way to have protected the house would have been not to occupy it. Once quartered there, and with soldiers around, the consequences had to be what they were. The troops would leave in this mansion what they left everywhere: dirt and destruction. The appearance of the beautiful entrance hall a few days after the guard had been stationed there was an indication of what might be expected. Everything was dirty, neglected, stained, on the verge of falling to pieces.

The very drawing rooms, which the soldiers rarely entered, gave mute evidence of the treatment they had received. The visitor who did not drop ashes or matches on the priceless rugs scorched the beautiful wood of the floors, or stained the draperies and curtains with his dirty fingers, or left the muddy imprint of his shoes on the silk-upholstered chairs. Lucio had stationed an orderly there just to watch out for the cigarette butts: as soon as one was thrown on the floor, he was to pick it up; or when one was forgotten on the furniture, he was to take it away. Useless precautions! Man's capacity for destruction, if no internal force restrains him, is unlimited. With a few exceptions nobody came to Don Joaquín Casasús's house who did not leave a trace of his passing. There was every degree: from those who stood up on the delicate little tables to those who entertained themselves for hours at a time by letting themselves drop with all their weight into the easy chairs again and again to see how the cushions regained their resiliency as soon as the weight was removed. After doing this long enough a moment arrived in which the cushion stayed flat.

This was all a depressing indication of what was to be expected. On the one hand ideals were degenerating, and on the other inanimate objects and instruments, worn out and abused by unappreciative or deliberately perverse hands, seemed to lose their properties as though convinced of the futility of trying to serve mankind.

3 AN AMBUSH IN THE PALACE

Lucio saw the President and brought away from the interview a fairly encouraging impression. Carranza, to be sure, had avoided any reference to Villa or Breceda or us; but, at the same time, he said nothing to confirm our suspicions that Breceda was plotting something.

"In a word," Blanco wound up, "either Carranza already suspects me and has approved Breceda's plans, as we fear, or there isn't any plan. The worst part of the whole situation, as I see it, is that you fellows aren't going to want to keep out of sight the time it takes for the doubt to be cleared up. Why don't you play safe and go with Villa?"

And, in truth, Domínguez and I could not bring ourselves to stay shut up. That very afternoon we went out for a walk in the hope that everything would be all right. One comforting thought buoyed us up: we did not doubt that Breceda would stop at nothing, no matter how low it was, for he was capable of everything. But, pretending to be friends with us, as he did, why should he double-cross us like this when he could so easily get somebody else to do it?

So we set out from Blanco's house seeing everything in a rosy light.

About five o'clock that afternoon on Plateros Street we met General Saucedo and General Santos Coy. Saucedo asked us to come with him to La Esmeralda.

"There's something I've been wanting to do for several days," he said. "First of all, I want to buy Lucio a present. I owe it to him. And I want to give each of you a little token to remember me by. This is a good time, come along with me. I'll get your remembrance and you help me pick out something nice for General Blanco."

It took a long time in La Esmeralda. Saucedo wanted something out of the ordinary for Lucio, and nothing they brought out satisfied him. He even selected the souvenirs for Domínguez and me with meticulous care. We took a long time to look over and consider the various things that Blanco might like, and while we were about it, Breceda suddenly appeared in the store. How in the world had he happened to run across us? It was astonishing.

He walked straight over to Domínguez and me and began in a half-friendly, half-indignant tone:

"A nice mess you made of things this morning! You certainly got me in bad with Don Venustiano. He made an appointment with Villa for the conference by telegraph; Villa was there on the dot; the Chief was waiting in the telegraph office; and when I went to get you, you were gone. Don Venustiano was furious with me, but he put off the conference till this afternoon and he expects you. I've been looking everywhere for you for three hours. So please come with me, for I won't face the Chief without you."

Could he be telling the truth? Anyway, he got the better of our suspicions.

"This morning," Domínguez answered, "we waited three-quarters of an hour. Then, as you didn't come back, we supposed the thing had fallen through and we went home."

"Well, the important thing is for you to come now, right away. Do it for my sake."

"All right, we'll go whenever you want us to." And turning to Saucedo, meaning for Breceda to hear me, I said by way of leave-taking, "General, you see that Don Venustiano has sent for us. So you'll have to excuse us. Many thanks for the remembrance, and forgive me if I do not return the favor at once."

Domínguez and Breceda also made their adieus to the two generals, and the three of us left the jewelry shop. As soon as we were outside, Breceda said:

"Listen, fellows, if it's all right with you, I'm going ahead in the car and you can walk over. That way there'll be time enough to get things ready so you won't have to wait as you did this morning. I'll be in the private office. You come right up there."

He got into the car and drove off.

Domínguez and I followed along the avenue to the square. We hardly spoke a word all the way. Only as we crossed the Fócalo, he said to me:

"Well, what do you think now?"

"I don't think anything," I answered. "But anyway it's better to take the bull by the horns."

We entered the palace by the main gate. As we passed the flag of the company on guard, we respectfully removed our hats. In front of the stairway leading to the private offices stood an automobile; strangely enough, it was pulled up so close to the door that there was barely room for one or two people to get by. I paid no attention to it at the time; it was only later on that I thought about it. The chauffeur had a military bearing. It seemed to me that behind a pillar near the car and the entrance I caught a glimpse of the brim of a hat very much like the one Breceda was wearing.

Domínguez and I went to pass between the car and the

door. I was going first and he after me. But just as we were pushing the door open, eight or ten soldiers appeared on the stairs, covering us with their rifles, which had the bayonets fixed.

"Hands up!"

Our first instinct was to step back and reach for our revolvers. But before we could try it, we discovered that two sergeants, who had stepped out of the other side of the car, were resting the muzzles of their pistols against the small of our backs. Domínguez, smiling, put up his arms. And I, who could feel that one of the soldiers was doing more than merely threaten me with his bayonet—it was going into my stomach —took hold of the gun with both hands, though offering no resistance, and I did not mince words telling the brute what I thought of him. Another minute and he would have run me through.

"Hand over your weapons!"

"Either 'Hands up' or 'Hand over your weapons,'" Domínguez answered. "We can't do both things at the same time."

The sergeants behind us settled the argument by taking our pistols out of our pockets, and after making sure that we had no other weapons, they made us step back to the door of the car.

The poor soldiers and the two sergeants looked terrified. They must have been told that we were dangerous, and that it would be a hard job to arrest us. They eyed Domínguez and me like a pair of wild animals. This explained the very elaborate plan and everything else, including the vigor with which the soldier had handled his bayonet.

The sergeants indicated with their pistols that we were to get into the car. One of them came inside with us and sat facing us so he could cover us both with his pistol. The other, in front with the chauffeur, had his gun ready too. And the car started off, followed by the curious glances of the few people who had witnessed the scene. In my final recollection of the courtyard, as I saw it that day from the inside of the car, there appears again behind a pillar the brim of a hat like Breceda's.

The car went by the company on guard, drove round the Palace, and turned into Correo Mayor toward Lecumberri.

"To prison," I said to Domínguez.

"It looks that way," he answered.

And as the sergeant sat there with his pistol cocked and his eyes glued on us, Domínguez said to him:

"Put your pistol down, brother, and put it away. We haven't any intention of escaping, among other reasons because it doesn't suit our plans. If it did, you may be sure your pistol wouldn't stop us."

The unmistakable note of authority in Domínguez's voice so cowed the sergeant that he obeyed. He first lowered the pistol and finally put it into its holster.

4 In Prison

General Carlos Plank, the warden of the prison, was never without a smile on his lips, and in the smile a pipe. He was like an overgrown child, all rosy, fair, and blue, perfectly blue, from the iris of his eyes to certain attributes of his soul.

That afternoon when he saw Colonel Domínguez and me brought into the prison by two sergeants and a considerable escort, his astonishment knew no bounds. His smile faded for a minute; his pipe came out in his hand.

"You prisoners? How's that?"

And while the necessary preliminaries for our entrance were being attended to, he kept looking at us again and again, with a growing expression of incredulity on his childish, smiling face. When he was left alone with us, he said:

"Boys, I just can't get it through my head that you're here as prisoners. And as nobody can make me believe it, I'm going to treat you like guests, not prisoners."

Plank installed us in his own house; that is to say, in the quarters he occupied as prison warden. He gave us several

large, airy, sunny rooms. The largest of these had windows
on the street and on a courtyard. What a temptation to a
prisoner those windows were, fifteen feet from the ground! A
sheet tied to the railing and a horse waiting below were all
we needed. But I must say that it never entered our minds
for a minute to pay Plank for his courtesy and consideration
toward us in such a way.

We spent our first hours of captivity as people do when
they move, fixing up our new house with a view to making it
comfortable. Plank put a boy at our service immediately, and
he helped us arrange the furniture as we wanted it. We decided to use the large room as a sitting room, the one next to
it as a bedroom, and the other as a dining room. To see us so
busied with all these tasks, anybody would have said that we
were delighted to be in jail.

The fact is that this seclusion which had been forced on
us, far from seeming the harbinger of some tragic denoue-
ment, was to us more like a game or one of the trifling ups
and downs of our political adventures. Don Venustiano still
preserved among his scant virtues a very praiseworthy one:
not to kill. So it was possible to be in his clutches without
feeling oneself in mortal danger. And, knowing this, we
promptly consoled ourselves with the small amenities of our
prison life. Two hours after we reached the penitentiary, we
received our first visit, from Miguel Alessio Robles whose
presence initiated us in the double life a prisoner led. It was
enough to see him enter, affable, exuberant, with his stiff
mustache like the Kaiser's, and his clumsy walk, to realize
that our thoughts and emotions followed two different channels: the one commonplace and immediate, within reach of
our hand and desires, and hence lacking in appeal and glam-
our; the other remote and out of the ordinary, forbidden and
apparently inaccessible, and for that reason dazzling as a
promise or hope. He came to express his sympathy and offer
us his help.

"That stubborn old fool," he said, applying to Carranza an
odd and double epithet which fitted him only by half, "is

going to be the ruin of the Revolution, with his vanity and his treachery."

And he went from Don Venustiano to his most intimate colleagues, flaying them in his best style; he was already a formidable propagandist, and with time he was to launch his ideas from loftier platforms than the comfortable prison sitting room where we were at the moment.

He talked vehemently with us on his constant theme of how the Revolution could be freed from personal intriguers, and when he left, an hour later, he was overflowing with active plans. He went off determined to do away with Carranzaism and every other *ism* that departed from the pure constitutionalism which should restore the law and avenge Madero's assassination. Toward the end of his visit Plank came in, and in a burst of enthusiasm Alessio Robles said to him:

"See here, Charlie, why don't they arrest me? Just tell me why. For I am absolutely anti-Carranza."

And he went down the stairs repeating this so that everybody who had ears could hear him, from the jailers and officials to the Yaqui soldiers on guard. Good, generous old Miguel! From the windows I watched him disappear in the gray twilight. A kind of murmur accompanied his uneven footsteps: probably the wake of his vociferations in defense of his imprisoned friends. And he did not stop at merely defending us, as we should learn later. For that night we received from the Café Colón, in his name, a delicious dinner, complete from entrées to cigars, and during the whole time of our captivity the same thing was repeated morning, noon, and night, without a single exception.

Don Venustiano's efforts to stamp out opposition did not stop with us. The day after our arrest other politicians connected, or supposed to be connected, with the dissident groups of Sonora, Sinaloa, and Chihuahua were taken into custody and sent to the penitentiary. These were Luis G. Malváez, Don Manuel Bonilla, Enrique C. Llorente, his brother Leopoldo, and two or three days afterward José Ortiz

Rodríguez and Luis Zamora Plowes, at the time editor of *ABC*. Apparently Carranza was now throwing off all pretense and had completely yielded to the temptation of becoming a despot, which is irresistible to the redeemers and liberators of Mexico. But so far all he got by this was to inflame the opposition in the street by the very prestige that he himself gave to the opposition in prison. The truth is that, prisoners though we were, we did not waste our time. On the one hand, Carranza put his opponents out of the way in prison; on the other, Domínguez and I, with these same politicians, formed a colony there in the penitentiary that in activity could be properly compared with a beehive. Plank made no objection to our request to have Luis G. Malváez come and live with us, and it wasn't hard to have Don Manuel Bonilla and his companions assigned to the rooms next to ours. In this way we were all together on the top floor of the main building, and our rooms opened on to a hall that overlooked the garden. This hall, our communication center, was to become the channel for the most vehement anti-Carranza plotting.

Our political activities could bear fruit, thanks, on the one hand, to the kindly tolerance of Plank and Martínez Urristra, the assistant warden, and, on the other, to our unbroken contact with the outside world through our continual visitors. For there was hardly a revolutionist that didn't visit us then, from the most daring to the most indifferent: Lucio Blanco, Alberto J. Pani, Luis Cabrera, Obregón, Acosta, Saucedo, Villarreal, Vasconcelos, Santos Coy, even Alfredo Breceda himself, who had the brazenness to pretend that he hadn't the slightest idea why we were in this situation, and who offered to do everything he could on our behalf so the First Chief would set us free. If my memory does not fail me, the only one of our friends who forgot us at this time was Isidro Fabela; this was especially hard on Enrique C. Llorente, who loved him like a brother and who almost wept at the thought of his indifference.

But the visits of these exalted personages were not the only ones that interested us. There were others, like those of the secret police agents, that while less agreeable were more interesting. Domínguez and I—especially I—had had a hand in organizing the first police service in the city under the revolutionary régime, and as, after that, we had seen to it that we should be informed daily about what we wanted to know, it became a habit with several of the agents to report to us. Even though we were in prison, this custom was not interrupted; the agents came to see us every morning to tell us what they knew. In this way we learned about all sorts of schemes and plans, some of them pretty shady, like the one to have the "Gaucho Mújica" kill Villa, and we were thus enabled to take a hand in the game ourselves. The plan for the gaucho was typical. Mújica was to go to Villa, win his confidence, and then, when a favorable moment came, strike. (This plan was similar to the one which with certain military touches was to be used later on to assassinate Zapata.) But we had time to interfere and spoil the plot against Villa, as will be seen further on.

Nor did we suffer for lack of other distractions, not political. Every afternoon Lucio Blanco used to send us a military band. The musicians gathered in a circle under our windows and played for hours on end whatever we asked for. We also liked to have them come inside and play in the corridors, which Plank—or Martínez Urristra—out of pity for the prisoners was always glad to allow. The metal framework and gratings of the cells echoed with the reverberation of the brasses and the cymbals and the shrill vibrations of the flutes and clarinets. And to see the miracle which *La Adelita* or *La Valentina* worked on the most hardened criminals made one believe in the myth of Orpheus.

Some mornings we used to stroll through the corridors and inside courts and we often discovered scenes and details that were interesting or moving, even if not pleasant. We would spend a long time trying to decipher inscriptions the dissident congressmen had left on the walls; we would enter into long discussions with the most dangerous prisoners on themes of human values, and sometimes they would tell us the story of their lives. And occasionally we would observe from a distance and with a strange curiosity—as though they were creatures from another planet—the supporters of Huerta and the reactionaries imprisoned there. Among these were men of high standing: Nacho de la Torre, always ailing, stretched out on his cot and covered with rich blankets and comforters; General Enrique Mondragón, aged and pale; and any number of officers and civilians of every origin, appearance, and political leaning.

We could not help feeling a certain sympathy for these adherents of Porfirio Díaz and Huerta who were prisoners there like ourselves. And for two of them we even felt gratitude—a very peculiar kind of gratitude—for, without knowing it, they were responsible for the best moments in our penitentiary existence. We owed them what I used to call the "pathetic hour" and the "Dionysiac hour," both so significant, though in different ways, that we used to look on them as the outstanding event of each passing day, and look forward to them as the supreme happening of the day to come.

The "pathetic hour" was the daily arrival of Doña Amada Díaz de la Torre, to see her husband. At first her frequent visits met with certain difficulties, as they were against the rules. But afterward, as a result of Domínguez's and my efforts, about which she knew nothing, Plank and Martínez Urristra, like the excellent fellows they were, smoothed out everything, to our great satisfaction. Our efforts were more than repaid by the sight of the beautiful lady.

She always arrived in a cheap hired cab, and from the moment she set foot on the ground her whole being radiated an air of serene, profound melancholy which charmed and captivated us. Her dark slender silhouette combined dignity and grace in the perfection of its lines. From our windows we would watch her descend to the sidewalk and, inside the building, cross the courtyard, enveloped in an atmosphere that she created as she moved. There are supreme majesties, in nature as among mankind, which triumph by their mere appearance. Thus the swan is itself the herald of its grace; and when Doña Amada Díaz appeared, everything around her seemed to fade into shadow that she might shine alone. Ten years before, I had seen her arrive, dressed in red velvet and sparkling with rubies, at a fashionable ball given by the School of Mines; now she walked alone and in mourning through the sinister court and corridors of a prison. But she was not a whit less under these circumstances than she had been before. On her beautiful Indian face, half hidden by a simple, becoming hat, grief and suffering had left no trace; there was only a calm, melancholy dignity, so assured and poised that something of it was left in the atmosphere that surrounded her. At such moments it was as though I were reading, written on the flagstones of that prison yard, the two famous lines of Díaz Miron's, and I repeated them as I looked out on the dingy vehicle waiting in the street, and which seemed raised, as by magic, to a privileged category.

The "Dionysiac hour" was the daily morning appearance of the daughter of one of Huerta's generals who was imprisoned there. Her coming was like that of spring; the most hidden sources of life and desire sprang into being at her approach. We used to crowd out on to the balcony for her coming, so tightly packed together that we got in each other's way. We would watch her come walking across the square, and then, as she went into the hall, we would all rush across to the corridor, as though the end of our prison term depended on getting there. From there we could contemplate the conflagration lighted by her brief transit through the courtyard. I used to think that a sixth sense had been born in all of us, for without anybody's announcing it everybody knew when she was going to arrive, and became all expectancy: jailers and prisoners, criminals and law-abiding men. Up in the corridor we would hang over the railing, and our glances formed an inverted cone, the tip of which moved with her from one end of the courtyard to the other.

She moved with the most extraordinary cadence of soft, flexible rhythms. Her feet as she walked seemed to follow

along one straight line, with the most exquisite movement of
the ankles. That graceful walk was reflected first in her waist,
and from there it rose in delicate undulations to her torso,
her throat, her head—exquisitely beautiful head, throat, torso
—rippling out to the movements of her arms. Her body was
like a flexible wand, and shed about it the fragrance and
vigor of her youthful beauty, which as she passed seemed
to flow from her into the ground and from there up the walls
with the sole object of bringing to life that great stone organism and all the little organisms within it, bound during
those moments with double chains.

5 Prisoners on the March

The Military Convention in session in Aguascalientes ordered Carranza to set us free. He did not obey the command,
however, but decided on his own authority to put us on the
train and send us to General Nafarrate, the military commander of Matamoros, with orders to take charge of us until
we reached American territory. Don Venustiano was trying
to kill two birds with one stone by doing this: first, not openly
to disobey the Convention; and, second, not to let us go unpunished, or, better still, to administer to us his favorite
punishment. For Carranza, who used the death penalty spar-
ingly, had a great predilection for exiling his enemies, especially personal ones. Who but he re-established the system of
ostracism (so contrary to the spirit and the letter of the
Mexican code) to which our revolutionary governments since
him were to adhere to so enthusiastically?

Naturally, we did not in the least mind being taken to the
other side of the border. Once we were in Brownsville, nothing could stop us from going to El Paso and entering Mexico
again by way of Ciudad Juárez. And Ciudad Juárez meant
Villa and Villa meant the Convention. But the thing we did
not like so much was that General Nafarrate was to see us
over the border. His fame as assassin rather than general was

too great not to make us uneasy. Besides, there was another obvious question that added to our worry: what was the reason for expelling us by way of Matamoros when Laredo was much nearer?

The enigma puzzled us very much, and our attractive sitting room in the penitentiary became more animated than ever and then settled down to meditation. Everybody turned the matter over in his mind, and we all agreed that what Don Venustiano had up his sleeve was to get rid of us through some one of the many resources at the command of the large and small Nafarrates in the country. (Nor were these suspicions unfounded. It was this same Nafarrate who a few months later was to shoot Aguirre Benavides, Bolaños, and the other delegates from the Convention who gave themselves up to him, trusting in the safe-conduct Pablo González had given them.)

In view of these fears some of our friends—particularly Pani and Lucio Blanco—tried to have our route changed. But their attempts proved fruitless, as was to be expected. Besides being stubborn, Carranza was despotic, which made it impossible to argue with him once he had reached even the most trifling decision. There were few things he enjoyed more than being surrounded by supplicants and ignoring them. As a matter of fact, of all the revolutionists produced in Mexico up to that time—since him there have been worse— he was the most profoundly and sincerely hostile to the rights of man. (Naturally, I am referring to those revolutionists who had some sense of responsibility for their acts and their obligations.)

At last the moment came to leave that prison, where, thanks to the kindness of General Plank and Martínez Urrista, we had not had such a bad time. To tell the truth— perhaps, in a measure, because of the fears that assaulted us—we felt a parting pang. Our imprisonment had not been without certain pleasant features, a certain novelty, and had taught us certain lessons. While there we had plotted successfully, we had acquired a firsthand knowledge of the mysterious, sometimes terrible prison world. Our acquaintance with the imprisoned followers of Huerta had taught us to weigh better the responsibilities of the politician of second rank—in a word, we had learned to be more tolerant, more understanding, more human. And we were filled with a sense of melancholy at the thought that all this, whatever it was, now lay behind us forever.

Half an hour before we left, Plank came to the rooms we had occupied, and said to us:

"Nafarrate is a bandit. You want to be careful with him. Just to be on the safe side, I'm returning your revolvers. Hide them carefully and don't give me away. If Don Venus finds out about it, I'll lose my job."

And he laughed with the sunny laugh of a blond, pink baby.

Carrying arms under those circumstances was a knife that might cut both ways. They might serve for our defense, or they might serve as a pretext to apply the escaping-prisoner law or some similar one. Still, Plank's advice seemed good, and we followed it. Plank had always been our friend, but on this occasion he was more than just that. He talked to us like an experienced revolutionist, one who knows all the tricks of the trade. It was he who advised us not to leave Mexico alone, but to take our families with us.

"The more women and children, the better," he said. "That way there can be no doubt about your peaceful intentions, and Nafarrate can't say afterward that you got rough and he had to liquidate you."

It was late afternoon when we left the penitentiary, to the excitement and astonishment of the neighborhood. The less the spectators could understand all this movement of soldiers and civilians in a strange promiscuity, the more interested they became. And from the point of view of a spectacle the affair was not devoid of a certain profound and typically Mexican interest. Carranza had ordered that we be taken to the station on foot, and for greater pomp and safety—whether his pomp or ours I cannot say—he had sent an escort large enough to take care of twenty criminals.

From our big middle window, where we stood looking out for the last time, we had watched the soldiers approaching, followed by a crowd of people. When we came downstairs, the soldiers stood in formation to the right of the street door. There Plank went through the formalities of turning us over to the captain who had been detailed to take charge of us. The latter, for something to do, looked us over first, and then counted us off, like heads of cattle, pointing to each of us with his finger as he said:

"One, two, three, four. . . ."

But once we were in his charge, he did not know what to do with us. It seemed to embarrass him to have to conduct a string of prisoners that didn't look like prisoners; he could not screw his courage to the point of issuing orders to people before whom he felt inferior. He could not get any further than saying to us: "All right, now let's get into formation and start off."

But he gave no order. He was a man well along in years, and he had an humble, almost servile air. His uniform, like most of those of that period, displayed more dirt and patches than martial attributes—which was quite as it should be, for, aside from his pistol and the three bars on his broad-brimmed hat, there was nothing martial about him, either in his words or in his bearing.

For the third or fourth time he repeated: "All right, now let's get into formation and start to the station."

But what he did was to take a cigarette out of his pocket and light it.

Evidently he was overawed by us. We were something new in his experience and he was reluctant to proceed. In his modest role as custodian of political prisoners, he was undergoing the same experience as our Napoleons before battle: they didn't know what to do with their troops. We—soldiers and prisoners—got tangled up like the brigades or divisions

under the rudimentary strategy of those generals, the ones
who said: "You go right, you go left, me in the middle,
and God help the one who chickens out." Finally we grew
impatient. Domínguez exchanged a few words with us and
then turned to the captain and addressed him in these impressive terms:

"You know that I am a colonel?"

"Yes, Colonel."

"You know what the rules provide for a case like this? I am
referring to my prerogatives, my rank, my rights. . . ."

"Yes, Colonel."

"Then, Captain, you won't object if, in spite of the fact
that I am under arrest, I take command of the squad?"

"At your orders, Colonel!"

No sooner said than done. Domínguez took command and
did not relinquish it. His first act of authority was to order
eight or ten taxis. Then he put the prisoners in some, the
soldiers in others, he and I got in with the captain, and in this
fashion we set out toward the station.

Mexico then was not the desolate city it became in
later years. San Francisco still preserved much of the gentle
but imposing tranquillity of the years 1905 and 1906. As we
rolled slowly down the avenue, our cars plunged into the
rising tide of brilliant joyous existence. After our long imprisonment it was like feeling a breeze from the sea or the
mountains in our faces.

We rode past the jewelry-filled windows of La Esmeralda,
which brought back the memory of Alfredo Breceda. We
left behind the fence of La Profesa and in its rear the colonial temple. From time to time familiar glances and smiles
came to us from the passing carriages and cars. We passed
El Globo, with its bright interior of a Parisian confectioner's
shop; we caught the fleeting gleam of great glass jars of al-
monds, and of caramel-colored customers and waitresses.
Iturbide . . . San Francisco . . . La Imperial . . . Guar-
diola. . . . Then the car rushed along the Alameda, cool in

the dusk of shadows splotched here and there with green clarity.

Lucio Blanco and other friends were waiting for us at the station and with them our families, ready to accompany us into exile. Altogether we were going to form a numerous caravan.

The train was already filled with passengers. Domínguez advised the captain to give orders that room was to be made for us. And the captain, who bristled with energy when somebody else was in command, ordered a first-class coach vacated "for the needs of the service." The passengers made vigorous and noisy objections. But in five minutes the coach was empty, and all of us, escort, prisoners and families, got in and made ready to settle ourselves. Our thirty soldiers immediately filled the car with their customary reek. The ladies of the party could not stand it, and Domínguez took steps to remedy the difficulty. It was not much trouble to persuade the captain to make certain modifications in the plans for the trip; the "needs of the service" made it necessary to distribute the soldiers through the second-class cars, with the exception of the captain, who was to stay with us.

The train finally started. We hung out of the windows to wave good-bye to Lucio Blanco, who brandished his gold-headed riding crop above the heads of the crowd on the platform. As the train rolled out of the train shed, I heard the sound of music. I listened attentively; on the other side of the fence they were playing *La Golondrina*. Lucio? Of course, Lucio had thought of it. He had stationed a band there to send us off in good revolutionary style.

6 IN THE SHELTER OF THE CONVENTION

Nobody would have believed that our car was in reality a traveling prison of politicians who had fallen on evil times. General Plank's advice had met neither deaf ears nor refractory wills. We were accompanied by our mothers, our

wives, our children, our sisters; and their presence created
such an atmosphere of domesticity and contentment that it
was hard for us to remember the reason for our journey and
its possible outcome. Besides, the contrast between the seclusion in which we had been living the preceding days and
the sense of freedom we felt as we rushed ahead in the train,
masters of mountain, plain, and valley, was so vivid that it
took away the sense of a journey into exile. The train rolled
on for hours, days; and we, so recently emerged from the
narrow prison horizon, gave ourselves over to the delight of
drinking in the scenery, feasting our eyes on the luminous
purity of the immense perspectives. No doubt the lack of
anything better to do contributed to the popularity of this
form of amusement.

For, aside from a few more than ordinary inconveniences,
this trip in itself was not very different from others we had
made, or if there was a difference, it consisted in the fact
that there was less novelty to it. Naturally, the prolongation
of our association, after the long days together in captivity,
could offer us few surprises. Only an occasional one of us—
gifted in certain aspects with a richer personality—could now
and again evolve something worth noticing; as for instance,
Enrique C. Llorente, for whose impeccable neatness my admiration reached its climax on this occasion. He gave proof
of how great and mysterious was his capacity for the exquisite
grooming of his person, of the unalterable poise of his manners, and of his marvelous ability to look at all hours as
though he had just stepped out of a bandbox. In the course
of the trip all of us, sooner or later, became hopelessly dirty,
and our interpretation of the rules of travel etiquette grew
more and more lax. Not so Llorente, however; just the opposite happened with him; his clothes seemed to press themselves, his collar whitened instead of darkening, his bearing
grew steadily more erect, his hair lay smooth, and the points
of his mustache bristled, blacker and stiffer than ever. And
everything else the same way. To rest or sleep, we others
used to lie back or stretch out on the seats; Llorente was

never seen to vary by an angle of ten degrees, to the right or left, backward or forward, from the most ceremonious sitting position. This was true even when sleep, closing his lids, gave his face the anatomical dignity of a statue instead of the laxness of muscles it produced in the rest of us.

There was one thing that Don Venustiano had overlooked when he ordered us into exile, and that was the authority—fleeting, it is true, but great—of the Convention at Aguascalientes. And even less had he allowed for the fact that it was presided over by an upright man: Antonio I. Villarreal. Carranza thought himself so strong that he believed his arbitrary orders were going to be respected even in the areas under the control of generals sincerely in favor of the Convention. But Villarreal showed him in our case how ridiculously mistaken he was, for he made short work of Carranza's disregard for his and the Convention's orders. Villarreal was still imbued with his early revolutionary spirit; he had not yet been bitten by the tarantula of presidential ambitions. He preserved—not yet clouded as in 1922, or completely obscured as in 1923—his sound human and political criterion and the strict sense of justice that made him one of the fairest, if not the most brilliant, of the leaders of the Constitutionalist Revolution.

Villarreal commanded that the orders to put us at liberty be carried out as issued, and this was done when the train we were on reached Monterrey. Nothing was further from our minds, and at first we were surprised and alarmed to see a large detachment of soldiers stationed on the platform, who surrounded our car as though they meant to take it by assault. But the smiling air with which Colonel Alfonso Vázquez (Poncho Vázquez, everybody called him) jumped on to the steps, opened the door, and came in, quieted our alarm.

"Nothing to worry about, gentlemen," he said, shaking hands with us; "my soldiers are here only to protect you, even if it doesn't look like it. We had to do things this way to keep your escort from putting up any resistance."

He was young, friendly, and enthusiastic. His voice rippled gaily as he talked.

"Let's see, now," he went on, assuming a more military tone, "who's in command here?"

"Colonel Domínguez," answered the captain in whose custody we had been placed.

Vázquez looked puzzled. "You?" he said, turning to Domínguez.

"Yes," the latter answered. "I'm in charge, but only by chance and for reasons of expediency. Don't pay any attention to that, though; the real commander here is the captain."

Vázquez then turned to the captain. "What are your orders?"

"None, Colonel. I mean, nothing special. Just to escort these gentlemen to the border, and if I am requested to do so, to leave them in charge of General Nafarrate at Ciudad Victoria or Matamoros."

"Very good, very good," interrupted Vázquez, laughing heartily, as though the captain's orders were extremely funny; "but now things have changed. General Villarreal, president of the Convention at Aguascalientes, has ordered me to relieve you so that you may return at once to Mexico City with your men. As you know, he is the highest authority in the Republic. From this moment the prisoners you are escorting are under my orders."

"Just as you say, Colonel," answered the captain, "only I'd like to have it in writing."

"Of course; you go right over to headquarters and they'll give you the official documents."

As we did not understand exactly what this change of custody might mean, we bombarded Vázquez with questions. He gaily explained the situation in a few words:

"Nothing, except that Don Venus just reckoned without his host this time. General Villarreal ordered me to assign you an escort to accompany you to Aguascalientes, not as prisoners, but as free men. He just told me to ask you, when you got there, to present yourselves at Convention headquarters. If you want to, you can rest here tonight and leave tomorrow; otherwise you can take the train that will be coming by in a little while."

We had been shut up in the discomfort and dirt of our car for forty-eight hours, and it had been very hard on the women and children. But we were so overjoyed that we decided not to stop off in Monterrey, but to go straight on to Aguascalientes. We communicated our wishes to Colonel Vázquez, who gave the necessary orders.

Soon afterward our car was uncoupled from the northbound train and coupled to the southbound, and a few minutes later we began our way back by night, as far as San Luis Potosí, over the same road we had just covered by day. But now our escort was from the Convention's troops, not from Carranza's, as before.

San Luis Potosí seemed to us, the day we spent there between trains, little short of an enchanted city, especially watched over by good fairies. Was it because the Revolution, still in its beginnings, had not yet stamped its destructive seal on it, as it did afterward on practically all the cities of Mexico, which before had been beautiful and flourishing? Or was it rather because of the unique glow that everything takes on when one has recovered his lost liberty? Be that as it may, San Luis Potosí seemed to me a species of urban paradise: such clean, well-paved thoroughfares; such intimate, inviting squares; such well-laid-out streets; such pleasant architecture! At night it gave the impression of a city covered by a great transparent roof through which one could see the stars. And this same sensation, of something protected from the inclemencies of the weather, was not dissipated by daylight. There was something urbanized and domestic in the surrounding country, a certain refinement which seemed to radiate from the city to the countryside, from the city to the sky, and had a civilizing influence on all alike. Even the vegetables in the nearby gardens seemed to acquire a degree of perfection unknown elsewhere.

Our impressions in Aguascalientes, when we finally got out of the train, were different, but no less pleasant. The slow dimming of the afternoon, the faint twinkle of the stars above, the slow lighting of windows and street lamps on the street, the walk from the station down the long, tree-lined avenue to the city, all tended to submerge the spirit in a gentle melancholy. And in this sensation of autumnal warmth, of twilight well-being—neither dark nor bright, neither sad nor joyous, the remoteness of the limbo—lies the essence of all Mexico. . . .

Leaving our families for the moment where best we could, the whole group of us went straight to the theater where the sessions of the Convention were being held. Just as we went up the stairs, a clock somewhere struck eight.

We waited for a few minutes in the vestibule to be announced. In a little while we heard a burst of applause from the room, and then a commission of three delegates came out to welcome us and invite us in. As we walked in through the middle door, all those present got to their feet and turned toward us. The orchestra, the boxes, the gallery overflowed with light and people. Once inside the door, we stopped, somewhat embarrassed, for we did not really know what it was all about. But we saw that the members of the committee in charge got up from their seats at the rear of the stage, and one of them walked over to the footlights, making signs to us to come ahead. We then walked down the aisle to the front row. The commission of delegates and the officer in command of our escort had entered with us.

Villarreal, who was presiding, tapped the bell for silence; he was about to speak. One had only to look at him to see that more or less the same thing was happening to him as to us: he was bewildered by all this ceremony. For the moment he was at a loss for words. His handsome head of a Europeanized Moor bent forward for a few seconds; the intense blackness of his thick hair, of his heavy mustache, of his eyes gleaming darkly from their deep-set sockets, shadowed by heavy brows and surrounded by unbelievably deep circles, seemed to catch all the light in the room.

Finally, with perfect simplicity of word and gesture, he said: "Gentlemen, the Convention has ordered that you be put at liberty. That is all: you are free."

The Convention broke into applause of an uncertain nature. Some seemed to applaud this sovereign decision; some, I do not know why, seemed to applaud us, the outpost of the Carranza opposition. When the applause died down, Don Manuel Bonilla, as the eldest of the group, expressed our thanks for the act of justice that had been done us. And next, amidst further applause, we mounted the platform to shake hands with General Villarreal and the delegates around him, and then we sat down in one of the boxes beside the stage.

BOOK IV

The Cradle of the Convention

---

1 EARLY CONVENTION DAYS

Aguascalientes led a troubled existence in those days, owing
to the excesses—unbelievable at times—of the revolutionary
troops. *Revolution* and *the Revolution* became synonymous,
and probably for this reason the names of certain figures of
the Constitutionalist epic sowed panic by their mere sound.
"Bañuelos" or "Domínguez" was heard, and people rushed
to take refuge in the most hidden nooks, especially if there
were handsome virgins in the family or other equally desirable
treasures. The wealthy inhabitants or even those in moder-
ately comfortable circumstances would have given a great deal
to have been able to hide their property, their stores, their
homes. To combat the danger of losing everything they tried
one of two plans: either they hid everything they could, or
else they made open display of it, in order to ingratiate themselves with the new group power, and in this way save
their possessions through their new friends.

Thanks to this latter attitude, Aguascalientes, which nor-
mally could not have accommodated two or three hundred
outsiders without overflowing, on this occasion managed to
make room in its small hotels and its not too spacious houses
for the thousands of people the Convention brought with it.
The rooms for rent were all taken in a minute; but no sooner
had this happened than offers of comfortable rooms, of whole

houses, of mansions, began to pour in, all *gratis et amore*, merely out of enthusiasm for the cause.

At first I was puzzled by this phenomenon, so contrary to my notions on political economy. It represented a depreciation of capital and an indifference to interest so sudden and spontaneous that I could not make it fit in with what I had studied on the subject. The law of supply and demand did not work at all. And, as is customary with me, in search of a ray of light to illuminate the mystery I let my imagination run away with me. Apparently—so I reasoned with myself at first—we were preceded wherever we went by the fame of our opposition to Carranza, and this made us very popular and assured us a warm reception from those who shared our attitude. This is to say, without expecting it or deserving it we were beginning to be looked upon as great men—a typical revolutionary phenomenon—and to enjoy the advantages connected with a reputation of this sort, even though we were not and did not feel like heroes.

The fact is that no fewer than six prominent citizens came to call on us the morning after our arrival, and each of them, vying with one another in hospitality, placed his home at our disposal with such urgent cordiality that we could not say no. These were moments of great political satisfaction to us. We felt popularity dropping on us like manna from heaven, and the Revolution and its hopes seemed to open before us in an infinite horizon. The brief springtime of the ideals we had so long cherished bloomed in our hearts, and it touched us deeply to see how these ideals—by the mere strength of their altruism and purity—were triumphing among people who did not even know us.

But the spell was of brief duration, for very soon our eyes were opened once more to the true state of affairs, and political economy resumed its normal laws. The truth, the sad truth, was that the well-to-do residents of Aguascalientes, than whom there are no better economists, sized up the new revolutionists as they arrived, in search of the least suspicious-looking faces, and as soon as they found a man who made a

good impression on them, they overwhelmed him with attentions in the hope of making use of him afterward. At
any rate, this seemed to be the rule—with exceptions, of
course—and, in any case, it was advantageous to both parties.
Thanks to this, we found lodgings in less time that it took
to ask for them. I do not recall where my eight companions
and their families stayed; I had a beautiful room in one of
the main streets, not far from the Morelos Theatre, where
the Convention met.

As we were not generals or generals' delegates, we were
not entitled to sit on the platform during the Convention.
But our role as early victims of Carranzaism surrounded us
with an aureole and we were treated with great deference;
from the night we were declared free, those in charge of the
assembly had assigned us a box so that we could be present at
the sessions. It was an orchestra box next to the stage, and
from there we could see all the theater. The speaker's table,
which was at the extreme left of the platform, was right beside us, and a few feet away was the chairman's table.

I had only to take one look at that military assembly to be
convinced that nothing would come of its deliberations.
It may be that the moral and cultural level of the Convention was not so low as in some of the congresses we have since
had in Mexico—congresses in which the deputies sold themselves to the highest bidder, where friends and companions
were sold out, where legislators who could barely sign their
names plotted and at times passed laws. But, nevertheless,
the Military Convention revealed at a glance that it lacked
the civic consciousness and the far-seeing patriotism that
was needed at that moment. The problem it faced was to
save the Revolution by ridding it of two perils: Carranza—
the greater—and Villa—the lesser. The first represented the
betrayal of the purpose of the Revolution and the return to a
struggle of personal ambitions in the fight for leadership. The
second represented unrestrained brutality, which could be
controlled only by wise guidance. But the majority of the
generals who had gone into the Revolution, on a vague

though noble collective impulse (and backed up by personal ambitions, not so vague nor so noble), were not as a rule capable of converting into a disinterested idea what had been a nebulous urge in them. To the touchstone of patriotism the majority responded with their little personal ambitions, so petty and so mean that, as one looked at them, it did not seem possible that they could have been the authors of the Revolution, and less still that they deserved to be.

Eduardo Hay, who was one of the best men there—at least as far as intentions were concerned—uttered a phrase at one of the early sessions which revealed the dominating spirit of the assembly. "We are here," he said amidst resounding applause, "on our honor." The instantaneous popularity of these words showed up to what point the sentiment they expressed was false—not on the part of Hay, who spoke out of sincere conviction, and who would hold no traffic with the chicanery and combinations of those who sold themselves for power—but on the part of the military politicians who took it up with such display of enthusiasm. It was evident that the rarest thing at the Convention was honor, and this would be clearly seen a little later on when nearly every one of the generals, some for one reason, some for another, would go back on his agreements on the most trivial pretexts. Being on their honor reduced itself to the generals', or their representatives', writing their names under the eagle on the flag, and a few days later, denying it, signature and all. The sincere efforts of some of the outstanding men at the Convention were doomed to failure, as in the case of Villarreal and Angeles and Obregón. It must be admitted (though some of us do not relish it) that at the Convention there were few who could compare with Obregón in generosity, and none so ready as he to conciliate opposing groups. His lack of success may have been due to the fact that he was too ready, or his tone was too humble, and this detracted from the prestige he had acquired on the field.

The Convention underwent a serious moral and cultural decline with the entrance of Zapata's delegates and his aides-de-camp. They arrived one morning, accompanied by Angeles and the other officers who had gone to bring them from the "mountains of the south." Their appearance aroused, not enthusiasm, but a positive frenzy. They were received as though they bore the truth and the Gospels, and as though, once Chihuahua and Morelos were united, the rest would take care of itself. Yet there were those who felt, just from looking at them, that they would be harmful rather than helpful to the work of harmony.

The group, motley and yet homogeneous, was headed by Paulino Martínez, Díaz Soto, and Alfredo Serratos. The first was a snake in politics; the second affected a plebeianism that was unexampled, even among the humblest figures of the Revolution; and the third was a strange mixture of a good man at heart and a politician without any guiding principles, who was at swords' points with his own better impulses. For a cheap audience the three were good speakers, better, on the whole, than those of any of the other groups in attendance, better than those of Carranza, Villa, or those representing the tendency personified by Villarreal, Eulalio Gutiérrez, and Lucio Blanco. But the oratory of the three of them—this was evident in their first speeches, acknowledging the ovation they had received—was inspired in a negative passion, even a hatred of everything that did not mean an inversion of values so that the most barbarous, the most primitive, the most uncivilized elements should become the leaders in the progress of mankind.

Díaz Soto used to wear at that time the tight trousers of the Mexican *charro*, a cotton jacket, and a broad-brimmed hat. Anybody who did not know him would have taken him for the driver of a pulque wagon. But those of us who were familiar with his connections, his profession, and his education had the sensation, when we saw him make this deliberate, unnecessary show of himself, that he was trying to act as a symbol, an allegory of Zapatism, by giving it, in his own person, a local habitation. Was he a faithful symbol of the real Zapatism? Zapata is still an enigma, but an enigma that

admits of only two answers: it is either the white cotton
pants and the leather sandals of the *pelado*—which the
depth of his suffering makes worthy of all respect—or it is
the tight trousers and broad-brimmed hat of the *charro*,
which (outside of the theater and the ranch) stand for the
degradation of all cultural values, having all the spiritual
poverty of the *pelado*, but without the humility and the
resignation that redeem him; having the insolent material
ambitions typified in trousers and shoes, but without the
higher aspirations that would justify them. And the Zapatism
that spoke through Díaz was the second and not the first,
and the same was true of Paulino Martínez, though one
could also hear the small-town lawyer in him, as well as of
Serratos, although in him it was overlaid by an agreeable
frankness.

2   CONVENTION SCENES

But if the Convention was doomed to failure as a political
achievement, as a show it was a brilliant success. I used to
take my seat in the box in the same frame of mind as if I
were going to see a performance of one of Reinhardt's pro-
ductions or some other theatrical offering in which all of
us—actors and spectators—would soon be taking part in the
action, though the emotion was more intense and absorbing
in this case, as one felt here that it was a question not of
feigned but of real truth. At times the show provoked laughter; at times it left one perplexed and bewildered; at other
times it produced its catharsis, for it was a tragedy in fact if
not in form, with its fatal struggle between two irreconcilable
forces. Two profound aspects of the same nationality were
locked here in a death struggle: one, the diffuse but desperately earnest and noble longing for a better social fabric;
and, as opposed to this, the deep-rooted incapacity to direct
the turbulence of this aspiration and convert it into something feasible, organic, and co-ordinated. The visible dra-

matic motive was the political passions, untrammeled, brook-
ing neither let nor hindrance; and the presiding power at the
crossroads of action was the pistol—here elevated to the role
of fate in the classical tragedy, or of character in the modern
drama—the ready, ruling, definitive pistol.

The leading man of the Convention show was usually
Roque González Garza. Villa had appointed him his personal representative, and his choice would seem to have been
shrewdly made, for with his friendly manners and his honorable intentions he offered the military gathering a softened
replica of the too crude figure of his master. Roque possessed
other virtues besides. He was loyal to the core and honest
in his convictions, and, for an affair of this sort, he possessed
no end of parliamentary tricks, which were no less useful because they provoked the amusement of the more serious-
minded and learned.

One morning Roque arrived at the Convention absolutely
convinced that he had found the solution to the Villa-Car-
ranza dilemma. He radiated satisfaction and mystery and,
though bursting to confide in his friends, nevertheless restrained himself. He got several of us who were unquestionably anti-Carranza into a corner in the hall and intimated to
us the importance of his idea, though without going into
details.

"It will be," said he, "the test. Carranza either goes or he
is done for as a leader."

"And what about Villa?" we asked.

"Villa doesn't matter here. The important thing is that if
Carranza tries to hold on, it's all over with him."

How or why Carranza was done for if he did not retire
was not explained. And so when we saw him go into the
room where the meeting was in session, we followed in a
few minutes, skeptical and smiling. For Roque was so good-
hearted and so eager to find a solution for every difficulty
that even his best friends often had their doubts as to his
mental capacity.

My reaction was the same as that of the others, or perhaps stronger, inasmuch as my opinion of him was colored by my memory of his amusing intervention in another political assembly, that of the Liberal Progressive Party in 1911. His behavior there, which came from his excess of good faith, from his ingenuous optimism with regard to the simple, the sincere, had been nothing short of fantastic, and was an inexhaustible source of anecdotes. How, for instance, could anyone forget his tenderhearted attitude—so different for this reason from the disgusting atmosphere that prevails at political meetings—the day the conflict between the supporters of Vázquez Gómez and Pino Suárez came to a head? Roque listened to the beautiful and lying summation of Urueta against the first of the two candidates, in which the great orator led off with this mordant phrase: "The brain of the Revolution!" He then listened to the powerful defense of Luis Cabrera, pregnant with wise counsels and intimations of the future. And Roque, moved to his soul by the rapture of the moment, filled with a sense of duty, and given this opportunity, arose to say that the final reason to settle the conflict was contained in certain official documents in his possession, whose testimony could not and should not be disregarded. However, as he did not have those papers with him, he asked for time to go and fetch them. An hour later he returned, dressed in formal attire—double-breasted frock coat, white vest, silk hat—and mounted the rostrum with all eyes riveted on him. He was so moved and nervous that to calm himself in preparation for what he was about to say, he laid his hand on his heart, as though to subdue it.

"Make ready, gentlemen here assembled," he began, his voice filling the silenced hall, "make ready to live this solemn moment. "Here," laying his hand once more on his breast, "here I have the memoirs of my brother Federico. . . . You shall hear them. . . ."

Whatever he was going to say was drowned out in the uproar that suddenly blotted him from sight, as though some supernatural force had cast him into a Tartarus of booing, from which he emerged after a little, the tails of his coat rumpled, the knot of his tie askew, and his false cuffs out of place.

Naturally, no scenes of this sort took place in Aguascalientes. Three years of intense political activity had elapsed since the beginnings of the Madero uprising, three years which had given Roque—much more alert and wily than anyone would have thought at the beginning—a thorough training. Nevertheless, the amazing suggestion by which he now hoped to settle the conflict between Villa and Carranza, as we who were his friends realized the moment he announced it, was in close keeping with that he had put forward three years earlier to resolve the struggle between Vázquez Gómez and Pino Suárez. Only this time, with the benefit of his experience, and operating on a different level and among different men, he came as close to the guerdon of applause as on the earlier occasion to the ignominy of scoffing and booing.

With fervid phrases Roque described the great civic spirit of General Villa, and his readiness to make every sacrifice for his country. And he wound up by reading aloud a document in which the Chief of the Division of the North, in his eagerness to remove every obstacle from the path of the revolutionary enterprise, offered to take his life with his own hand if Carranza would commit suicide together with him.

This was heroic Villaism's finest hour.

But from the point of view of dramatic interest nothing could compare with the tempests that Antonio Díaz Soto used to stir up. His unbroken stream of oratory made this possible, and the corrosive ideas he was championing almost made it a duty. Díaz Soto did not believe in God or the Devil, in good or evil, in country or family, in mine or thine. He did have a feeble belief in the divine, mysterious origin of the Zapata gospels and in Emiliano Zapata as a superhuman being. He used to describe him, among his mountains in the south, at the moment in which he revealed to a few faithful the Ayala Plan. His descriptions of these scenes were couched in biblical terms that evoked Moses and Mount Sinai, and if the four hundred leaders there assembled did not fall to their knees at the sound of this strange oratory, half lay, half religious, Díaz Soto flayed them in spirit, upbraiding them for their ignorance, their inconsistency, and their servile submission to stupid prejudices unworthy of the Revolution's anointed.

One day it came to his mind that there was such a thing as socialism, and that Karl Marx had written the Communist Manifesto and *Capital*, and that patriotism and other similar inventions were but ruses devised by the classes in power to weld more tightly the chains of the proletariat. And as the poor Convention generals were not very well up on this, he decided to enlighten them, with the vehemence of gesture and the vigor of phrase characteristic of him.

Somebody (Angeles, perhaps, or some other revolutionist uninitiated in the mysteries of the International) had placed a Mexican flag fastened to its pole on the stage near the speaker's table, that it might fan the patriotic ardor of the orators. The three colors of Iguala and the pre-Cortés eagle presided like a tutelary divinity over all that was thought and uttered in that tribune. From time to time, at the voice of the orator or the breeze set in motion by his gestures, the folds of the national ensign rippled as though affirming his statements or emphasizing his gesture.

There were also those who, engrossed in the elucubration of their own thoughts, almost laid their hands on the cloth, unconsciously longing to caress it, or to calm their nerves by doing something. And there were those who dragged the flag into their speech, with the clear design of winning over their hearers, stirring them, arousing them.

Up to that morning Díaz Soto seemed never to have noticed the flag. But this time, as he was marshaling his ideas to begin his speech, he began toying with the cloth, lifting it, and letting it fall again. I cannot recall exactly what his speech was about that day, but as usual it had to do with the excellence of Zapata's ideals and the imperative need for bringing them down from the mountains of the south to the central and northern plains of the Republic—all this delivered with the pyrotechnical, repetitive eloquence at which Díaz Soto was unrivaled. There was one beautiful passage, with sweeping historical touches, demonstrating that mankind is one in origin and destiny. In another he led in magnificent procession before the rapt gaze of the Convention the great leaders of humanity who had admitted no distinction of nationality, race, or color; Buddha, Jesus Christ, Saint Francis, Karl Marx, and Zapata. This was followed by a veritable paroxysm of oratory denouncing the perverse division of humanity into countries and nations, flagellating imperialist ambitions, refuting the ideas of a fatherland and repudiating those childish emblems that men in their folly invent to make war on one another.

During the latter part of his speech Díaz Soto tried to suit the action to the word, and, gripping the folds of the Mexican flag that hung beside him, he began to apostrophize it with exclamations and rhetorical questions.

"Now, what is the good," he asked, shaking the flag and sweeping the front rows of his audience with an impassioned gaze, "of this dyed rag, bedaubed with the image of a bird of prey?"

Naturally, nobody answered. Shaking the tricolor banner once more, he asked, or shouted:

"How is it possible, gentlemen of the Revolution, that for a hundred years we have been venerating this silly mummery, this lie?"

At this point the revolutionary gentlemen, as though slowly shaking off the spell Zapata's best orator was weaving around them, began to doubt the evidence of their eyes and ears and to look around at one another in astonishment. A tremor ran through their ranks, and, to a man, they got up just as Díaz Soto, on the point of tearing the flag from its staff, to judge by the way he was tugging at it, was rounding off his idea with these words:

"This rag and all it represents is but a mockery, an empty show, against which we must all . . ."

Four hundred pistols flashed out of their holsters. Four hundred pistols gleamed on high, their bright fingers of light pointing straight at Díaz Soto's breast. The room became a babble of scraps of phrases, fierce insults, and vile interjections:

"Let go of that flag, you dirty . . ."

"Zapata, son of a . . ."

"Take your hands off that flag, or . . ."

Díaz Soto was never more admirable than at this moment. Under the aim of the revolvers and the rain of the vilest insults, he stood pale but firm beside the table, his arms folded, waiting for the storm to wear itself out. All he said was:

"When you have finished, I'll go on. . . ."

3 The Death of the Gaucho Mújica

While we were still in prison, Berrueco had come to us one day with a long story of how "Gaucho Mújica" had been released from Belén prison a few days before.

Berrueco was one of the various secret agents that I had put on the police force. He seemed so insignificant that at first I had paid scant attention to him; but he showed himself so faithful and active that little by little he completely won our confidence. Of all the group to which he belonged he was the most assiduous visitor Domínguez and I had while we were locked up. General Plank knew perfectly well the capacity in which Berrueco was employed, and, besides, we ourselves had told him that he was the channel through which we received most of our political information. Yet Plank never interfered with his coming up to the quarters which served as our cell, and much less did he inform Carranza of the frequency and nature of his visits. When Plank had to choose between duty and friendship, the latter always won.

"I know you won't believe me," Berrueco told us on this occasion, "but it's the God's honest truth. One of the generals that is closest to Carranza has fixed it up with Gaucho Mújica to go and assassinate General Villa. The gaucho is already out of jail (and you know he was held for murder), and the general I'm talking about has promised him a big sum of money and his complete freedom if he carries out their agreement. He must be on his way to Chihuahua already, and what he plans to do is to worm his way into Villa's good graces and, the first time he gets a chance, kill him."

Berrueco did not tell this in the calm way I write it; he was in a state of great excitement, stammered even more than usual, and was so pale and nervous that one had only to look at him to see the importance he attached to his discovery. His nervousness was at least partly justified; in view of the gaucho's reputation as a killer, the plan really represented a danger to Villa's life, and this touched our agent in a sensitive spot. Berrueco, to be sure, did not know the Chief of the Division of the North, and owed him no personal allegiance; but he never forgot—on this he based his hopes for the future—that it was I who had given him his job in the secret service, not to serve Carranza, but, on the contrary, to further our own plans, and the trump card in our deck was Villa. For this reason, through his loyalty to us, Berrueco came to feel almost the same concern as we about anything that referred to the formidable *guerrillero*.

Domínguez, who was exceptionally brave and daring, laughed heartily at what Berrueco was telling us. And, to be sure, heard offhand like that, it did sound too silly to take seriously. Only when one stopped to think that the person selected to carry out the plot was the gaucho Mújica, and recalled the man's daring and his criminal astuteness, did one realize that the thing might not be so incredible as it appeared at first glance.

"Berrueco, old man," said Domínguez, "you're just seeing things. It's plain you don't know Villa. . . ."

"Well, neither does the gaucho," answered Berrueco, who was nobody's fool.

"That doesn't make any difference," Domínguez answered. "Either the gaucho isn't so smart as they say, or he ought to know that the gaucho hasn't been born yet who can pull the wool over Villa's eyes. You don't fool around with Pancho Villa."

"Well, Colonel, you can think what you please. But I swear to you that everything I've told you is so, and if you don't believe me, just wait and you'll see." So great was Berrueco's solemnity as he took his oath that for the moment he stopped stuttering.

It seemed to me that the first thing to find out was where he had got his information, whether we believed it or not. So I began to question him.

"Now, first of all," I said, "tell us who this general is."

He answered without a moment's hesitation: "Don Pablo."[1]

It was my turn to be skeptical.

"Don Pablo? I don't believe it. Don Pablo isn't capable of such a thing. . . ."

"Don Pablo," Berrueco insisted.

"Well, but how do you know it?"

"From two different sources, two of the best."

"What are they?"

"We know it (I'm not the only one, there are other agents who know it, too) from a person who is close to Don Pablo, and from another who's in touch with Mújica. . . ."

"Who are they? What are their names?"

"I can't tell you any more about the first one. The second is a woman."

"A woman?"

"Yes, sir. A woman who is on intimate terms with the

[1] Pablo González, one of Carranza's most important military leaders.

gaucho. Please don't make me tell you her name; we, too, have
our professional secrets."

Berrueco departed and we were left perplexed and troubled. Domínguez's first impression had changed. Now it did
not seem so improbable that somebody might have been
found bold enough to make an attempt on Villa in his own
territory. On the contrary, now it seemed to him perfectly logical. "That's the only way they'll ever get Villa," he said, "some
coward assassinating him by surprise. A man with a heart in
him would never do it." But my skepticism remained unshaken, more as regarded the supposed intervention of Don
Pablo than about the gaucho. I could not bring myself to
believe that one of the leading generals of the Revolution—
in rank if not in achievements—would descend to such low,
cowardly plotting, and against the very man to whom the
Revolution owed its most important military victories. To accept this meant to renounce the noblest revolutionary hopes
and ideals, everything that Carranzaism was openly to repudi-
ate later on, when it planned and exulted over the dastardly
assassination of Zapata.

We finally came to the conclusion that it was our duty not
to judge Berrueco's report too farfetched, and, on the strength
of the possibility, to send word to Villa about the reputed
intention of the gaucho and his accomplices. It would not do
to send a letter or a telegram, so we decided to have one of
our friends, Cabiedes, a brave, loyal young chap, deliver the
message in person. He was to repeat to Villa word for word
our conversation with Berrueco.

Now that we were free in Aguascalientes, we decided at
once to go to see Villa, among other reasons, to find out how
the matter of the gaucho and his plans had worked out. It
was three weeks since Cabiedes had left, and he had not returned nor sent us any word as to the outcome of his mission,
and we had heard nothing from Villa.

So Domínguez and I started out toward Zacatecas, and

about evening we found the Chief of the Division of the North in his headquarters, a little beyond Guadalupe. He seemed greatly surprised to see us.

"Well, where did you boys drop from? I thought the old man had had you shot. . . ."

"No, General, not yet. . . ."

"And how about Nafarrate?"

"We haven't even seen him."

"You can thank your lucky stars that you got off safe, believe me. To tell the truth, I was sure something was going to happen to you, especially to this fellow," and he pointed to Domínguez as he said this.

Domínguez asked: "To me, General?"

"Yes, to you, my boy, to you. Because you talk too much."

Domínguez turned red with rage, and flashed Villa a myopic, angry glance; but Villa, who had intended no offense, but merely a friendly warning, went on talking—fortunately for us—without noticing Domínguez's anger. He was in good spirits, almost jovial, and it showed in his eyes, which were less bloodshot and restless than usual, and in the gentler movements of his lower jaw. His expression was almost human.

Patting Domínguez on the shoulder with his left hand, he said:

"And thanks for the warning. That devil of a gaucho! If he wasn't on my trail already!"

"Did he actually get here?" I asked.

"Twice, partner. The first time he fooled me good. He said he admired me without knowing me, just by my reputation, and he wanted to join me. He was telling me how many men he'd killed (to win my confidence, you know), and finally he got me to give him money for a trip to the north, saying he'd soon be back. Then that friend of yours came along—what's his name?"

"Cabiedes."

"That's it, Cabiedes. Well, he came and told me what was up. You can guess how I took it. I almost put a bullet through

Cabiedes to teach him to travel a little faster. But after a while I calmed down, thinking that the gaucho would soon be back, and that's just what happened."

"And then what did you do?"

"What did I do? Oh, everything was tended to. I've got him buried now."

"Buried, General? Where?"

"What do you mean 'Where'? Why, where would it be? In the ground. And would you believe the son of a bitch almost got away from me? Because these lawyers around here told me that as he was a foreigner we couldn't just up and kill him like anybody else. But I said I'd like to know why this dirty double-crosser of a gaucho shouldn't get his just because he was a foreigner. So we held what they call an international trial. He confessed every last thing, for I told him I knew everything, and that if he lied to me I'd let daylight into him, but if he told the truth, we'd see about it. Mr. Carothers, the United States consul, heard the confession and signed the declarations. Then we read them over again and I had some more seals and signatures put on them, and then I ruled that it would be only justice to sentence the gaucho to the same punishment he had wanted to give me. Mr. Carothers said he'd do the same thing in my place. When the gaucho found out that I was going to do him in, he went all to pieces, and he began to offer me things. He promised over and over that if I'd only let him off, he'd go and kill Carranza. But I asked him since when he thought I needed traitors to kill my enemies. 'You dirty skunk,' I said to him, 'I'm a man and I can do my own killings.' He soon saw it was no good; so he shut up. We shot him right on the spot."

After a long pause Villa added:

"Where's Cabiedes now? You know, I'm kind of sorry for the way I treated him because I thought he'd been too slow about getting here with your message. Tell him to come to see me. I want to give him a present. He's a nice fellow, serious, thoughtful, and dependable. Who knows?—maybe if it wasn't for him I wouldn't be here now."

4 THE ART OF THE PISTOL

The next morning Villa, who had a passion for firearms, brought the conversation around to them. As always when this happened, I found myself, in contrast to Domínguez, with little to say. On this occasion, however, I did not want to remain completely mute, and so I mentioned to Villa, in an offhand manner, as though it were unimportant, something that had greatly impressed me some months before in Sinaloa: the exceptional gifts of General Felipe Riveros which made him the outstanding pistol shot in the ranks of the revolutionists.

"General Riveros," I said, "is a remarkable shot. He can put a bullet in an empty cap of the same caliber at twenty paces."

Villa was just raising his hands to turn back the brim of his hat. He remained as though frozen to a point, his arms on high. In a dubious tone he repeated:

"A bullet in a cap of the same caliber?"

"Yes, General."

He then rested his elbows on the table, looked out of the window opposite him with a bemused expression, and finally said, recovering his customary self-assurance:

"That's not possible."

To tell the truth, I had not been an eyewitness to Riveros's feat of marksmanship; I had heard it from a third party. But those who told me about it had given it such an air of verisimilitude that I accepted it as a fact, without ever thinking to ask Riveros to do it in my presence. So, as I was convinced of it, I insisted:

"Yes, General. It is."

"Well, if it is," answered Villa, "we're going to prove it right this minute, for if he can do it, I can do it. You wait and see."

And without an instant's delay, he got up from where he was sitting.

We stepped down from the car, he, Domínguez, I, and a little later several officers joined us, among them Luis Aguirre Benavides.

Villa stood on the embankment for a few minutes, looking around for a suitable target. It was a superb morning. The dewy and wondrously transparent air enveloped everything in its clarity, a perfect clarity which seemed to saturate everything without touching it. The least differences in the terrain nearby stood out as clearly as the huge folds of the remote blue mountains. Except in perspective there was no near or far; the inner eye exactly reflected the slightest detail of the landscape.

Some hundred yards from the railroad track stood the ruins of an adobe wall. Villa walked toward it, we at his heels, and stopped there. In silence he studied the relation of the surface of the adobes with respect to the sun. On one side of the wall its rays broke into light and shadow; on the other, the shadow was soft and uniform. Villa went feeling the cracks between adobe and adobe on the latter side with the tips of his fingers until he found one that suited him. He took a bullet out of his cartridge belt, and holding it in his mouth and twirling it with his fingers, he managed to separate the bullet end from the cap. The nickel reflections of the shell lighted up his lips for several seconds and remained there while he kept his eyes on the little heap of gunpowder he was emptying from it into the palm of his hand. Finally, as he let the powder fall to the ground, he spat out the cap as though it were a cigarette butt. As it fell, the projectile became a momentary meteorite.

It was plain that Villa did not intend to take a back seat for General Riveros, for he went about all his other preparations with the greatest care and forethought. At exactly breast level he drove the cap between the adobes, giving it the slightest backward slant, as though he actually knew the mathematical trajectory his shots took. Then he moved back twenty paces from the target, took aim, and then altered almost imperceptibly the position of the cap. He repeated this operation, and then again, and still again.

To me this was a new Pancho Villa, an almost infantile Villa, whose pastime, in spite of the sanguinary memories his pistol evoked, was strangely in keeping with the smile of the light and the profound peace of the countryside. I watched him come and go, bend over, straighten up, advance and draw back arms and legs, in part fascinated by the athletic vigor with which he began and completed each movement, and in part troubled by a vague uneasiness. For, in the midst of all those preparations, I was beginning to be worried about the outcome. Suppose the feat attributed to General Riveros was not possible? And if it wasn't, how would Villa react? To my right, Domínguez was watching all that was going on with the curiosity of a professional marksman. To my left and a little in the rear were the other officers.

Finally Villa got ready to fire. But before squinting along the line of sight of the empty shell, he turned to me and said:

"You heard what I said, friend; if the thing can be done, I'll do it. Now, we'll see."

He brought his pistol up slowly and took aim. But just as I thought he was going to fire, he lowered his arm again. Then raising it quickly, and without taking time to aim, he pulled the trigger. The report rang out, light, sharp, dry, as clear as the outlines of that morning of light.

Everyone ran toward the ruined wall, except Villa, who walked toward it slowly, and myself, who followed a little in his rear, my eyes fixed on the shiny handle of his pistol, back in its holster. Gleaming in the light, the butt stood out in relief against the brown wool of his sweater.

"You did it, General!" shouted one of the officers.

"Right in the cap?" inquired Villa.

"Yes, General, right on the nose."

"Let's see," said Villa, as he came up to the group.

I, too, poked my head forward. The bullet had hit the cap

squarely, but without going completely through the opening; what it had done was to shoot away most of the edge.

As soon as Villa saw it, he said:

"What this friend claims General Riveros does can't be done."

I kept quiet. Domínguez spoke up:

"Why don't you try it again, General?"

"Again? What for? It would just be wasting bullets."

Then he looked again, this time closer, at the effect of the bullet. After a few seconds he said:

"You know what? When I stop to think about it, I begin to think the stunt is not so difficult nor impossible. Maybe I'm going to have to admit that our friend here was right. Yes, my lad," and he leaned against the wall looking at me, "when I was an outlaw in the hills I could have done what you say General Felipe Riveros does. For there I spent eighteen months without laying my hand on a woman, and my body was in first-class shape. It is not the same here. Here, no matter how hard you try, your hand isn't quite steady. Take my word for it, friend, a woman is a marksman's worst enemy, and, so they say, a bullfighter's."

That face-saving explanation seemed to me extremely plausible, and I would have backed it up with numerous arguments and theories, if Villa had not gone off on a tangent, asking me suddenly:

"And what kind of a marksman are you, friend?"

I felt myself between the Devil and the deep blue sea, but, of the two, I preferred the Devil.

"Very poor, General."

"Come on, come on," said Villa. "You can't be so poor when you're mixed up in all this mess. Let's see you try your hand."

My answer was to move over to the spot from which Villa had fired a few minutes before. I pulled out my pistol and took slow aim. I fired.

The bullet missed the cap by five or six inches.

"Pretty bad," Villa shouted at me. "Now fire without taking aim."

I raised my arm quickly and fired. The bullet went half a yard wide of the cap.

"You really are bad," was his comment.

And then, as I walked toward him, he said:

"Friend, I wonder that you are still alive. How the devil do you manage to protect yourself from the Carranzaists?"

Naturally, he imagined that I went around trading shots morning, noon, and night. But as it would have lowered me in his estimation to set him straight, I merely answered:

"I look after myself as best I can, General."

The answer did not satisfy him. He countered immediately, shaking his head admonishingly:

"No, my boy, no. You are on dangerous ground. One of these days they're going to kill you."

And he fixed those eyes of his, which were never at rest, on me. I felt him looking me over from head to foot the way the Yaqui Indians do with whatever meets their glance: as a possible target. Then, throwing one arm over my shoulder, he drew me toward him and led me away, walking slowly, to the adobe wall. There, with our backs to the group of officers, Aguirre Benavides, and Domínguez, he went on in a low voice, meant for me alone to hear:

"I like you, friend, and for that reason I think you deserve a better fate. So I am going to give you a piece of advice— good advice, you can take my word for it. Follow it and don't forget it. Here, give me your pistol. You pull the trigger with this finger, don't you?"

"Yes, General, with this one."

"Well, when you shoot without taking aim don't use that one, but this one," and he pointed to the middle finger. "Instead of using the forefinger to pull the trigger, hold it like this. You understand?"

"I do."

"But pay attention, friend; exactly like this, for everything

that doesn't work out the other way you do it depends on this.
. . . That's right, like that."

And sure that he had made himself clear, he added, as he
pushed me by the arm:

"Go on, now. Try it out."

He rejoined the group of the officers and Domínguez, and
once more I stationed myself at the proper distance from the
target. I held the pistol exactly according to his instructions.

When Villa saw that I was on the point of firing, he shouted
encouragingly:

"Go ahead, it's going to be all right."

Almost without taking aim I fired. The bullet was lost in
space.

"That way I do worse, General," I said.

"That's what you think. Try it again, remember you've got
me for a teacher."

I fired again. The bullet landed half a yard from the cap.

"You're improving. Try again, without aiming," he said
emphatically.

I obeyed. The bullet came within six inches. With a teacher's pride, he exclaimed:

"There you are! Does that convince you? You practice like
that a little every day and you'll see."

Domínguez eyed me with curiosity and surprise. But, although I pretended to be elated to flatter the amiable attitude of Villa, and acted as though it all seemed to me very
natural, I could not get over my amazement at finding that I
possessed such marksmanship.

On the way back to Aguascalientes that afternoon, Domínguez was determined to worm the secret out of me. At first I
refused to tell him, but in the end friendship won out.

"All right," I said, "I'll tell you, but only if you promise
not to tell it to anyone as long as Villa lives."

And with his solemn promise, I passed on to him the magic
advice, or what I understood as such.

5 The Film of the Revolution

History has not yet assessed what lay at the bottom of Don Venustiano's predilection for being photographed, whether it was a primary desire, or a political maneuver of a hidden and transcendent nature. Did he take pleasure in his own image, perhaps aware of the attraction his features held, highlighted by the oratorical references to his "patriarch's beard"? A touching narcissism in a man of sixty! Or was it rather that, annoyed by the pictures of Madero he encountered at every turn, the First Chief hoped to replace them with his own? Possibly his future biographer will opt for a thesis somewhere between the two, and claim that Don Venustiano found the martyr President's photographs as displeasing as he found his own to his liking. This theory could be substantiated, on the one hand, by the First Chief's willingness to pose for the photographers, and, on the other, by the suffering he underwent as a result of the panegyrics of Madero with which he was invariably received. Those of us who accompanied him on his entry to large cities or out-of-the-way villages during the first months of the struggle know something about this. Wherever he went there was always a photograph of Victoriano Huerta's victim, bedecked with garlands and wreaths. Cheers for Madero arose from the crowds—ingenuous and trustful of their new leaders—and the First Chief, whether on foot or on horseback, wrapped himself in the mantle of his annoyance, smiling and aloof, as he witnessed that Carranza stood out in neither the photographs nor the cheers.

The fact is that the figure of Don Venustiano and the photography of the Revolution became one. Carranza arrived in Sonora, not only on the run, but dirty, ragged; and when everyone was expecting that he would ask for a bath—soap and water to rid himself of the dirt and lice—it caused real amazement to hear that all the commander of the Constitutionalist army wanted was a photographer. This had far-reaching consequences for the photography of the Revolution; its awareness of its role as an activity that would give rise to great things dates from that moment, as did the stimulus, first great and then overwhelming, to its economic possibilities. For from then on Don Venustiano cultivated the determined and overriding inclination to lavish himself in effigy; and his kindly smile and glittering glasses soon came to be the harbinger of a rich harvest for the photographers: a golden, tinkling harvest. In Hermosillo the bills for the First Chief's photographs ran into thousands of pesos. This was as nothing compared to the outlay for those made in the North American studios of California to which, because of the paucity of such establishments in Sonora, the large-scale commissions were entrusted—the printing of a hundred or two hundred thousand copies, on special paper or with ornate design. And this was only the beginning of the photographic era, for later on the supreme directors of the Revolution, not content with still-lifes of the First Chief, resorted to films.

The Convention was halfway through its agenda when one of the official photographers of the Constitutionalist movement appeared in Aguascalientes. Was it Abitia in person, or one of his assistants or imitators? Whoever it was, the photographer came—and this is an important point—to show the gentlemen of the assembly the film of the achievements of the Revolution taken on location. His mission was not only artistic but political, and as such very shrewd and constructive. For nothing could have been more opportune at the hour of an appeal for unity than to bring before the eyes of the leaders of the dissident groups the sight of themselves, even though only on the screen, fighting together for the military and political cause whose scenes were recorded on the celluloid strip. There Carranza was seen surrounded by the very ones who were now denying him. There was Villa at the head of the formidable armies with which months before, in the name of the Constitutionalist plan of Guadalupe, he had captured Ciudad Juárez, Chihuahua, Torreón, Zacatecas.

There, after the victories of Orendaín and Castillo, Obregón and Lucio Blanco marched side by side. There Don Pablo and Eulalio Gutiérrez, Villarreal and Zapata, Dávila Sánchez and "Roba-Vacas," Robles and Benjamin Hill, Iturbe and Raúl Madero, were one in brotherhood. And all of them, bent on a single aim, joined in a single effort, consummated the triumph of the revolutionary arms, the forerunner of the civic enterprise waiting to be carried out. What better exhortation to the deliberating leaders to forgive one another their weaknesses and agree to agree! Compared with this, the self-willed oratory of Eduardo Hay, the almost inaudible sermons of Villarreal, of Obregón, of Angeles were as nothing, nor the generous efforts of the noblest and most disinterested group of all: that of young, austere officers of the type of David Berlanga, to whom the Revolution was an object of religious devotion rather than a cause for enthusiasm.

But passions were already running too high for anything or anybody to be able to restrain them. The idealistic motive, which still persisted in a few, had lost its potency for the majority, had practically disappeared. It was not the Revolution they were fighting for, but its spoils. And even those who were sincerely striving to save the work of the Revolution— the historic mission of the popular movement which would either fail here or take on increment—did so without losing sight of the personal fruits of victory. Each one was in favor of the alignment most advantageous to his interests, not those of the cause being invoked.

For this reason the predominant sentiment of the Convention was anti-Carranza. Carranza, dictatorial and corruptive, who responded to the bootlickers and the toadies and was the enemy of free men (think back on his favorites), was, without doubt, a complete travesty on the spirit of the Revolution. It was already apparent that he was headed straight for an inferior imitation of Porfirio Díaz, without the latter's military distinction or public austerity. But this was not what the majority of the delegates to the Convention, devoid of the most elementary notion of Mexico's historic destiny, found most objectionable. What they could no longer tolerate was for Don Venustiano to go on parceling out the spoils of the Revolution and, still less, for him to use them as he pleased to reward his unconditional supporters to the disadvantage of the others. Inversely, though to a lesser degree, Villa, the savage victor of the decisive battles of the Revolution, and Zapata, the apostle of barbarism made idea, were beginning to stand out as a threat of supposedly imminent and terrible acts of vandalism. But neither was this the reason for the opposition to them of the handful of Carranzaists of good faith, but the fear that by allowing Villa and Zapata to acquire further power, they would soon do away with the privileged status of those they looked upon as their enemies.

The night the film of the Revolution was shown we saw, too, how deep and capable of the worst excesses was the anti-Carranzaism of the Convention, which on occasion colored the sessions of the assembly.

Lucio Blanco and several of those of us who were his friends were strolling about the city when we got word, at the last minute, that the show was about to begin. When we reached the theater we could not find seats or even standing room. The entire Convention was present en masse, and with it the horde of friends and acquaintances of the delegates. The aisles were full to overflowing, every available inch of the boxes was taken, and the orchestra could not have held another pin.

After a brief effort to find a place, we became convinced that it was impossible, and were on the point of giving up when Blanco had an idea:

"I'd be willing to bet," he said, "that nobody has thought that we can see just as well from behind the screen, which is of cloth, as we can here. Let's go backstage, and there we can even get armchairs if we ask for them."

No sooner said than done. Behind the cotton curtain which doubled as a screen there was nobody but the stagehands. We found them seated on a pile of ropes and in a state of quiet comfort that was in sharp contrast to the crowding outside. When they saw us come in they divined our intention; evidently this did not annoy them, but, on the contrary, they smilingly offered to share with us the seats they had improvised. Blanco, always the perfect gentleman, would not accept their offer, and on the grounds that it would be better for all—and putting his hand in his pocket—he asked them to bring us the best chairs they could find among the props. Set against the rear wall, they were ideally comfortable. We did not even need to raise our heads to see; for some reason I do not recall, most of the lighted screen was at eye level.

Like a good revolutionary audience and under the influence of the circumstances of the moment, that one behaved in really extraordinary fashion. First, while the lights were on, delegates separated by the width of the theater carried on conversations at the top of their lungs. The words reached our hiding place, at times underscored by the laughter of certain groups, at times by the booing of others. In spirit, if not in the timbre of the voices, it was like the chatter of boys suddenly let out of school.

"They are in a joking mood," said Blanco, "for they are beginning to get bored by the Convention."

When the lights were turned out, the hubbub grew: jokes in feigned voices, answers half humorous, half insulting; guffaws. The darkness was broken by screeches, savage peals of laughter, the guttural howls of valley and mountain. The slides flashed on the screen by way of prologue did not interest anybody; the uproar grew by what it fed on. But all of a sudden everything changed. Laughter and catcalls, stamping and whistling turned into a deafening ovation as the title of the revolutionary epic adapted to the screen appeared in gleaming letters. And then I knew what the unanimous applause of a whole theater as the curtain falls is like; I tasted in imagination the glory of great actors.

A loud hoarse voice roared:

"Long live the Revolution."

"Long may it live."

Then silence.

The vibrations of the projector, neither very new nor very good, could be felt throughout the theater. On the screen the figures of light and shadow flickered. But the noise of the machine was unimportant; now the attention of the audience was unmindful of the ear and was concentrated in the eye.

Marching past within the luminous frame went the interminable file of Yaqui soldiers, grim, sinuous as the trails of their craggy hills. Their burnished cheekbones glowed in the sun as though made of bronze; their hats, adorned with ribbons and feathers, moved to the feline rhythm of their steps. When the tall, slender, lean Yaqui who was beating a drum the size of a toy appeared, the same stentorian voice as before cried:

"Long live the victors of the West!"

"Long may they live!"

And an ovation followed.

Then alongside a vast store of artillery captured from the enemy, Obregón stood with his officers. Once more the applause broke out, and the cry:

"Long live the Army of the Northwest!"

"Long may it live!"

Carranza emerged on the screen, corpulent, solemn, hieratical, at the moment of his triumphant entrance into Saltillo. Another voice cried:

"Long live the First Chief."

But instead of the enthusiastic, unanimous chorus, disorder followed. There were "Long lives" and "Down withs"; applause, stamping, protests, hisses.

Then immediately afterward, as though the operator had planned it so, astride his superb, prancing horse and bathed in light, came the magnificent figure of Pancho Villa, legendary, all-conquering. The unanimous applause drowned out the voices and only like a postscript to the salvo did this cry manage to make itself heard:

"Long live the Division of the North!"

"Long may it live!"

And the applause broke out anew.

For an hour, or perhaps more, the parade of the standard-bearers of the Revolution and their hosts went on, haloed by the light of the screen and the glory of their deeds.

We, however, did not see the end of the film for, without warning, something happened which made us leave our places behind the curtain with all possible speed. Don Venustiano, naturally, was the figure who most frequently returned to the screen. His repeated appearances were becoming more and more displeasing to the Convention audience, as might have been expected. The hisses mingled with applause that greeted him on his first appearances were turning into unalloyed hissing; then into hissing that verged upon hooting; then into open booing, and finally into an uproar. Stage by stage, it reached its climax in the scene where Carranza was making his entry on horseback into Mexico City. At this point it became a kind of hellish din that culminated in two shots.

Both of them perforated the curtain at the height of the First Chief's breast, and buried themselves in the wall, one half a yard above Lucio Blanco and the other still closer, passing between Domínguez's head and mine.

If the First Chief had entered Mexico City on foot instead of on horseback, the bullets would have found their mark in us. Ah, but if he had entered on foot, he would not have been Carranza, and if he had not been Carranza, there would not have been any shots, for there would have been no Convention!

6 Pancho Villa on the Cross

The Convention was still in session when war broke out again. That is to say, the attempts at conciliation failed in practice before they failed in theory. To tell the truth, the reason they failed was that this was what the majority on both sides wanted. They had armies, and they were close at hand, so how could they resist the temptation of putting them to fighting?

Maclovio Herrera, in Chihuahua, was one of the first to begin hostilities again, flouting Villa's authority.

"The damned big-eared son of a bitch," the Chief of the Division of the North fumed; "why, I made him! All he knows about fighting he learned with me. How does the treacherous, ungrateful cur dare to turn on me like that?"

His wrath was such that only a few days after Herrera's rising the troops Villa had sent in pursuit of him were hemming him in. The encounters were bloody, desperate. Both sides were Villa men, and it was a case of hurricane against hurricane. It was kill or be killed.

One of those mornings Llorente and I went to see Villa. It made our blood run cold to look at him. The glitter in his eyes made me realize suddenly that mankind is not of one species, but of many, and that these species are separated by limitless space, have no common denominator. An abyss cleaves them, and it may cause vertigo to look from one of these worlds to the other, which lies opposite. As fleeting as a ripple on water there passed over my soul that morning, face to face with Villa, the giddiness of fear and horror.

To our "Good morning, General," he replied in a sinister voice:

"Not good, my friends. There are more hats around than we need."

I did not understand what he meant by the expression, nor do I think Llorente did, either. But whereas he selected the part of wisdom, keeping quiet, I asked with stupid, almost crime-provoking tactlessness:

"More whats, General?"

He took one step toward me and answered with the deliberation of a person who can barely control his anger: "More hats, my educated friend. Since when don't you understand the language of real men? Or don't you know that on account of Big-Ears (the damned son of a bitch, if once I get hold of him!) my boys are killing one another? Now do you understand why there are too many hats? Do I talk plain?"

I didn't say a word. Villa paced up and down the car, as if keeping time to the internal rhythm of his wrath. Every three steps he would say between his clenched teeth: "The damned son of a bitch. The damned son of a bitch."

From time to time Llorente and I exchanged glances, and finally, not knowing what to do or say, we sat down, close to each other. Outdoors the morning shone bright, its perfect harmony broken only by the distant noises and shouts of the camp. In the car, aside from the palpitations of Villa's rage, nothing was heard but the ticking of the telegraph apparatus.

Bent over his table, facing us, the telegraph operator worked on. His movements were precise, and his face as expressionless as his instrument. Several minutes elapsed in this fashion. Then the telegraph operator, who had been transmitting before, said, turning to his chief:

"I think they're here now, General."

Taking his pencil from behind his ear, he began to write slowly. Villa came over to the little table where the apparatus stood. His air was at once agitated and icy, impatient and calm, revengeful and indifferent.

He stood between us and the operator, in profile, leaning forward. On one side of the dark blotch of his silhouette against the wall the energetic line of his under-jaw and of his arm folded across his breast stood out, and on the other, concluding the powerful angle that descended from his shoulder, the curved, dynamic outline of his pistol butt. This morning, instead of his slouch hat, he wore a gray sun helmet, with green facing on the brim. This headgear, always odd on him, seemed to me more absurd than ever that day. Strangely enough, instead of taking away from his height, it seemed to add to it. Seen close, and against the light, his stature seemed to increase enormously; his body stopped all the light.

The operator tore off the pink pad the sheet on which he had been writing, and handed the message to Villa. He took it, but handed it back immediately, saying:

"You read it to me, friend, but read it carefully, for I think this means business now."

There was a sinister inflection in his voice, so portentous and threatening that it was reflected in the voice of the operator. Separating the words carefully and pronouncing every syllable, he began in a low tone: "I have the honor to inform you . . ."

As he read on, his voice grew stronger. The message, which was laconic, gave notice of the defeat that Maclovio Herrera had just suffered at the hands of the troops pursuing him.

Villa's face seemed to pass from the shadows into the light as he listened. But instantly, as he caught the final words, his eyes blazed again, and his face flamed with his most terrible rage, his uncontrollable, devastating wrath. The commander of the troops, after giving the list of his casualties, had ended by asking instructions as to what to do with the hundred and seventy of Herrera's men who had given themselves up.

"What to do with them?" shouted Villa. "What a question! What should he do except shoot them? I honestly believe every one of my men is going bad, even the best ones I absolutely relied on. And if they're not, what in hell do I want with these generals that get friendly even with the traitors that fall into their hands?"

He said all this without taking his eyes off the poor operator, through whose pupils, and then through the telegraph wires, Villa perhaps hoped to make his anger reach the very battlefield where the corpses of his men lay.

Turning to us, he went on: "What do you think of that, gentlemen? Asking me what to do with the prisoners!"

But Llorente and I hardly returned his glance, and, without answering a word, looked off into space.

This did not disturb Villa in the least. Turning to the operator, he ordered him:

"Come on, friend. You tell that damned fool I don't want him using up the wires on nonsense. He's to shoot the hundred and seventy prisoners immediately, and if he hasn't notified me in an hour that the order has been carried out, I'll come there myself and put a bullet through him so he'll know how to manage things better. You understand?"

"Yes, General."

And the operator began to write out the message.

At the first word Villa interrupted him:

"What are you doing, not obeying me?"

"I'm composing the message, General."

"What do you mean, 'composing'? You send that off the way I said it to you and that's all. Time wasn't made to be lost fooling with papers."

At this the operator put his right hand on the transmitter and, pressing the lever with his little finger, began to call: Tick-tick, tiqui; tick-tick, tiqui.

Between a pile of papers and Villa's arm I could see the knuckles of the operator's hand, tense and vibrant from the contraction of the tendons as they produced the homicidal sounds. Villa did not take his eyes off the movements that were transmitting his orders seven hundred miles to the north, nor did we. I kept wondering—with that stupid insistence we have in dreams—at exactly what moment the vibrations of the fingers were spelling out the words "Shoot immediately." For five minutes that was a horrible obsession that blotted out every other reality, every other sensation.

After the operator had sent off the message, Villa seemed to grow more calm and sat down in an armchair near the desk. He sat there quietly for a little while. Then he pushed back his sun helmet. Then he buried the fingers of his right hand in the reddish tangle of hair that hung over his forehead, and scratched his head as though he were trying to get at some inward itching of the brain, of the soul. Then he sat quietly again.

Motionless, silent, we watched him. Perhaps ten minutes elapsed.

Suddenly he flung around toward me and said: "What do you think about all this, friend?"

I answered evasively: "Were you talking to me, General?"
"Yes, to you."

Hedged in like this, I tried to get out of it by using the language of real men: "Well, there are going to be a lot of extra hats around, General."

"Maybe I don't know that. That wasn't what I asked you. What about the consequences? Do you think it's right or wrong, this business of the shooting?"

Llorente, braver than I, cut in ahead of me: "General," he said, "to be frank with you, I don't think that order is fair."

I shut my eyes. I was sure that Villa was going to get up—or, without even getting up—and whip out his pistol to punish this criticism of his conduct in a matter which had flicked him on the raw. But several seconds went by, and then I heard Villa ask, without getting up, and in a voice whose calm contrasted strangely with the storm that had so recently preceded it:

"Well, let's see. Why don't you think my order was fair?"

Llorente was so pale that it was hard to tell his skin from his collar. Nevertheless he answered firmly:

"Because, General, the message says the men surrendered."
"Sure. What of it?"
"When they are taken that way, they shouldn't be killed."
"Why not?"
"That's why, General. Because they surrendered."
"You're a funny fellow. That's a good one. Where did you ever learn such things?"

My shameful silence had become unbearable. I broke in:
"I feel the same way, General. It seems to me that Llorente is right."

Villa enveloped us both in one glance.

"And what makes you think that, friend?"
"Llorente explained why: because the men surrendered."
"And I say again, what of it?"

As he repeated it this last time, a certain uneasiness was apparent which made him open his eyes still wider to take us both in with his restless glance. From the outside I could feel the pressure of that look of his, cold and cruel, and from the inside, an irresistible impulse to talk, which was pricked on by the vision of the distant executions. I had to hit quickly on some convincing formula. "The person who surrenders, General, by so doing spares the life of others, since he renounces the possibility of dying fighting. And this being the case, the one who accepts the surrender has no right to order the death sentence."

Villa looked at me steadily, and his eyeballs stopped rolling from one to the other of us. Jumping to his feet, he shouted to the operator: "Listen, friend, call them again, call them again."

The operator obeyed. Tick-tick, tiqui; tick-tick, tiqui.

A few seconds went by.

Villa inquired impatiently: "Do they answer?"

"I am calling them, General."

Llorente and I could not sit still, and we, too, came over to the instrument table.

Villa asked again: "Do they answer?"

"Not yet, General."

"Call louder."

The operator could not call louder or softer, but it was plain from the contractions of his fingers that he was trying to make the signals clearer and more exact. There was a short silence, and in a little while the receiving instrument began to tick.

"Now they're answering," said the operator.

"All right, friend, all right. Now you transmit as quickly as you can what I am going to say to you. Pay attention: 'Hold up shooting of prisoners until further orders. General Francisco Villa.'"

Tick, tiqui-tick, tiqui. . . .

"Finished?"

Tick-tiqui, tiqui-tick.

"All right, General."

"Now tell their operator that I'm right here beside the in-

strument waiting for the answer, and that I'll hold him responsible for any delay."

Tiqui, tiqui, tick-tick, tiqui-tick, tick. . . .

"Have you told him?"

"Yes, General."

The receiving instrument began to tick.

"What does he say?"

"He says he is going to deliver the message himself and
bring the answer."

All three of us stood beside the telegraph table: Villa
strangely restless; Llorente and I weak with anxiety.

Ten minutes went by. Tick-tiqui, tick, tiqui-tick.

"Are they answering?"

"It's not them, General. It's another station calling."

Villa took out his watch and asked: "How long ago did we
send the first order?"

"About twenty-five minutes, General."

Turning to me, Villa asked: "Will the counterorder get
there in time? What do you think?"

"I hope so, General."

Tick-tiqui, tick, tick. . . .

"Are they answering, friend?"

"No, General, it's somebody else."

Villa's voice was husky with an emotion I had never heard
in it before, and it grew deeper each time he asked if the call
was the answer to his counterorder. His eyes were riveted on
the little lever of the receiving apparatus, and every time
this made the slightest movement, he asked as though the
electricity of the wires were reaching through to him:

"Is it him?"

"No, General, it's somebody else."

It had been twenty minutes since telegraphing the counterorder when finally the operator said:

"Now they're calling," and picking up his pencil, he began
to write.

Tick, tick, tiqui. . . .

Villa bent farther over the table. Llorente, on the contrary,

seemed to stiffen up. I walked over beside the operator to
read what he was writing.

Tick-tiqui, tiqui, tiqui, tiqui, tick-tick. . . .

After the third line Villa could not curb his impatience
and asked me:

"Did the counterorder get there in time?"

Without taking my eyes off the paper, I nodded my head.
Villa pulled out his handkerchief and mopped the sweat
off his forehead.

We stayed and had dinner with him that afternoon, but
he made no reference to what had happened that morning.
Only as we were leaving, late that evening, Villa said, without
any preamble:

"And thanks, friends, for that thing this morning, that business of the prisoners."

7 A PERILOUS SLEEP

The natural gifts that made Villa a vivid and entertaining
talker were revealed to me one night in the little town of
Guadalupe, in the state of Zacatecas.

Enrique C. Llorente, José Vasconcelos, and I had reached
Guadalupe that afternoon. All three of us had come to talk
with Villa about a number of different things and we planned
to leave again in a few hours. Llorente was going to Washington, Vasconcelos to Aguascalientes; and I had to make a short
trip to Chihuahua. After we had finished the official business,
Villa said he would keep us company until our departure.
But as the trains from Ciudad Juárez and from Mexico City
did not come through until one o'clock in the morning, in
order to do this he had to give up his invariable habit of going
to bed early. Such a delicate attention on his part surprised
me beyond words, for I knew him so well that I could not understand it. Partly because of his rude upbringing and partly
because of his disposition, he never observed the forms of

courtesy with anybody. What was behind this unusual amiability? My astonishment and my suspicion—I could never free myself from my distrust of Francisco Villa—put me somewhat on guard, and I watched the General with more than ordinary attention. I analyzed his least movement, I watched his gestures, I studied his expressions, his words.

Our conversation took place in the lounge of the special car that Villa used for traveling or campaigning. The servants had cleared the table where we had had dinner. Villa's desk was closed. Every now and then the telegraph instrument clicked with what seemed, to us, idle messages going by. Through the little windows of the car we could see the pleasant valley, with its pools of water here and there, as it lay blue and mirrorlike in the light of the moon. On the other side the silver of the moonlight and the ocher of the abrupt, barren lands gave touches of enchantment to a landscape devoid of all beauty by the light of the sun.

The miracle of the autumn night finally took possession of us, and we stepped out on the platform to contemplate the vague dreamlike confines that lay limitless beneath the nocturnal covering of the glittering sky. It was chilly. On one of the steps a sentinel stood guard, all wrapped in a dark serape, and humming an endless, melancholy air in a voice as light as the glow of his cigarette. Another, half stretched out on the platform, was sleeping with his head resting against the brim of his hat, which he had bent down to make a pillow. His smooth and rhythmic breathing seemed to be keeping time to the light-flooded night. The moonlight was so bright that we could see his chest rise and fall as he breathed. Villa had been looking at him ever since we came out, and had not taken his eyes off him while Llorente, Vasconcelos, and I were admiring the view.

"What a mystery sleep is!" said Villa as we went back into the car. "What a mystery sleep is!"

And his restless eyes, always roving about as though possessed by terror, suddenly came to rest; they seemed to fix on some vague, distant point.

"Sleep is the strangest and most mysterious thing there is."

Vasconcelos had pushed the back of his chair up against the desk. On the other side, to the left, Llorente's bust rose from behind the telegraph table. I sat directly across from Villa, and to be more comfortable I had tilted my chair back against the window sill. As he talked, Villa seemed to be looking at me; through my eyes there passed that invisible ray by which he contemplated the images he was calling up.

"One time," Villa began, "when I was escaping with my pal Urbina, I found out that sleep is the strangest and most mysterious thing there is. For a week the mounted police had not let up for a minute in one of those brutal pursuits of theirs in which we came within an ace of being killed. My pal and I were hiding in the Durango sierra, and every day we thought they'd surely catch us as we slipped from one of our caches of provisions to another. We had left the last settlement we knew far behind us, the last wood chopper's cabin, the last shelter of the forest guards. And yet it took us longer to dismount than for the mounties to appear and make us start our cruel journey over again. In all this time we had hardly rested or slept, and when we did, it was only for a few minutes. Our horses were ready to drop. Urbina was getting so worn out he'd doze off on his horse until he slipped out of the saddle. Several times I had to wake him up and talk to him and scold him so he wouldn't give up. In spite of my powers of resistance, I was getting utterly exhausted, and I couldn't get over my surprise that we couldn't shake the mounties off our heels. How did they do it? Had they planned it all out beforehand and sent men on ahead? Didn't they sleep, either? Didn't they rest?

"Finally one morning we thought we were safe. From the cliff where we had managed to work our way through the heavy woods and thickets we could see the whole plain below, and there wasn't a sign of our pursuers. We were on a peak as high as a watchtower, and as hidden as a varmint's den. Two hours before anybody could find us we could see the approach, not only of a troop, but of a single rider, and we'd have time to climb farther into the sierra.

"We unsaddled. We fed the horses. We got ready to go to sleep.

"'Look pal,' I said to Urbina, 'I guess there's no danger now. Still, I don't feel easy. One of us had better watch while the other sleeps, and then we'll change. As you are more worn-out, you go to sleep first while I watch. In two hours I'll wake you up and then I'll go to sleep.'

"All Urbina said was: 'All right, pal.'

"He couldn't keep his eyes open. He lay down, put his head on his saddle, and went straight to sleep.

"What a mystery sleep is! My pal slept just as calm and easy! There was nothing but peace and rest about him as he lay there. As I looked at him, I couldn't believe that for a week he had been within an inch of being killed or taken prisoner several times. It seemed to me that either I was dreaming then or I had been dreaming before. His breathing was even; his face had the repose of a man who has never known danger. I remember he had on a pink shirt, and the button was off at the collar—I can still see it—and the folds of it would open and close with every breath. The light moving of the pink cloth on my pal's hairy black chest seemed to be such a part of the loneliness of the mountain, the quiet rustle of the trees, the steady munching of our drowsing horses, that I began to be afraid. The peace of his sleep terrified me, it was so different from that struggle to the death we had been mixed up in for so many years, God only knows why. And yet I couldn't take my eyes off that regular movement of Urbina's shirt, just as though I had been bewitched. Maybe I was beginning to go to sleep, too.

"But I came back to myself. To shake off that obsession I looked up. Away off, in the distance, down the mountain, where the mounted police might come, I saw a little white speck moving. But as I was still bewildered by the drowsiness that was overcoming me, I had to make an effort to realize what I was looking at in the valley. 'That's what it must be,' I said, and I jumped right up. Sure enough, it was the mounties. They were on our trail again; they'd soon be up to us!

"I shook Urbina.

"'Hey, pal, wake up, they're coming. Wake up, the mounties are after us.'

"But sleep is the queerest thing there is. My pal didn't hear me. His pink shirt kept on moving the same as before. There was the same peaceful expression on his face that descended on it from the quiet solitude of the mountains, the smooth, steady rustle of the trees.

"To save time I went and brought up the horses and saddled mine. All the time I kept calling my pal and shaking him with my foot. When I had my horse saddled and bridled, he was still asleep. I took hold of his head and shook it hard. He went right on sleeping just the same; his breathing didn't change at all, and to look at his face you would have thought that instead of pulling his hair and rubbing his ears I was smoothing his pillow so he would sleep better. When I saw that he wasn't waking up, I pulled the saddle out from under his head and let it hit the ground, and started to saddle his horse. And all the time I kept yelling at him. When I had finished, I gathered up our guns and the serapes. I rolled up our saddlebags. I fastened everything to the saddles with the straps. . . . My pal didn't wake up. Then I began to call him as loud as I could. I yelled so loud that I didn't recognize my own voice. I had never heard my voice like that before and I never have since. And still my pal didn't wake up. Then I pulled out his pistol, lifted up his head with one hand, and with the other I fired off two shots right beside his ear. Urbina kept on sleeping. His breathing was just the same as when he went to sleep an hour before. His pink shirt barely moved.

"Afterward, when I remember what an agony I went through that morning, I often think I should have lighted a match and held it in his hand until he woke up. But I didn't think of it then. The dark spot that was the mounties was getting clearer and clearer down below, and I couldn't think straight. Dimly I compared the helplessness of my pal with the danger that was flying toward us, and it seemed to me like a dream when your knees give way under you and you want to run and can't.

"Sleep is the most mysterious thing there is! I picked up my pal, threw him face down across his horse, and tied him tight. Then I got on my horse and made for the sierra.

"That's the most terrible day I ever went through in my life. I had to look for the worst path I could find so as to throw the mounties off the track, and at the same time I had to watch out on those bad trails to keep my pal from getting hurt against the rocks and tree trunks. Several times I had to double back on our trail. At others I had to travel long distances on foot and open the way for Urbina's head, which was hanging over the side, or hold it up to keep it from being bruised. And I fled like that for more than three hours, more than six, more than eight. Finally, late that afternoon, I reached a place that offered some protection. I felt safe there and made camp.

"When I took my pal off the horse, his face was black with dust, and purple, for all the blood had rushed to his head. Yet he went right on sleeping, just as easy. I unsaddled the horses. I threw myself on the ground. I slept."

A long silence left Villa's last words echoing in our ears. Llorente, whose admiration for the guerrilla leader was boundless, smiled with an expression half moved, half triumphant. "What do you think of my man?" it seemed to say. Vasconcelos, who was always quick to show appreciation and respect for every manifestation of real humanity, whether fleeting or enduring, was pale with emotion. I just watched.

In a little while we heard the whistle of an engine. We got ready and went out. We said good-bye alongside the train.

A few minutes later from one of the train windows I saw Villa pass by at a distance, with a woman who, I believe, had come in on the train from Ciudad Juárez. To judge from her bearing and her silhouette she was young, perhaps pretty. Had he not said he would keep us company until the trains came in? Villa had his arm around her waist and was leading her toward his car. Now, probably smiling to himself in the dark, he was revealing his real reason.

BOOK V

Eulalio Gutiérrez

---

1 A PRESIDENT OF THE REPUBLIC

I was up Chihuahua way when I heard that the Convention had named Eulalio Gutiérrez President *pro tem*, and not Antonio I. Villarreal, as we had all expected. Apparently Eulalio had appeared as a dark horse (as the Yankees say) at the last moment, a compromise candidate who satisfied the different factions because of the negative virtue of not representing any one of them too strongly. And this was enough to bring home to me, even at a distance, how deep-seated the division was, and how the optimists were fore-doomed to failure: the cautious, like José Isabel Robles, and the senseless, like Serratos. The latter, without doubt, had again proposed, to obviate conflict, his great electoral pro-cedure, a true expression, as simple as it was practical, of the democracy of a town meeting. For General Serratos, fer-vidly pro-Zapata, was in favor of reducing the vote for the presidency to a simple heads-or-tails formula: eagle or sun. I am even of the impression that one day, to illustrate his point with an example, he put his hand into one of the straight pockets of his charro pants, pulled out a half peso and, throwing it up in the air with a skill worthy of the great dilettanti, said to the audience before him, "Well, friends, what will it be: Villarreal or Angeles? . . . Eagle or sun?"

At a time like this, when the most absurd ideas—such as

trying to save the situation by appointing a president for twenty days—ran riot, Villarreal might have seemed to many a better and less spectacular choice than Eulalio. Villarreal, moreover, was extremely popular; he was liked, esteemed, and respected. In a way he was the real type of civilian hero of the Revolution, a private citizen who had become a soldier in response to the exigencies of the situation and had taken up arms without any taste for military glory, though all his life he had been a man who had fought for his ideas. He used to say: "I have been in many a quarrel, but I can say without boasting that I have never fired a pistol or a rifle." His words were in keeping with his appearance, for his whole being radiated goodness and honesty; and his frank, open look and sincere smile were of the sort that set apart the truly generous from the truly hollow.

But at the same time it cannot be denied that it would have been hard to find a braver, cooler, shrewder person than Eulalio. In spite of his ironic smile and gentle voice, in those days Eulalio represented the ideal of the Mexican revolutionist, whose last thought is of saving himself. He used to give me such a feeling of actual and potential bravery and audacity that my imagination adorned him with the prestige of some fictitious character, one of the heroes of the daring exploits of the Spanish Main. He, too, I felt, would have been capable of carrying in his own hand the lighted torch to blow up the powder magazine and perish with ship or fortress.

If, then, he was so brave—one may ask—why did he name Villa commander-in-chief of the Convention's armies at a moment when to do this was nothing but cowardice? This at least was the contention of all those who wanted to wriggle out of their Aguascalientes compromise, the conventionists who found it more convenient not to honor the signatures they had affixed with great solemnity a few days before between the serpent, the eagle, and the cactus of the Mexican flag. But Gutiérrez could have answered that if he appointed Villa, it was because of the defection of those very ones who were later to censure him bitterly, at the same time that they backed up Carranza in those wily tricks of his which made all solutions impossible.

The Convention had voted, on the one hand, to do away with the post of First Chief, and to this end had appointed a provisional President; and, on the other, had voted that Villa should hand over his command of the Division of the North. But whereas the independent generals and the enemies of Carranza obeyed the edict, about whose meaning there could be no question, giving Eulalio Gutiérrez their unconditional support, the generals in favor of Carranza decided to support him—which was an open act of insurrection —until the terms he laid down for his retirement had been observed. Now Carranza had no right, in the face of the sovereignty of the Convention, to lay down terms of any kind, and he never would have done it if he had not counted on the support of the generals who would back him up. He would simply have been deprived of his office, and that would have been the end of the matter.

Nor was there any possibility for Villa to interpret or twist to suit himself the order about giving up the command of his troops. What, then, was the duty of the generals who were sincerely opposed to such factiousness? Would it not have been better to stand behind Gutiérrez so he could have enforced orders? But instead of doing this Carranza's partisans fled Aguascalientes and then sent messages from Mexico City or Orizaba notifying Eulalio that they would support Carranza and not him until he had obeyed the order to remove Villa. This was not only disloyalty and an unjustified rejection of the agreement that they had just signed, but a piece of low trickery. They were trying to hold Gutiérrez and the few who supported him to an agreement that had been made on the understanding and basis of unanimous cooperation, which was only feasible this way. By the same token the enemies of Carranza could have refused to support Eulalio as long as he did not put out Carranza. And this would have put the provisional President in the grotesque position of having to fight the two opposing factions singlehanded.

Whichever way one turned it, it was evident that the problem of putting out Carranza and getting rid of Villa resolved itself into a military question, because there was no doubt that both would offer armed resistance. But this problem which the Convention had unloaded on Gutiérrez's shoulders could not be undertaken without the immediate aid of the majority of the generals in the Convention. United, these would form the strongest group, but divided—each group hanging back until the other was brought into line—the old personal contentions would begin all over again. Inasmuch as Carranza's backers had destroyed the unity of purpose of the Convention by demanding that Gutiérrez dismiss Villa when he counted on no other support, Gutiérrez did what anybody else would have done in those circumstances: he temporized with Villa, even did everything he could to lull his suspicions until a favorable moment when he could remove him from his command, and, if necessary, take the field against him. But this could not even be attempted unless Carranza's generals behaved reasonably.

Those were the days when each of us rode around in his private train as though it were a cab. The majority of our political conversations, weighty or trivial, took place to the accompaniment of moving wheels and scenery and were permeated with the smell of smoke and hotboxes. The trains of generals and the trains of civilians ran up and down the main lines, passing each other at the stations or on the sidings. The freight service had practically disappeared and the passenger service barely existed. There was nothing but military convoys or engines pulling a drawing room and a caboose, transporting with lightning speed the armies and the ideas of the revolutionary tempest. When the trains met at the stations, the engines greeted each other, the train crews joked together, and if the passengers were politicians of rank, they would get down and talk importantly with one another.

That was the way Vasconcelos and I met one morning somewhere between Torreón and Fresnillo, or Fresnillo and

Zacatecas, and I learned through him that General José Isabel Robles was impatiently waiting for me at Aguascalientes to offer me a post in the new government.

"But Robles hardly knows me," I demurred.

"That doesn't matter," said Vasconcelos. "Eulalio and I aren't acquainted and still he's going to appoint me Minister of Education. Whatever it is, you ought to accept. We all have to pull together now."

And during the brief layover we hotly argued these two attitudes, each defending his own position. Immediately afterward, Vasconcelos's train resumed its trip north and mine hurried southward. The two trains were speeding in opposite directions as though in a frenzied race; in a few seconds his had diminished against the horizon until it seemed a mere dot clinging to the edge of a cloud. Why were we in such an absurd hurry? There was always a touch of unreality, something inexplicable, fantastic about the trips of the revolutionists at that time. Trips that basically resembled the voyages in *Persiles y Segismunda*.

In Aguascalientes Robles informed me that he would probably be made Minister of War and invited me to be his assistant. I laughed and then, in a more serious tone, I explained my reasons:

"A year ago," I said, "General Iturbe offered me, the day after the capture of Culiacán, the rank of lieutenant-colonel on his staff. If I had accepted, by this time I should be a general and I could, without blushing, consider your proposal. I would in all probability be delighted with it. But as I did not accept then, I am still a civilian and I lack the necessary rank to act as your assistant in the War Department."

"That doesn't matter in the least," answered Robles, "because it's as a civilian that I need you."

"In that case, you'd regret your choice in twenty-four hours. Take my advice as a friend, General: make another general, who has troops of his own, your assistant and if possible let him be a friend of yours and a man you can trust."

Fortunately for me, Robles took my advice, or at least acted as though he had, for shortly afterward he selected for the post General Eugenio Aguirre Benavides, an intimate friend of his. But still he did not want to deprive himself altogether of my supposed services, and he finally persuaded me to accompany him on his cabinet adventure as adviser. For this purpose he invented certain official functions *sui generis*, designed specially for me, which were neither those of a private secretary (these would be entrusted to poor Bolaños) nor those of chief of staff (which would be discharged with great flourish and good sense by General Serratos).

I do not know whether Eulalio Gutiérrez knew about the proposal Robles had made me. But, once Robles and I had made our arrangements, we immediately went to see him, and I soon found myself forming part of the intimate clique where the weightiest problems of the new government that was coming into existence were discussed. Gutiérrez was surrounded at this time by the pick of the anti-Carranzaists, both military and civilian—that is to say, the best of Villa's and Zapata's followers, dissolved or made one thanks to the miraculous waters of the Convention. But the truth is that nobody was willing to abate a jot or tittle of any personal claims he might have, and in consequence the new government was born sickly, premature, feeble; and nobody seemed to know what to do with it. The one who seemed to know most and say most was Antonio Díaz Soto y Gama, though if one listened closely, it was evident that he was as ignorant as the rest.

What did we talk about? What was discussed? What was decided at that political gathering? The details now escape me. All I can clearly recall is that at one point Eulalio came over to me, took me aside, and, in a low voice, asked me to suggest a candidate for Minister of Industrial Development. Without a moment's hesitation I answered:

"Don Valentín Gama."

"And who is that gentleman?"

"An authority in the field, and a distinguished teacher. Also a great citizen. He organized the Independent Civic Union under Madero."

I had overoptimistic and consequently absurd ideas at the time about the possibility of elevating the politics of Mexico. I still believed that the ministerial posts should be filled by men of outstanding intellectual and moral gifts, and I even considered it the duty of good revolutionists to refuse important posts so they could be given to the most fitted and the most distinguished.

"Gama, you say?" Eulalio asked, low-voiced and thoughtful.

"Yes, Gama; Valentín Gama. He's a relative of Díaz Soto."

At this the provisional President frowned.

"That does not matter," I went on. "He is the best man for the job; he thinks and acts independently. There is nothing to be afraid of."

And so it worked out. Eulalio was not afraid.

2   A Minister of War

Carranza and his generals fled toward Veracruz, and Eulalio Gutiérrez, with the burden the Convention had placed on his shoulders, made ready to transfer his government to the capital of the Republic.

It was a sight to behold how all the railroads were jammed with interminable cordons of our military and civilian trains, hurrying on, not because of strategic or political needs, but because of our impatience to take possession of the magnificent booty that the Carranzaists had left behind in their flight—the city of Mexico. Of course we had a feeling (or, to be more exact, the certainty for reasons that were fairly obvious) that Eulalio's government was sure to go on the rocks; but we also knew that in Mexico's national sport, civil war,

Mexico City is like the cup in an athletic tournament: the one who has it savors the joys of victory and feels himself the winner in the political contest; he maintains his title against his rivals, even though he is in constant danger of losing it at any minute to the many opponents who long to snatch the prize from his hands.

My close friendship with José Isabel Robles dates from that trip of conquest to the capital of the Republic. Robles was more set than ever on having me with him and had given me the room next to his in his own private car, and for several days we were together at all hours except to sleep. And this association, at least for me, was a revelation and laid the foundation for a deep, intelligent regard for him.

Judged superficially, General José Isabel Robles seemed a centaur, a somewhat mythological incarnation of primitive warlike and equestrian virtues. But at close range one immediately discovered, under the epidermis of his ignorance, a certain quiet austerity, a certain delicacy of perception, which in anybody else would have seemed acquired traits, but which in him could only be innate and spontaneous and had the effect of raising him above himself. The semi-fabulous hero of the cavalry charges, whom I had been able to imagine only galloping at the head of his brigade of horsemen, sowing terror with his glance, his hat fallen back, his arm brandishing a smoking pistol, became transformed, without any effort on his part, into a gentle, serene, sensible man, more than willing to judge everything calmly and to settle all disputes and difficulties without any other consideration than the justice of the case.

This dual aspect of his personality was revealed to me one day in all its force when I surprised him reading, of all things, Plutarch's *Parallel Lives*. And I say surprised, for he was so absorbed in his book that he did not notice me for some time after I had come into the room, and it embarrassed him considerably.

"That's a good book, General," I said, somewhat mechani-

cally, for I was thinking less of what I was saying than of
the amazing fact that one of Villa's right-hand men should
be reading Plutarch, the moralist, with such absorption.

"It is a good book, isn't it?" he answered.

But as I had not yet recovered from my astonishment, I
merely nodded.

He went on:

"I found it the other day when we took Torreón from the
Federals. Aguirre Benavides and I went into a house where
there were lots of bookcases, and just out of curiosity I picked
up some of the books; some were in Spanish and some were
in foreign languages. After I had looked through a lot of them
that I didn't understand or didn't like, I found this one,
and I put it in my pocket. And whenever I have a little time,
I take it out and read it. I'm sorry now I didn't take the other
volumes, for there were several of them. If a person could
only have lived in the days of Greece and Rome!"

"To a man that's a man, General, all times are alike."

"No, my friend, don't you believe it. Why, without going any farther, while we were in all this mix-up of the Convention, I kept thinking to myself: 'Among all these speechi-
fiers, there's not a single Demosthenes. And that's why we're
in the fix we are.'"

This serious, sober side of Robles's character, which was
not immediately apparent, explained the sway he had over
Villa. One could understand why the Chief of the Division
of the North, so overbearing in word and deed toward his
subordinates, except in the case of Felipe Angeles, for whom
he felt a superstitious admiration, should treat Robles as a
father treats a son. Robles was as brave as a lion in the hour
of danger, and austere as a hermit afterward, and thus he
seemed to Villa twice perfect. This made him immune to
all criticism and entitled to every privilege.

Robles was permitted by his chief to counsel, advise, re-
prove, and even protest in situations where others had to
keep quiet. That "fluky" pistol of Villa's, so ready to punish
on the least suspicion, for the most trifling mistake, would

have pardoned real disloyalty in Robles. It was a pistol that had learned to bow its head before Robles, as was clearly proved on the occasion when Obregón was on the point of being sent before a firing squad by Villa. Obregón got off with his life that time not merely because two or three of Villa's generals intervened for him, but because Robles came to his aid, and Robles's moral force, his untarnished valor, his undisputable superiority were qualities which tipped the rude scale on which Villa weighed his responsibilities. It was the tacit recognition of human virtues on a man-to-man basis.

But it must not be thought from what has been said that, off the field of battle, Robles altogether renounced his somewhat primitive virility. When necessary, he knew how to impose his will and make himself obeyed in peace as well as in war. Despite his small stature and his slight frame he could on occasion behave like a gang boss or the quartermaster of a brigantine. But always his violence was tempered by a sense of justice, rather than an excess of brutality, which without detracting from the severity and efficacy of the punishment, purged it beforehand of the possibilities of hatred.

What happened in San Luis Potosí the afternoon we left for Mexico City is a case in point. One of the staff officers was half drunk, and for several hours he had been trying to pick a fight with his brother officers. When Robles heard about it, he ordered him put under arrest. But instead of submitting, the officer barricaded himself behind one of the pillars in the station and, pistol in hand, and more insolent and quarrelsome than before, threatened to shoot anybody who tried to lay a finger on him. Under other circumstances his defiance would probably not have prevented the execution of the order, but as the station was full of people waiting for trains, the officers who had been ordered to take him into custody thought it more prudent to avoid a showdown rather than risk a massacre.

It was about four o'clock in the afternoon, and our train was ready to start as soon as General Robles should arrive. From that time on until six o'clock, when Robles and the group of persons that was to accompany us to Querétaro finally got there, that drunken officer was the lord and master of the station: he hugged and kissed the women, insulted the men, and the minute he saw or thought he saw anybody make a move toward him, with the wiliness of the drunk he quickly got into a position where he could drop the first person who should take a step. And while he stood there with his pistol leveled, not a soul dared to come within two hundred yards of him.

Robles had been informed about what was going on before he reached the station, but when he saw with his own eyes the spectacle one of his men was making of himself, his wrath knew no bounds. I saw him as he passed by me, and his face was colorless, and his hand trembled as he pulled down the chin strap of his hat. His close-clipped black mustache contrasted with the pallor of his skin, and stood out against it almost as much as his eyes, which were glittering.

He walked straight over to the nearest group of officers. One of them was wearing his sword, and Robles pulled the blade out of its scabbard, while he shouted:

"Everybody stand still!"

And then, holding the sword in a position for striking, not for thrusting, he started straight toward the rebellious officer. When the latter saw that someone was finally taking up his challenge, he raised his arm and took aim. The other officers, without moving from their places, called to him:

"Don't, Martínez; it's the General!"

Martínez's eyes grew as big as saucers; he swayed for a minute and then took two steps forward, ready to hand over his pistol. But Robles was not to be deterred by this gesture; carried away by his sense of outraged justice, he brought the flat of his sword down with all his might on the officer's back.

The officer lowered his head, bent double with the pain. Robles struck him again.

"Down on your knees, this minute," he said as he struck him.

The officer flinched as he bent over, but did not obey the command.

"On your knees, you hound!"

The officer, still on his feet, covered his eyes with the hand in which the pistol still gleamed. He was trembling and sobbing with pain. In a low voice, he said:

"No more, General."

From the row of officers came sympathetic voices:

"Let him off now, General!"

But far from paying any attention to their pleading, Robles redoubled the fury of his blows. Every time he struck, he repeated:

"On your knees! On your knees!"

And he did not stop until Martínez, unable to endure any longer the pain in his kidneys, his back, his neck, finally dropped to his knees and then fell full length, in a faint, on the stone floor of the platform.

When Robles got into the train, he was his calm, pleasant self again. But there was a trace of bitterness in his voice as he said, sitting down beside me:

"You see the kind of things we have to do. This isn't much like what we were reading last night."

And, in truth, it did not resemble it, for we had been reading Plutarch's life of Cicero.

3 MILITARY JUSTICE

A large number of military convoys had gathered near Tacuba on the eve of the official entry into Mexico City of the Convention government. On the railroad tracks nearest the suburb, the trains of Villa, Eulalio Gutiérrez, Robles, Eugenio Aguirre Benavides, were lined up in parallel rows. The assemblage of passenger coaches that had been converted into headquarters and offices, and of freight cars that were used for the troops—with cradles swung between the wheels, and primitive shelters on top of the cars—turned into one of those typical camps of the Mexican Revolution which day and night afforded the oddest and most varied scenes and noises.

A little after dark I left the small office I occupied in Robles's car and went to see Villa, without any other object than to talk with him. The conversation of the revolutionist from Durango fascinated me; his remarks were often original, unexpected, and surprising. On the way from my train to his I stopped several times to look at the stars which have a peculiar brilliance in the valley of Mexico. Farther down along the slopes of the railroad embankment the soldiers were scattered in little groups, sitting around their campfires with their women, their cookery, and their songs.

When I came in, I found Villa absorbed in making roses with a lariat. The chairs and tables had been moved out of the way, and Villa was standing in the middle of the car in his shirt sleeves, his hat pushed back on his neck, holding in both hands, at the height of his thighs, a design resembling a rose, which the bright line of a new lariat had traced in the air. It was a highly complicated figure of exact geometrical proportions, held in place by the stiffness of the rope. Villa's secretary and four or five others were sharing in the warrior's pastime, and they were all standing with their backs to the wall of the car so as to leave him as much room as possible. When I came in, Villa said to me:

"How do you like this rose?"

"Which rose?" I asked, as I did not grasp what he was referring to.

"This one here in my hands."

"Oh, is that a rose? It's pretty, all right."

"Isn't it!" And he studied it complacently for several seconds. Then he went on, explaining to me:

"Yesterday when I was in San Juan del Río I bought these lariats"—and he indicated with a gesture of his head a number of lariats on his desk, all smoothly rolled like flat buns, and as white as the one he had in his hand. "I bought them to see if I had forgotten how to use them, but you can see I haven't. Say, are you any good at this?"

I smiled and was going to say I had never thrown a lariat in my life, but he went on without pausing:

"I'll bet anything you want that you can't make a rose like this. I'll bet you five thousand pesos that you can't make even the simplest one of my roses."

"It can't be done, General, because, among other reasons, I never bet."

"All right, then, we won't bet. Or rather, we'll make it a one-sided bet: I lose five thousand pesos if you can do this same thing with a lariat."

While he talked, he undid the design he had in his hands, and as he finished the last words, he gave two or three quick turns to the rope and it made another rose, not so complicated as the first, but quite as pretty.

"That's really very difficult, General," I answered; "I'm sure I can't do it. Anyway, it wouldn't be fair for you to bet five thousand pesos without my risking anything."

"That doesn't matter. You risk your reputation."

"My reputation?"

"Yes, your reputation as a lariat thrower."

"Very well," I said, "I accept, but with the condition that you make the rose again so I can see you."

"All right. Now watch."

He straightened out the lariat and took hold of it in two different places with each hand; he made two wide loops without a knot, turned them upside down, crossed them, pulled out the two loops they formed in the center, and, putting his hand between them, opened them out into a large, beautiful rose. All his quick, precise movements had not taken more than a few seconds. I watched every single move he made, without missing a one, for I had set my heart on winning that bet of five thousand pesos against my ability as a lariat thrower.

"Now you do it," said Villa, handing me the rope.

I don't know how I did it, for I have never been able to

repeat that night's achievement since. What I did was to imitate like a monkey everything Villa had done. I adopted the same posture as he, took the lariat in my hands just as he had done, and followed detail for detail, imitating even the rhythm, the movements he had made. And, without quite knowing how, out of my hands there emerged a rose just like his, though not so perfect.

"And this is the fellow," he said as he looked at it, "who pretended he didn't know how to handle a lariat!"

And turning to Luis Aguirre Benavides, he said, in the most unconcerned fashion:

"Luis, my boy, give this gentleman five thousand pesos."

Aguirre Benavides went into one of the inside compartments of the car and returned in a minute with a sheaf of bills, which he put in my hand. They were new and smelled of printer's ink. Their pink-and-blue designs had the gleam of pages coming off the press. I was still looking at them when the door opened and an officer came in. He was tall and of a muddy color, and there was a strange air of sinister humility about him. His gray uniform might have been part of his skin, and the same was true of his shoes, his leggings, and the dirty handkerchief that was knotted around his neck. When he took off his hat, it revealed a thatch of lank, black hair which grew back from his forehead as though his skull ran up to a point. He included all in his salute and said, turning to Villa as he handed him an envelope:

"Here's the list of my prisoners, General."

"What prisoners are you bringing in, friend?" asked Villa, without looking at or opening the document.

"Those five counterfeiters, General."

"Oh, the counterfeiters. Listen, Luis, those prisoners are to be taken to the court-martial car, and I want them tried this very minute and shot tomorrow."

Aguirre Benavides went out to give the necessary orders.

A little later, by putting my face against the windowpane, I could make out the outlines of the group of prisoners and their guard moving toward the train where the offices of the

military court were located. In spite of my efforts I could not
make out their faces. I wondered who they were. By this
time they must have learned from the lips of the meek and
baleful officer the fate that was in store for them. The supreme will had sentenced them to death without even finding out what their names were, and for a crime which he himself, the judge, committed: manufacturing money for his
personal use. And sentenced to death beforehand, as they
were, they were now going through the farce of a trial, at
midnight, as is our practice in troop mutinies and revolutions.
Summary trials to cover up assassinations!

That was one of the most horrible nights I had ever gone
through in my life.

When I got back to Robles's train, I found a group of
women from Mexico City waiting for me beside the car
steps, weeping and lamenting. They were the wives and
mothers and sisters of the five counterfeiters, some of whom
belonged to the better class. They had heard of the punishment that was going to be meted out to their relatives and
they were desperately knocking at the door of anybody who
might be able or willing to help them. In some way they
had found out about my friendship with Villa and my intimacy with Robles and Gutiérrez, in whose hands they
imagined the final decision rested, since the one was the
Minister of War and the other the President of the Convention government. They all surrounded me and tried to
talk at the same time.

"You, sir, you can save them."

"Aren't you the person who was with Villa just now when
they brought our husbands in prisoners?"

"Won't you please ask General Robles or the President . . ."

I was startled out of my own melancholy reflections, and
at first I did not know what to answer. For a few moments
I had the horrible feeling that I was an accomplice or an
accessory to the crime that was going to be perpetrated, and,

like a criminal caught red-handed, I felt the five little packages of thousand-peso bills that Aguirre Benavides had just
given me scorch my fingers. It seemed to me that for a moment the conscience of the Revolution had become personified in me, with all its contradictions and excesses. To be
sure, the Revolution had not falsely coined the money to pay
its troops to overthrow Huerta. But what about that which its
generals threw away on their extravagant whims, their gambling, and their orgies?

But I pulled myself together and tried to answer them:

"Ladies, you don't know how sorry I am. . . ."

"Oh, no, no, don't refuse us, for God's sake, don't say no!"

"You look like a good son!"

"We know that if you just speak a word with General
Villa . . ."

"Ladies, please, try to calm yourselves a little, and I'll do
anything I can for you."

"Yes, yes, whatever you say."

"Now, tell me what you want." Really I didn't know what
to say. "I am ready . . . to do anything for you . . . that's in
my power."

At this, one of them, controlling herself by an effort, spoke
for the group. By the light that came from the train windows
I could see how her face was swollen with crying. She had a
black lace shawl over her head, and where the ends crossed
on her bosom, the color contrasted with the yellow silk of her
dress. It was plain that the poor soul had dashed out of her
house, snatching up the first things she found.

"For your mother's sake," she said, "we beg you to inter-
cede with General Villa not to shoot Daniel or his companions."

"But, madam, what you ask of me is impossible, or, at any
rate, useless. You do not know General Villa. If I go to him
now to ask him to revoke an order he issued in my presence,
the only result will be that he may order me shot, too."

" 'Too,' you say? That means that it has been decided already? Then you know they're going to shoot them?"

"I don't know anything, ladies, but I cannot deceive you, either. You have to take what I say literally."

The weeping and wailing and lamentations knew no bounds. And all that suffering seemed to me so unnecessarily cruel and senseless that if I had not been completely surrounded by the women I should have taken to my heels. Besides, a crowd of soldiers and women and children of the camp had gathered around us, attracted by the noise of the women's grief. I noticed, too, that several men had come with the prisoners' relatives, but none of them spoke a word. They probably realized—and they were completely right—that it would be useless for them to try to secure by words what the women could not win by their weeping.

With her voice broken by sobs, the woman with the shawl spoke again:

"At least, let us see the Minister of War or the President."

"I'll be glad to do that," I said, and I drew over to the steps of the car, inviting them to come up, prepared to ask Robles to see them at once. But just as I was going to help the first woman up, the officer on guard on the platform bent down and whispered to me:

"General Robles has ordered that no stranger be admitted to his car. If the ladies are coming in, you'd better see him about it first."

All my efforts to convince Robles were futile. And not because he was indifferent to my arguments or in favor of Villa's decision, but because he knew that it was impossible to argue with his chief on matters of this sort, and therefore it was better not to try it. In a word, in spite of his position as Minister of War, and in spite of his prestige as Villa's best and most trusted general, he was in exactly the same situation as I. The only thing he agreed to do was to help me to get Eulalio Gutiérrez to intervene.

Meanwhile the tribulation of the prisoners' families had permeated the whole camp and had even penetrated the ingrained lack of feeling or unconcern of the non-commissioned officers and the soldiers. Nobody talked about anything but the shootings that were to take place the next day.

Eulalio Gutiérrez vented his indignation even before we began to talk.

"Everything you are going to say to me," he began, "I've already thought myself. Villa is bringing off an assassination, and you and Robles and I and everybody else who is mixed up in this business are going to seem like accomplices. You say I'm President. President! President in name is what I am! Who has the power here? Who has the troops here? Who has control of the railroads? Villa. We might just as well admit it: we are more insignificant to him than to that autocrat of a Carranza. At least one could talk with him!"

"Well, then we'll be a pack of fools and cowards if we go on like this," I answered, looking at Robles, who nodded his approval.

"No, we won't," answered Eulalio, "because we won't go on this way; you leave that to me. But just now all we can do is to put up with it. What would you have me do? Make a fool of myself telling these women that I do not approve of the execution of their sons or their brothers or whatever they are, and then have Villa shoot them, snapping his fingers in my face? The world is full of ups and downs, and these poor devils struck a bad moment, and there's not a soul can save them."

When I heard Eulalio talk like that, I realized it was useless to try to do anything, for I knew, both from hearsay and personal experience, that he was neither stupid, nor cruel, nor a coward, but, quite the contrary, a man of exceptionally keen intelligence and kind heart, and absolute integrity, as he proved a few days later when he broke with Villa.

But nevertheless I wanted to do all I could to satisfy my conscience and I went over to Villa's car. I wanted to see if it was really some immutable law of God or nature or history that our Revolution should be directed only by assassins and their henchmen. At the steps of the car one of Villa's *dorados*[1] blocked my way. An orderly then appeared on the platform, who said:

"The General has retired for the night. He has given orders not to be disturbed under any circumstances. If you want to talk with him, come back tomorrow at nine o'clock."

"But tomorrow morning at nine o'clock there'll be nothing left of the counterfeiters," I replied.

"That's as may be, but I don't think the General will be up before that time."

I spent the rest of that night in Mexico City and deliberately kept away from the camp at Tacuba until late in the morning of the next day. It must have been close to eleven when I got back there. The glorious sun of November threw a kindly veil over the drought-cracked earth and the stubble of the surrounding cornfields. Had the execution been carried out? I wondered when they had got rid of that tragic group of women.

Robles was not in his car. I sat down in the lounge and was absent-mindedly staring out of the window when I saw a squad of soldiers followed by a throng of spectators coming up through one of the cornfields. The soldiers' muskets threw back the rays of the sun. The furrows made it difficult to keep step, and the soldiers were not in formation. They formed two uneven rows, and between them came five men whose arms were tied behind them with ropes that passed from elbow to elbow, and who tried to keep as close together as possible. Some of them stumbled at every step; others walked with the precision of marionettes. They all had a dazed expression, as if they were perceiving everything about them too acutely or too faintly. Some seemed engrossed by the very stones their feet encountered; others seemed not even aware of the dazzling sunlight that enveloped them. One of them—fair and of a ruddy complexion—looked in my direction with such wild eyes that his look hurt, like the pain

[1] Villa's famous bodyguard, whose uniforms were resplendent with gold braid and ornaments; hence their name, "the gilded men."

of a wound. They were on their way to the cemetery. The sensation they left with me as they walked toward it was that those five men were bearing their own corpses on their backs to the open graves in which they would be buried as soon as five or six bullets had been put through their bodies.

4   ZAPATA'S TROOPS IN THE PALACE

Eulalio Gutiérrez wanted to visit the National Palace before he installed his government there. So that same afternoon he, José Isabel Robles, and I presented ourselves there. Eufemio Zapata, who was in charge of the building, came out to the main entrance to receive us and began to do the honors of the house. To judge by his air, he was taking his momentary role of receiving the new President in his government abode and showing him the splendors of his future drawing rooms and offices very seriously. As we got out of the automobile, he shook hands with each of us and spoke like a rough but affable host.

While the greetings were being exchanged, I looked around me. The car had stopped just past one of the arcades of the large patio. In the background the two lines formed by the white masonry of the arches and the shadow of the openings met at an angle. A short way off, a group of the Zapata soldiery stood observing us from the sentry chamber; others peered from between the columns of the massive white arches. What was the attitude of these men? Meek or suspicious? At the time, they aroused in me curiosity more than anything else, because of the setting of which they formed a part. That place, which I had seen so many times and which always seemed the same, gave me on that occasion, practically empty as it was, and in the hands of a band of half-naked rebels, the effect of something new and strange.

We did not go up the main stairway, but used the staircase of honor. Eufemio walked ahead of us, like a janitor showing a house for rent. He was wearing the tight trousers

with a broad fold down the two outside seams, a cotton
blouse tied at the belly, and a huge broad-brimmed hat; as
he mounted step after step, he seemed to symbolize the historic days in which we were living, in the contrast of his person, not meek, but uncouth and clumsy, with the cultivation
and refinement presaged by the staircase. A flunky, a coachman, an official, an ambassador would have been in place
there; each would have had the dignity, small or great, that
went with his position, and that had its place in the hier-
archy of dignities. Eufemio looked like a stableboy who was
trying to act like a president. When his shoe touched the
carpet, there was a clash between carpet and shoe. When his
hand rested on the banister, there was an immediate incom-
patibility between the two. Every time he moved his foot, his
foot seemed surprised at not getting tangled up in brush and
undergrowth. Every time he stretched out his hand, it seemed
to feel in vain for a tree trunk or boulder. One only had to
look at him to see that everything that should have formed
his setting was lacking, and that everything that surrounded
him was superfluous as far as he was concerned.

But at this moment a terrible doubt assailed me. What
about us? What kind of impression would the three of us
who followed Eufemio have made on anybody who saw us—
Eulalio and Robles in their stetson hats, unshaven and with
their unmistakable plebeian aspect, and I with that everlasting
air of the civilian in Mexico who at the hour of violence goes
into politics, a mere instrument assuming the attitude of intellectual adviser to a successful military leader, at best—at
worst, of criminals passing themselves off as leaders?

After we had ascended the stairs, Eufemio took great pride
in showing us one by one the different rooms of the palace.
Our steps alternately were echoed on the waxed floors, so
polished that we could see ourselves dimly reflected in them,
broken by the different colors of the marquetry, or were
hushed by the velvet of the carpets. Behind us we could hear
the soft slapping of the sandals of the two soldiers who followed us at a short distance through the empty rooms. It was

a meek, gentle sound. Sometimes it ceased for a long time while the two soldiers stopped to look at a picture or examine a piece of furniture. Then I would turn back to look at them through the long perspective of the rooms. They formed a double figure, strangely quiet and remote, as they stood close to each other, looking at things in silence, their heads with their lank heavy hair uncovered, and their palm-leaf hats humbly clasped in both hands. Something sincere and worthy of respect was unquestionably represented by their rapt, embarrassed, almost religious humility. But we, what did we represent? Was there anything fundamentally sincere and serious in us, who were making joking comments on everything we saw, and had not bothered to take off our hats?

Eufemio made some remark about everything we passed, and his observations were often primitive and ingenuous. They revealed a cheerful, childlike conception of the gubernatorial functions. "This is where the government meets to talk." "This is where the government eats." "This is where the government has its dances." It was evident that he supposed we had never seen a tapestry, nor had the slightest idea of the uses of a sofa or an armchair or a corner table, and he went along illuminating us. He said everything in such good faith that it positively touched me. When we reached the presidential chair, his tone became triumphant, almost ecstatic. "*This* is the chair." And then in a burst of enviable candor he added: "Ever since I've been here, I come every day to look at it, just to get used to it. Because—can you imagine it?—I always used to think when I heard them talk about the President's seat that they meant his saddle." Eufemio laughed heartily at his own ignorance and we laughed too.

For some time Eulalio had been aching to take a dig at General Zapata, and he saw his opportunity. Turning toward Eufemio and putting a hand on his shoulder, he fired this arrow in his gentle, modulated voice:

"Not for nothing is one a good horseman, partner. The day this seat becomes a saddle, you and your friends can all be presidents."

The smile disappeared from Eufemio's face as if by magic, and a gloomy, sinister look replaced it. Eulalio's witticism had been too cruel and perhaps too apt, and it had flicked him on the raw.

"Well," he said a few seconds later, as though there were nothing more worth seeing, "let's go downstairs now and see the stables. Then I'll take you to the rooms where my men and I are quartered."

We went over the stables from one end to the other, though with greater satisfaction on Eufemio's part than on ours. Amidst the array of collars, bridles, bits, and halters—all smelling of grease and leather—he displayed an amazing store of knowledge. And the same with the horses; he knew all about breeding them, training them, and showing them. His enthusiasm for these things took his mind off the incident of the chair, and then he led us to the quarters he and his men occupied in the palace. Eufemio—and in this he gave evidence of his sincerity—had found rooms to his taste in the poorest, most out-of-the-way rear court. He seemed well aware of how miserable his accommodations were, and to forestall criticism, he quickly explained why he had chosen them.

"I picked this place because I've always been poor and I didn't feel right in better rooms."

Really the place was abominable. I thought I should smother as I went in. The room was not large and had only one door and no windows. There must have been from fifty to a hundred officers from Zapata's army there, of all ranks, when we came in. The majority were standing up, side by side, or in groups with their arms around each other. Others were sitting on the table, and some were lying on the floor in the corners and along the wall. Many of them had a bottle or a glass in their hand. The air was foul and sour and a hundred different odors were mingled with the heavy pall of smoke. Everybody was drunk, some more, some less. A soldier stood by the door to keep it shut against the light or against inquisitive eyes. Two small electric lights glimmered feebly through the asphyxiating fog.

At first nobody paid any attention to us. Then as Eufemio went from group to group, whispering something in a low voice, they began to look at us without suspicion and even make certain signs of welcome. But they were faint, almost imperceptible expressions. We had, beyond question, fallen into a world so different from our own that our mere presence was a source of perturbation in spite of everything they and we did to overcome this. With the exception of a few, they avoided looking straight at us and watched us instead out of the corner of their eyes. Instead of talking with us they whispered among themselves. And every now and then they would turn their backs to take a long swallow from their bottles or empty their glasses.

Eufemio and those around him invited us to have a drink. "Here, let's have some glasses," shouted Eufemio. Timid hands reached out to set five or six dirty glasses on the edge of the table. Eufemio set them in a row and poured out fresh drinks of *tequila* on the dregs at the bottom of the glasses.

We drank in silence. Eufemio poured out more *tequila*. We drank again. Once more Eufemio filled up the glasses. . . .

As we drank, Eufemio began to warm up. At first he became happy, jovial, and then thoughtful and gloomy. At about the fifth or sixth glass he happened to remember Eulalio's joke about the presidential chair.

"This comrade," he said, addressing his men, "thinks that Emiliano and I, and others like us, will be presidents the day they saddle horses with seats like the one upstairs."

There was a profound silence, broken only by Eulalio's sarcastic laugh. Then the rustle of voices began again, but there was a vague new, note in it, excited and menacing. Nevertheless Eufemio went on serving *tequila* as though nothing had happened. Once more the glasses were handed round and we drank upon each other's sticky leavings. But at this point Robles began to look at me hard and then, almost imperceptibly, make signs to me with his eyes. I understood; draining my glass, I took leave of Eufemio.

An hour later I was back at the palace, and Robles's entire guard was with me; but just as we came up to the entrance, I saw Eulalio and Robles calmly walking out of the same door through which we had entered in the early afternoon.

"Thanks," said Eulalio when he saw me. "Fortunately we don't need the soldiers now. They were so busy drinking that they could not waste time fighting with us. But, anyway, the precaution was thoughtful. What amazes me is how you and Robles understood one another without saying a word."

5 A MINISTER OF INDUSTRIAL DEVELOPMENT

When General Gutiérrez decided that I should be the one to go and offer Don Valentín Gama the portfolio of Industrial Development, my idea no longer seemed to me quite so good as it had at first. Naturally, from our point of view the plan was highly desirable. The interests we represented, which, for the moment, coincided with those of the nation, in substance or in form, would benefit greatly by having the distinguished mathematician as a member of Eulalio Gutiérrez's cabinet. But this was reckoning without our host. What about the plan from Don Valentín's point of view, his interests and responsibilities as scholar and man?

The doubt kept gnawing at me as I ascended the slope which leads from San Diego Square in Tacubaya to the observatory. The cruel scenes of the executions the night before were still uncomfortably present in my mind. My soul was still reeling from the fumes of the brutish orgy the Zapata faction had just displayed before me in Eufemio's rank, frightening lair. Was it for this, I asked myself, to become an instrument of this, a party to this, an accomplice to this, that I was going to drag my university professor away from his books and his thoughts?

Nevertheless, I kept on my way to the observatory, even though in a kind of dreamlike state, my will divorced from my acts, like one of Dostoievski's split-personality characters.

Where the devil had I got the idea that what a government like that of Eulalio Gutiérrez needed was to have ministers like Don Valentín?

The tree-lined avenues of the observatory, the sand crackling under my feet, heightened even more my feeling of the absurdity of my errand. Perfect peace reigned there: the warm morning sun on the symmetrically laid out flower beds; the soft rustle of the breeze through the bright, lush foliage; the scent of the recently watered earth; the red-and-white buildings, crowned by the spherical eye of the domed observatory, which at a glance encompasses and contemplates the firmament. Not a soul in sight, not one human sound . . .

Beyond the shadow of a doubt what I was on the point of perpetrating was the equivalent of a spiritual fraud.

Barricaded behind piles of books and instruments, Don Valentín Gama received me:

"Good morning. Where did you drop from?"

His cordial hand was the same as always, his affectionate smile, his modest bearing, with its somewhat infantile quality. But the body which housed all this seemed to me smaller, gaunter, more fleshless. It was as though the matter were turning into spirit, as though the physical were being burned away in the unquenchable flame of the soul. His oddly shaped head, which in my student days I had associated with conic curves, seemed to have accentuated the dynamics whereby its elliptical, hyperbolical, parabolic surfaces had become fused with one another. More than ever, Mathematics now lived on the outside of his head almost as much as on the inside.

"Where did I drop from, sir? I wouldn't be too far afield if I were to say from hell; for I have come from the political arena, and this seems to me an astronomical paradise."

We talked first, in homage to the past, of scenes and events in which, alongside human figures, others had their place, such as the tables of Callet, the great equatorial telescope, the *Variations* of Lagrange, the *Differentials and Integrals* of Leibniz, the *Methodus Fluxionum* of Newton. Then, as I waited for the first opportune moment to broach my mission, we struck out through the underbrush of the political situation and its actors. At this point a brief skirmish ensued between Don Valentín's patriotism, well-intentioned and always alert, and the political urgency—on my side—of another patriotism already somewhat calloused by the encounter with overwhelming realities, realities dismaying in their violence, disorder, bloodshed.

After a brief interchange, we were both sliding down the slope of mutual consent.

"And do you think General Gutiérrez will go along with my ideas?"

"Unhesitatingly, sir; whatever they are, they will seem good to him. He is guided, more than by ideas, by intentions, impulses, and these are of the highest quality, I can assure you."

"And will I have a free hand in choosing my assistants?"

"From porters to under-secretary."

Don Valentín and I were in complete agreement on one point: the broad, heroic concept of citizenship. The gentle words in which he voiced this echoed, without his knowing it, my own ideas which, as I heard them from his lips, cured me of the fears and revulsion I had felt an hour before; I, who had come prepared to assume all the responsibility for whatever happened there, suddenly found that the civic impulse of Don Valentín, strong and unqualified, was freeing me, without my having sought it, from the least responsibility.

Without overemphasis he said to me, lifting his expressive face as though better to receive the light, which was reflected from his small spectacles:

"You came here to propose a sacrifice to me, that I know. Not by chance have astrology and astronomy been confused at times. But just because I am aware of this, I accept your proposal. Those who clamor for a fatherland, but sidestep the dangers and discomforts of bringing it into being, are the only ones who do not deserve it. I shall not be one of these, never. It is like preaching virtue and not practicing it. If I can be helpful in any way, here I am. Only the selfish, the sunshine patriots are too busy with their own affairs to help unless they are offered pleasant and gratifying posts like an embassy or something of the sort. Suppose one fails? What does failure matter when the intention was to succeed? What is wrong is not to attempt anything in order to preserve the illusion that 'if I had done it, it would have come out right,' that 'I would have succeeded'. The able who leave their country in the hands of the inept are, because of lack of faith or pusillanimity, more inept than the others, more inept socially."

What strange ideas at a moment like that! Old and new at the same time, unhackneyed and yet self-evident. His political conviction glanced off the book-filled shelves, the geographic and cosmographic globes, the delicate instruments of watchlike precision, and from all this that was pure science returned to me bearing the echo of our battlefields, idealized by the sense of civic aspiration and converted into the assurance that this aspiration could be achieved.

In his private car, between Atzcapotzalco and Tacuba, Eulalio made Don Valentín Gama's acquaintance. There the provisional President spoke for the first time with his future Minister of Industrial Development. Employing a kind of double talk, I introduced them to one another, first defining Don Valentín in Eulalio Gutiérrez's terms, and then Eulalio in Don Valentín's. With his agile mind and unerring eye, Eulalio instantly grasped the duplicity of my phrasing, and said with a simplicity I admire to this day:

"Luisito here [he pronounced the name with an *s*, an *i*, a *t* which the sweet sibilance of his voice almost converted into music] Luisito here has told me wonderful things about you, Professor. And as I have great confidence in him and know that by myself I could not evaluate the reasons on which he bases his regard for you, I have let myself be guided by his judgment to invite you to come and suffer a little with us. For, to tell you the truth, we are not in a bed of roses."

Don Valentín's eyes opened wide, surprised perhaps at so much humility on the part of a president in Mexico, and answered forthrightly and with his customary simplicity:

"To suffer for our country, General, I am always at your orders."

The rest of the conversation no longer interested me; the important thing had been accomplished. They went on talking while I savored my passing moment of political triumph. But my pride came less from looking upon myself as the creator of this alliance between the university and the aspirations of the people, than because Eulalio, incarnating the noble impulse of the Revolution, though roughhewn and formless, had known how to express it with decorum: nothing farcical or vulgar, neither hypocritically suave nor brutal. And this because, despite the assumptions of certain fools of the moment—and not a few later on—Eulalio's humble origins and his prowess as a *guerrillero* were no discredit to him. He carried out his duties as President under extremely difficult circumstances as ably as he had earlier blown up trains and checkmated Huerta's forces. In addition to being intelligent, he was sincere and humble, and this is rare among improvised military leaders and politicos. He was not trying to make the world over according to his ideas, nor did he look upon himself as a genius, nor obliged to correct the Divinity's plan. This explains why, in spite of his lack of education, he had the vision to discover men like José Vasconcelos (the only great minister the Revolution produced) and to accept collaborators like Valentín Gama (who would have done for Industrial Development what certainly none of those who succeeded him accomplished) and like José Rodríguez Cabo, whose thirst for reform and revolutionary passion—deep, uncontrollable, and, at times, unjust—was always respectful of human rights.

On this occasion, when Don Valentín discussed possible under-secretaries with him, he said:

"I will appoint whomever you want, Professor."

There was not a trace of political condescension in his tone, but only the sincere willingness to accept advice rather than give it.

Beside Eulalio's car, Don Valentín Gama and I took our leave of one another. The last thing I asked him was:

"And whom are you going to make under-secretary, sir?"

"Whom? Probably another of your professors, Don Agustín Aragón."

And he trotted off, active, full of nervous energy, though prematurely stooped.

For a moment I stood thoughtful, watching him disappear from sight. Then I walked along the track to Robles's car. The countryside, the dusty, sad, barren lands of Tacuba, made me feel once more the absurdity of the political situation in which we were involved. A little farther on stood Villa's train with its guard of *dorados*. Their air of gunmen, the presage of their cruelty, the harshness of their bloodthirsty and ignorant fatalism leaped to the eye. Beyond stretched the fields of corn stubble through which, twenty-four hours before, I had seen the five counterfeiters pass, condemned to death without trial or law. All this was like the frame of a picture which obsessed my imagination, in which I saw my old teacher, Agustín Aragón, explaining to his students before blackboards covered with alphas, betas, gammas, the laws of mechanics and the movement of the astral bodies. And interwoven with this, after the manner of Cubism, the covers of the *Revista Positiva*, glorifying Auguste Comte, dedicated to the religion of Humanity, and inscriptions in letters of gold: "Order and Progress," "Know in order to foresee, foresee in order to act."

BOOK VI

Villa in Power

---

1 A Form of Government

The generals who had left Eulalio Gutiérrez in the hands of Zapata and Villa, and, contrary to all the hopes of the Revolution, continued to support Carranza, had not put their money on the wrong horse. The Convention group represented the sense of moral responsibility of the Revolution and, therefore, the real danger for Carranza's corrupt, ambitious supporters. What better policy, then, could they have pursued than to let their real enemies wear themselves out struggling with an impossible situation? Because it was an impossibility for the Convention to maintain its moral prestige so long as it had to put up with Villa and Zapata to bring Carranza to terms, and an even greater impossibility to array itself at one and the same time against Carranza, Villa, and Zapata, and defeat them all, armed only with the excellence of its intentions. And between one impossibility and the other, after a few convulsive, useless efforts, would come dissolution, and with it what the Carranzaists wanted: a free hand in the struggle for power, and the chance to turn into a boss system, with certain trappings of social reforms, this Revolution against the previous boss system, which in its turn had been decked out with certain adornments of scientific and economic liberalism.

Eulalio, who was far from being a fool, took in our situation perfectly; three or four weeks in power (to give it this name for lack of a better) reaffirmed him in his first idea that the only thing that could be done for the moment was to play for time and look for some way of escaping from Villa without falling into Carranza. But while we waited, we had to defend ourselves against the most imminent threat, which was Villa and Zapata, and as a result we had to work out one of the most absurd and incongruous policies that could be imagined: we had to help our declared enemies, Carranza's followers, defeat our official supporters, Villa and Zapata, in order to relieve ourselves a little from the terrible pressure of these latter.

Robles, Aguirre Benavides, and I employed the system in the War Department with a cool efficiency whose success was accompanied by not a few dangers and difficulties for us. It went hardest with me because, being a civilian, I lacked the guard and the officers they had to protect them, and I had to face singlehanded the countless big and little Zapata chieftains who regarded me as the clumsy author of their defeats. And all this at a time when nobody was safe in Mexico, when every morning the city asked—as on so many other occasions in our long history of political crimes—how many murders had taken place that night, and when the most cruel and treacherous assassinations could and did occur nightly.

Robles had said to me: "As you understand, we can't do a thing against Villa at the moment. He doesn't need us at all, except as a sort of emblem. But it's different with the Zapatistas. Give them money when they ask you for it, though don't let them exceed the limits; but under no circumstances are they to get arms, ammunition, or trains."

And it was a sight to see how furious some of Zapata's subordinates got—mostly generals in blouse and cotton trousers, a rifle on a bandolier over their shoulders, and cartridge belts across their breasts—and how others thrived on the situation, these the generals in tight breeches, drill jacket, and silver-studded pistol holster.

During the days when Zapata's forces were trying to drive

Alvarado out of Puebla, I used up every pretext imaginable
to keep from supplying them with arms, ammunition, and
engines. As Robles and Aguirre Benavides rarely appeared in
the office, I was the one the leaders of the Army of Freedom
of the South besieged. They would come in to see me, followed by their numerous staffs, and the gloom of my office
would be lightened by the white blotches of their unbelted
cotton pants; their sandals flapped softly; and their enormous hats, which seemed wheels on invisible rails, would
set in motion a close, fetid breeze with every movement. I
would have them sit down in any order, without distinction
of rank, and then enter on a highly technical discussion of the
art of modern warfare, with and without ammunition, with
and without rifles, with and without trains. Everything was
fine as long as I was explaining how our factories of arms
and munitions and explosives could not supply us with the
hundredth part of what was needed, or when I pointed out
that, by the terms of our alliance, General Villa was the
only person authorized to supply them with what they
needed; but as soon as they saw or suspected that I did not
want to help them, they put me in the most difficult situation and sometimes almost started a riot. One group of them
that did not get what it came for revenged itself on me by
dancing in my anteroom, to the terror of some fifty people
who were waiting there, something that could be called "the
dance of the rifle and the pistol." And these were among the
tamest; others, without beating around the bush, simply
threatened to kill me, like the general who asked me for
trains to go to the support of Amozoc, which was being attacked by Carranza troops. I assured him we had no engines;
he said this was a lie, that he had seen them at such and
such a station, and when finally, to get rid of him, I offered
him one that was so old it still burned wood and was practically worthless, it exasperated him so that he said to me, very
calmly:

"All right, boss, I'll take it. But if I get licked, I know the
son of a bitch that's going to pay for it."

As he pronounced the insult, I picked up a glass paper-
weight and, raising my arm to throw it at his head, said to
him in a voice trembling with rage:

"Son of a what?"

"Nothing, boss, nothing, don't get excited. That just
slipped out. But I'm not taking back a word of the rest: if
I get licked, straight back here I come, and you'll get hurt."

And, sure enough, though I did not get hurt, he did come
back, not after the capture of Amozoc by Cesáreo Castro,
but after Puebla had been retaken by Carranza's troops. He
came back with some fifteen or twenty other generals who
believed us responsible for this other loss, and they were
not wrong. Because, naturally, from their point of view there
was no explanation, unless it was our bad management, for
losing ground all the time. Perhaps they already suspected,
without its being quite clear in their minds, that we were
acting more as Obregón's allies than as theirs.

As Robles said, we could do nothing against Villa's forces.
But they could do anything they liked, even laugh at the
government they affected to support with their arms. What
was not clear was just how deliberate their intention was in
behaving this way. Did they have an idea that they should
theoretically accept the authority of the Convention, or did
they think this authority existed like the padding in a ma-
niac's cell, to break the violence of his frenzied blows? However this may have been, the fact is that Villa, Urbina, Fierro,
and the other prominent figures of the Division of the North
behaved at this time in Mexico City as was their usual custom when they were far from it, and their excesses, seen
thus, without perspective, seemed wilder and more scandalous
than ever. Against this small, urban, civilian background, actions designed for a setting of mountains and woods acquired a lurid relief.

As, for example, Villa's amorous indulgences, which lost
their robust rustic harmoniousness in the city to the point
of giving rise at times to delicate international problems. His
doctrine, as he preached it to his officers, was very simple.

"You must never," he said, "do violence to women. Lead them all to the altar; you know these church marriages don't mean a thing. That way you don't lose your good time and you don't make them unhappy. Just look at me: I've got my legal wife that I married before the Justice of the Peace, but I've got others that are legitimate, too, in the sight of God, or the law that means most to them, which is the same thing. That way they're not shamed or embarrassed, because whatever slip or sin there may have been is mine. And what could be better than an easy conscience and a nice friendly understanding with the females you take a notion to? Don't pay any attention if the priest objects or grumbles; just threaten to put a bullet through him and you'll see how he comes round."

But Villa sometimes grew a little lax about his own rules or failed to apply them with the tact the circumstances required. Hence the terrific scandal he caused one day when he tried to marry the cashier of the Palace Hotel in his own fashion. Though, if the truth be told, there was more smoke than fire to the scandal, as will be proved the day these matters can be discussed without hurting anybody's feelings. To a few pusillanimous souls, simple folk who do not understand the workings of the feminine heart in general, and the French in particular, that scandal seemed appalling. But compared with the over-all picture of which it formed a part, it was a trifling matter. Villa did much worse things a dozen times a day and so did Fierro and Urbina.

The efficiency and skill with which Urbina had organized his system of robbery on a large scale was extraordinary. And he completely discredited the contention of the Carranzaists —who had invented it to justify similar holdups of their own —that Zapata and Villa stood for the reaction supported by the rich foreigners and the clergy. Because it was exclusively against the rich—natives and foreigners—that Urbina directed his activities. He practiced that variety of robbery which goes by the euphemistic name of "forced loan" or "immediate subsidy" with a skill nobody could equal, though many other generals tried it. His judgment in selecting his victims was

unerring, and his methods were as quiet as they were infallible. He never made a mistake and he never had to make
much show of force to get his money; they used to pay him
right up, "cash on the barrel-head," as he put it. He first
mapped out his campaign and then worked his territory district by district, block by block, street by street, and house
by house, preparing things beforehand with a network of invisible guards so that none of his victims should escape. And
he used to do it—glorying in his abilities, like a virtuoso of
the art of robbery—in broad daylight, in the offices of his
victims, right on the principal thoroughfares of the city, while
everybody was going about his daily occupations. He did it
all in such a quiet and orderly manner that nobody ever
suspected a thing.

Those of us who were in the seats of government did hear
about it, but in view of our inability to do anything, we,
too, kept quiet, like the victims, who feared worse reprisals
if they made a complaint.

What days those were, when murders and robberies were
like the striking of a clock, marking the hours that passed!
The Revolution which had dawned four years before as a
noble hope was threatening to disappear in deceit and crime.
What did it matter that a little group preserved its ideals
unsullied? Its very restraint and sense of responsibility had
already made it and would continue to make it the least
adapted to the struggle. This in itself was another of the
great contradictions of the Revolution: a movement essentially idealistic and generous had fallen into the hands of the
most selfish and the most unprincipled.

2 THE DEATH OF DAVID BERLANGA

One morning Rodolfo Fierro appeared at the Ministry of
War less self-assured and smiling than was his habit. Not
that his handsome appearance had changed in the least. He
was wearing, as usual, that magnificent pair of puttees which

on his legs acquired a vigor of line that was unique and complete. His white stetson hat, of the finest quality, had not lost, in the way he wore it, an iota of its vaguely provocative and indisputably menacing air. He still cloaked his words in the modulations of a low-pitched voice, eschewing all coarse or crude expressions. His eyes, which squinted slightly, preserved their direct, searching gaze. Yet, nevertheless, that morning his personality seemed dimmed; without being so, he looked faded, aged.

I thought he had come, as he so often did, after money, for besides being a good general and a good revolutionary, he was a great spendthrift. The hundreds, the thousands of pesos which slipped through his fingers as though he had a paper-money printing press in each hand! And inasmuch as ever since our entry into Mexico City the Ministry of War, as he well knew, was under obligation to act as his bank, every two or three days he came to my office and said in his softest, firmest voice:

"I want to give you a receipt."

"Out of the question," was my invariable answer. "We don't have a cent."

But he was an old hand at the game and, putting on an even greater display of verbal sweetness, he wound up with a voucher for at least part of what he had hoped for. Naturally, in this I acted in strictest keeping with the instructions José Isabel Robles had given me. "We have to keep Fierro in a good frame of mind," he had said to me, "no matter what it costs." And the fact was that the price we were paying for Fierro was not excessive in comparison with that of many others: not over two or three thousand pesos three or four times a week.

"All right," I asked when I noticed that after greeting me he said nothing, "how much?"

"Whatever you like," he answered. "That's not really what I came for. I wanted to talk to you . . . in private."

And, smiling, he underscored his last words with a look at the two stenographers near my desk and several officers who were waiting in the reception room across the way for their appointments.

I sent the stenographers away, and motioned Fierro to an armchair beside me.

"No," he replied. "It is going to be hard to talk here without interruptions. Take care of those officers, and then let's go someplace where we can really be alone."

I sensed that there was something serious in the wind, so, without further ado, I got up from my chair and motioned Villa's general to follow me. We crossed the waiting room and the minister's office, where at that hour there was no one but his orderlies; I opened the door, half hidden in the wall, which led into his bedroom, and we locked ourselves in there. I took a chair, and offered another to Fierro, but he preferred to sit on the bed, on whose green satin spread he tossed his hat with a barely perceptible air of weariness. He looked over, one by one, the furnishings, the curtains, the carpet, the hangings; he opened the drawers of the nearby night table, and finally he began to puff on the cigar he had in his mouth with such concentrated attention that one would have said that was all he had on his mind.

I, meanwhile, was studying him, trying to satisfy a two-fold curiosity: that aroused by our interview, already tinged with mystery, and that which the presence of that "handsome beast," as a Yankee journalist had called Fierro, never failed to awaken in me. The latter especially absorbed me. For Fierro, whose good looks put him in a special category, was also the subject of a sinister and fascinating legend; he was credited with feats and cruelties as hair-raising as they were heroic. There, with his handsome, Herculean legs crossed, his elbow on his knee, and his bust leaning toward his hand—while his fingers held the cigar and his mouth let out the smoke—his true nature, with its own light, its own wavelength, rose to the surface. His semisavage nature, dissembled a few seconds earlier behind a screen of civilized words, manners, and gestures, clashed violently with the atmosphere of the delicate mahogany furniture, the lace and brocade curtains, like a rough boulder spoiling and rending it all with its jagged edges.

Suddenly he looked me in the eyes, and said:

"I have just killed David Berlanga—and believe me when I tell you that I regret it."

"David Berlanga!"

The image of that noble lad, all abnegation and sincerity, disinterested, brave, generous, arose before me. His pale face, his head with its long, straight hair seemed to rise in the space between myself and the now indubitably brutal and sanguinary figure of Rodolfo Fierro. I recalled him a few weeks before, courageously denouncing before the Military Convention of Aguascalientes all the pettiness, all the corruption that flowed like streams of slime under many of the men of the Revolution. I reconstructed with a single stroke the complete orbit of his career as a young revolutionist, always passed over, always under secret attack by the shrewd operators who secured and held high offices by means of intrigue, lies, treachery. And under the gaze of that killer there before me, I suddenly had a horrible impulse, a vague desire, to become an assassin myself, like so many others whose atmosphere I had been breathing during the past months, and to stain with human blood the rich carpet of that room. I do not know if it was my better nature, or cowardice, or the strange air of supplication which haloed the fixity with which Fierro's eyes were riveted on mine; at any rate, the deep urge to reach for my pistol changed its course, and was sublimated in these two words, which were the tacit acceptance of the irremediable:

"But why?"

"On orders from the Chief."

And then Fierro told me everything.

"Berlanga," he began, "was having dinner night before last at the Sylvain. In a private room several members of the Chief's staff were dining with a group of women. You know what happens on such occasions: you eat too much, you drink too much, and when it comes time to pay, there's not enough money. I am not referring to Berlanga, but to the Chief's officers. So when the waiter brought the check, what they did was to sign an IOU for the meal and the tip. Naturally, the waiter did not want to accept it, but fearing the consequences of refusing, he went to ask Berlanga's advice who, apparently, was well known in the restaurant. Berlanga was outraged; he began to shout about the army personnel who brought discredit on the banner of the Revolution; he said that the Division of the North was a gang of bandits, that the only way we Villistas knew how to triumph was by stealing, and when he had worn himself out shouting and insulting the troops of General Villa, he paid the officers' IOU, so the waiter would not be out the money, and to keep the document—so he said—as proof of the way the Chief's men behaved.

"Naturally, the officers overheard everything Berlanga had said, and they went to Villa with the tale yesterday morning. The general was furious.

" 'Those whelps,' he said, 'that come barking at me and trying to nip my heels, I'm going to squash them like this.'

"And he raised his foot and brought it down with a fury that even I had never seen. Then he called me aside and ordered in a low voice:

" 'Tonight you get hold of Berlanga wherever he is and you shoot him.'

"And I, what could I do except obey orders? Besides, orders of this sort had never surprised or bothered me; we've been at this sort of thing for years, as you know. Now that Berlanga's dead is when I am beginning to regret it; for, on my word of honor, you don't meet many men like Berlanga. He showed it when he was shot. I'll never be able to kill another one like him, even if the Chief sends me to the wall.

"In keeping with my orders, I set out looking for Berlanga somewhere around midnight or one in the morning. I put a group of *dorados* in two automobiles, and I went to several places with them following me. Then I set out for the Sylvain. It had just come to my mind that Berlanga might be there, for I remembered having heard the officers say, when they were talking to General Villa, that he usually had dinner there.

"And when I got to the restaurant, there he was. As I went over to him I could see that it was some time since he had finished his dinner; I could tell from the cigar he was smoking, which was burned down about halfway, and which must have been a very good one, for the ash was still clinging to the end like a big bud. I told him that I had orders from General Villa to ask him to come with me, and that any resistance would be useless, for I had men enough with me to make myself obeyed.

"'Resistance,' he answered. 'What good is resistance in such cases?'

"He called over the waiter, paid his check, picked up his hat, put it on calmly—taking care as he did all this not to dislodge the ash of his cigar—and we went out.

"He did not say another word to me until we were driving through the gateway of San Cosme barracks.

"'Is it here they're going to lock me up?' he asked me.

"'No,' I answered. 'It's here we're going to shoot you.'

"'Shoot me? When?'

"'Right away.'

"And he did not ask for any further explanation. We got out of the cars and went into the guardroom. By the faint light of the lamp burning there I looked with a certain curiosity at that man whom we were going to execute without trial or formalities of any kind. I did it almost mechanically, and now I regret it, for at that moment Berlanga began to interest me. He was as calm as when I had come upon him in the Sylvain; not even the color of his face had changed. With the greatest composure I have ever seen in my life, he unbuttoned his coat. He went over to a table. He pulled out of his pockets a notebook and a pencil. He wrote several lines in the notebook, probably a good many, for it took him a while, and I did not see him lift the pencil from the paper, nor pause; he wrote without stopping, as though he knew beforehand all that he wanted to say. On a sheet he tore out of the book he wrote something else. He took a ring off his finger, several more things out of his other pockets and, handing them all to me, even the pencil, he said:

"'If it is possible, I would appreciate it if you would give those things to my mother. I have put her name and address on this paper. . . . And I am at your orders.'

"His face remained unruffled. There was not the least trace of emotion in his voice. He buttoned his coat, not automatically, but fully aware of what he was doing, and still taking care, as during all his previous operations, not to dislodge the ash of his cigar. In the time that had elapsed it had grown until the white bud was longer than the stub of the cigar to which it was attached.

"We went out. Our steps as we crossed the courtyards of the barracks sounded to me hollow, strange, unreal; I can still feel the noise of them in my ears like a nail. We could hardly see one another's face, there was so little light.

"We went through one door, then many others, and then we stopped. I ordered the squad of *dorados* to take up their positions in front of a wall, and I turned to Berlanga to tell him that everything was ready. At that he seemed to fix his eyes on me for a few seconds; then he bent his head toward the hand which held the cigar, and finally said, in reply to my attitude:

"'Yes, right away. I won't keep you waiting. . . .'

"And for several minutes, which seemed no time to me, he went on smoking. In spite of the darkness I could see clearly how he held the cigar carefully between the tips of his fingers. It was plain that, almost oblivious of his imminent death, Berlanga was finding pleasure in contemplating the enormous bud of ash which glowed with a faint salmon tint toward the lighted end. When the cigar was almost completely consumed, with a brusque jerk of his hand Berlanga made the ashes fall to the ground, like a brilliant and silent ember. Then he tossed away the stub, and with firm step, neither hurried nor slow, walked over to the wall and stood there with his back to it. He would not let his eyes be bandaged."

"It was a horrible crime," I said to Fierro, after a long pause.

"Horrible," he answered, and began pulling at his cigar once more, more determinedly than before, obsessed with watching the formation of the ash.

"The truth is," he added after a little, "I am not as bad as they make me out. I have a heart, too; I can feel and appreciate . . . what a brave man Berlanga was. And how strong. Look," —and he held out the cigar— "since early this morning I have been trying to smoke a cigar without letting the ash fall, but it's no use. My fingers, which I can't control, suddenly twitch and the ash falls. And it's not that the cigar is a cheap one, I can assure you of that. While he, Berlanga, could keep his hand steady as long as he wanted to, up to the very moment when we were about to kill him. . . ."

3 THE PRESIDENT SHOWS HIS FRENCH

In the midst of the wreckage of the Revolution's highest hopes Eulalio Gutiérrez did not forget the obligations he had assumed in Aguascalientes. He was doing everything he could to get Obregón to break away from Carranza at the same time that we freed ourselves from Zapata and Villa. We were secretly making preparations for our march to San Luis, ready, if it came to a showdown, to fight both Villa and Carranza. And it must be recognized that this decision reflects the greatest credit on the President *pro tem,* for it required almost as much faith in the ultimate destiny of the Revolution to convince Obregón of the dangers Carranza represented as it did bravery to prepare the break with Villa while still under his thumb. We were well aware of what this latter course of action would lead to. There was no question but that Villa would soon learn what we were about, in spite of all our precautions, and once he knew, nothing could prevent his falling on us with his usual violence.

The situation came to a head one Sunday morning. (Or if it was not Sunday, it was a day on which for some reason or other the offices were closed to the public.)

I had gone to the War Office to attend to a number of matters that were urgent. I had been going over papers and dictating letters and telegrams for three hours. Ugalde, my stenographer, was sitting across the table from me, transforming the words that fell from my lips into forceful little tracings with his yellow pencil, which slid agilely across the paper. We both felt happy. We were working in the quiet solitude of the office in the same frame of mind as if the overwhelming military incubus, which my words and his pencil handled so deftly, had no significance other than the detached reality that scientists attach to the object of their experiments.

About one o'clock the telephone rang. Ugalde took down the receiver and answered without raising his hand from his notebook or releasing the grip on his pencil. His voice was in keeping with the tranquil atmosphere of our work as he spoke:

"Hello. . . . Yes. . . . Yes. . . ."

I saw that he covered the receiver, putting it face down on the desk and from the depths of the paragraph I was mentally elaborating, I heard him say:

"They want to know if you're here, and if you are, they want you to come to the phone immediately."

I took the telephone from him and answered, like him, in a tone of complete serenity:

"Hello. . . . Yes. . . . Guzmán speaking. . . ."

But the state of affairs at the other end of the line must have been different. The voice that came from there was breathless, agitated, and catastrophic; at its words, notwithstanding my best efforts to remain unmoved, a shiver ran over me from head to foot. I could notice the effect of these words as I listened to them, more in Ugalde's face, which reflected stage by stage the expression of my own, than in myself.

When I set the telephone back on the desk, the magic of
our peaceful work had been dispelled. My silence bespoke
my perplexity. Ugalde, without taking his eyes from my face,
had put his pencil in his pocket and closed his notebook.
Finally, in a tremulous voice, which was in striking contrast
with that of a few moments before, he asked:

"Is it anything serious, Mr. Guzmán?"

"I have just been informed," I answered in a voice that
resembled his, "that Villa had just taken the President prisoner and has ordered the arrest of his Cabinet and the other
important members of the government."

I went out into the yard, got into my automobile, and
drove away. Outside, the bright winter sun, warm and comforting at midday, had a placid gleam; it radiated harmony
and seemed to deny the possibility of conflict. The streets
were alive with pleasant noise and jocund passers-by, all
conducive to a state of well-being. The Zócalo was a lake of
light; automobiles and streetcars seemed to move along it in
rhythm without a care. But my automobile carried a heavy
load of worry. And as I passed through the bustle of Plateros
Street, I felt more and more how alien I was at that moment
to the impulses that moved the crowds of men, women, and
children on the sidewalks and in the other vehicles.

As we passed the confectioner's shop, El Globo, the movement of my car was so slow that it seemed to exist only in
contrast with the rapidity of my thoughts: slow motion at the
service of vertigo. . . . But at that moment I happened to
see Colonel Domínguez in the shop, taking a package from
one of the salesgirls, who was offering it to him with a smile
and a boutonniere.

Jumping from my car, I threaded my way through bumpers
and mudguards into the store. Domínguez was standing near
the cashier's window, with his cane, his cigarette, his package, and his flowers in one hand, and his money in the other.

"Never mind about those cakes," I said to him in a voice
that was not so low as I should have wished, "and come with
me right this minute."

Several of the customers looked at us in astonishment and wonder. But Domínguez, with an air of perfect composure, put his package down on the counter and followed me.

I walked ahead, clearing a path through the crowd, until we reached the automobile, which had kept moving in the triple lane of cars. Once inside, Domínguez asked:

"But what's the matter?"

"This is the matter," and I told him what had happened.

By the time we reached the statue of Charles IV, we had made our plans. We would leave the car at the door of the garage that was on the Paseo de la Reforma, just across from Eulalio's house. And I would approach the house and do my best to get in touch with Gutiérrez. In the meantime Domínguez would try to telephone to Lucio Blanco, to warn him of the danger and ask his advice. If I had not returned in half an hour, Domínguez would come to look for me.

The first difficulty I encountered was the guard. Instead of the President's usual escort, I found Villa's *dorados*.

"You can't pass, sir."

"I can't pass?"

"You nor nobody, sir. Them's orders."

"Whose orders?"

"Why, General Villa's. Whose did you think they were? Don't you know who's the boss around here?"

It was no use to go on arguing, so I asked to see the captain of the guard. He repeated what the soldier had said; but I assured him that it was Villa I wanted to see, to consult him about certain matters connected with the service, and he finally let me come into the vestibule at the foot of the stairs.

"You positively cannot go any farther," said the officer. "Orders are very strict."

Downstairs none of Eulalio's men were to be seen. The *dorados* were everywhere. Groups of them were standing by one of the windows watching a cavalry column parading beneath the trees of the avenue. They were Urbina's men, who had turned up opportunely to add a menacing note with their presence. I watched them, too, for several minutes. The riders were only several abreast, and moving slowly, the better to impress the spectators.

"Has the general been here long?" I asked the officer.

"About an hour or so."

Then I began to walk up and down the room, affecting the patient air of a person who waits. As though sunk in thought, I prolonged my strolls into the next room. And a little later, when nobody was looking, I slipped out into the first patio.

It was radiantly clear out there; the green trees seemed varnished with sunlight. In one corner there was a staircase. For a minute I studied the layout, and then I went up it. It led to a sort of mezzanine, which seemed to be servants' quarters. There was nobody there; I walked through and managed, with some difficulty, to get into one of the larger rooms. The doors into this room from the rest of the house were locked, but one of them opened on to a little corridor with a window, and from this window I managed, after considerable effort, to climb through the next window.

I then found myself in another empty room, like the first two, but farther ahead I could hear voices. I went forward until I got near enough to make out what was being said. The conversation was going on in the next room.

I left my hat on a table and, with a nonchalant air, as though I were a member of the household, I walked past the door to see what was going on.

The voices came from a group of officers of Villa's *dorados*, who were calmly talking in the middle of the room. Some—the majority—were sitting on the table, swinging their legs, and the others were standing. Their indifferent talk did not disguise the fact that they were alert and waiting for some important event to take place. They made a compact group before the door of the reception room, which was closed. Without a doubt Eulalio was being held in there.

With the same easy air I walked through the room toward the next one, which adjoined the reception room. The officers turned to look at me. I greeted them familiarly, my hands in my pockets:

"How's everything . . . ?"

"All right. We're here with the Chief."

I went ahead. The room adjoining the reception room was a bedroom. Like the others it was empty. Here the voices in the waiting room were drowned out by others which came through one of the sliding doors, though the heavy hangings and carpets somewhat muffled all sounds. The new voices were harsh and argumentative, but they sounded as though the worst of the quarrel were over. The better to hear, I tip-toed over to the doors through which they filtered. The two halves of the door were ajar, but the portieres on the other side were completely drawn. Slipping between the doors and the velvet curtains, I could now hear Villa's voice, sharp and emphatic:

"You say Mr. Vasconcelos's life has been threatened. Well, why didn't you tell me about it? I'll give him a guard."

Eulalio's somewhat sibilant voice, high-pitched and ironic, came equally clear: "But that's not the way things are done. If I'm President, all the troops have to be under my orders, and I'm the one to assign the guards."

Villa's voice again: "Well, sir, but who says that my troops aren't yours, too? Aren't we all one government?"

At this point several voices were heard together. I could make out only an occasional word.

I drew the edge of the curtain away from the wall a little and peeped through. I could see a part of Roque González Garza's face and uniform and a little of Vito Alessio Robles's back and head. I pulled the curtain back a little more; a hand appeared, a hand that I recognized, but which seemed like something completely new, amputated from the body to which it belonged. It was Eulalio's. Close to it stood a bottle of cognac, surrounded by three or four little glasses. Higher up and farther off between two figures I could see a lock of Villa's curly auburn hair under the drooping brim of his hat. At times the movements of the hair were accompanied by the glittering flash of an eye, visible through the interstices of the fringes of the uniforms. Villa's face was very red and wore that set smile which accompanied his towering attacks of anger. By the arms and legs I could see, I judged that he formed the center of a large group.

Eulalio's hand took hold of the bottle and poured out cognac in one of the glasses. With three fingers he picked it up, and glass and hand disappeared from my range of vision. The mingled voices went on confusedly. Hand and glass appeared again. Eulalio said something in a clearer tone. A brief silence.

Villa's voice was heard again: "I gave that order, sir. If I turn all the railroads over to your government, how will I move my troops? Look at the territory I hold."

". . . ?"

"But anyway it's all the same thing. You've named me commander-in-chief of your troops, haven't you? Well, I'll protect you, and to protect you I'll keep under my command all the forces the situation warrants. Besides, they're my trains and my troops."

At this juncture I could make out Fierro's voice and, a little closer by, Vito Alessio Robles's. Eulalio answered something.

Villa's voice broke in again: "Well now, I'm telling you, sir: three thousand of my cavalrymen are on parade in front of your house, just so you can feel how strong I am. The guard I've stationed here is mine, too. You won't leave this place without my permission."

Eulalio's voice: "We'll see about that."

A buzz of voices.

Then Villa: "And if you did get out, a lot of good it would do you, because now, just so you'll know it, I'm going to leave you without a single train. How do you think you'd get away from me?"

Eulalio's voice came sharp, clear, serene, biting: "How? Don't you worry about the how. To get away from you I'd be willing to ride a mule."

"All right, you heard me; you try it and I'll lay you out cold."

This was followed by movements that the carpet muffled. I thought the quarrel was going to begin again, but then I realized that it was over for the time being. I swiftly drew back from the curtain into the middle of the bedroom. There came the sound of voices and of many feet. A door opened and footsteps were heard moving down the hall. Then steps and voices died away. There was quiet in the waiting room, quiet in the reception room. I walked over to the curtain once more and pulled it open. Nobody. I walked into the room.

Eulalio, seated in an armchair, had just poured himself another glass of cognac, which he was lifting to his lips. He was startled to see me at first, as I emerged from my hiding place; then he smiled, but said nothing and then eyed me inquiringly. I could not keep from smiling myself to see him sitting there so calm and mocking.

Nevertheless I asked him: "Well, General, what do we do now?"

"Now? Why, what you fellows say who read books and went to school." And his keen, intelligent eyes sought mine as the expression that preceded laughter came over his face.

"What we say?"

"Yes, you intellectuals."

"I can't think. What is it we say?"

"Why, *malgré tout*, Master Guzmán, *malgré tout*. Isn't that the way you intellectuals say it?"

4 Do You Think So, Mr. President?

In spite of everything, Eulalio held to his determination to break with Villa, and to this end he resumed—as soon as he was set free—the plans he had laid out. Now, beyond doubt, the material difficulties which confronted us would be multiplied, inasmuch as the head of the Division of the North was no longer unaware of our intentions. But even this did not dishearten the President named by the Convention, nor did the slight moral advantage that Villa now knew all bolster him up.

The Carranzaists, meanwhile, censuring Gutiérrez for his "alliance" with the Villa faction (or "the reaction," the term maliciously being applied to the dissident revolutionary group), which was no such thing, but only a way of marking time until they saw the error of their ways, persisted in their self-seeking and anti-revolutionary attitude. The victories of Puebla seemed to encourage them—victories which we had made possible by withholding support from Zapata's hordes —and this made it harder for us to win them over. Obregón now refused to have anything to do with the representatives of the Convention: he sent them to Veracruz (as in the case of Rodríguez Cabo) to lay before Carranza himself our intention of removing him from power.

In a word, Eulalio Gutiérrez was as firm in his purpose as before the quarrel with Villa, and his situation was not too different from what it had been at the beginning, when Carranza's supporters had demanded that Villa be stripped of the Division of the North while they betook themselves to safety.

I took a favorable view of the preparations for departure. Even more, I was anxiously awaiting the moment when we could exchange the influence of Mexico City—which left one drained when everything depended on the accumulation of energy—for the pure and purifying atmosphere of the country, the mountains, the villages. An unavoidable mirage led me astray. Had we not managed to finish off Huerta by marching against him, without other strength than the justice of our cause, from the most remote corners of the Republic? We could do the same, my reasoning ran, against Carranza and Villa now. Which means that I did not realize that a nation divested of great conscious groups (conscious of the need for serene, self-sacrificing, creative patriotism) was, if it was to arouse strong, irresistible popular movements, of necessity dependent upon the contingency of stirring events,

which are not repeated every day. I believed that what the
Mexican people had just accomplished they could do again,
without taking into consideration the fact that what had come
about as the result of a momentary enthusiasm based on emotion, would not *ipso facto* continue now that a deep and lasting enthusiasm, based on ideas, was needed. What was on
the point of happening was precisely the collapse of the primitive enthusiasm, its disintegration into rival personal ambitions; its factitious survival, under cover of three or four simu-
lacra of ideas invented for the use of the leaders by their
more obtuse or more servile intellectual advisers, or rather,
by those more dazzled by the tinsel of outward power than
by the austere virtue of inner ideals. But as I did not grasp
this at the time—nor, I think, did anybody—I cherished the
remnants of my political and revolutionary illusions.

Such worries as I had were concerned with the past rather
than the future; with certain of the men we were going to
leave behind rather than with those we would soon encounter.
The image of Don Valentín Gama obsessed me. What good
had it done us to drag him into the Convention government?
He would now be left exposed—inasmuch as he did not ven-
ture to follow us further—to reprisals and insults. If his association with us had not been translated into anything useful, it was not he who was to blame, but circumstances, too
unstable, precarious, and abnormal to allow of anything different. What possible use could be found for the talents and
noble aims of a technically highly trained man in the midst
of the barbarous crimes and rampant intrigues which hedged
us in? And now that the result of the Convention was on
the point of turning into a mere adventure of *guerrilleros* on
the run, the contradiction was even more evident.

The person of Don Valentín Gama, abandoned to the enemy as something useless to our side, and, moreover, un-
transportable, took on the quality of a symbolic example in
my eyes. In him I seemed to see, too, how in our country
true civic virtue found no outlet, nor recompense, nor glory,
whereas the simulators of devotion to duty or efficiency were

using the whole country for their own ends, and even piling up honors in this way. That illustrious teacher had offered a sacrifice on the altar of patriotism: he had laid aside his instruments and his books of astronomy to put himself at the service of a cause which he considered good. But such an act, far more valuable as a cure for the basic maladies of Mexico than many of the battles our generals were fighting, would never be appreciated at its ethical worth. On the contrary, many would consider it all a big mistake, something to be covered up and forgotten, inasmuch as the Convention movement was going downhill and to inevitable failure.

For the question of political triumph or failure has an importance for us which far exceeds the immediate effects of a struggle which might perhaps be justified by a certain narrow criterion. It touches upon the moral standard by which the public actions of each person are measured in themselves, seen in their historical context, in their ultimate transcendence for the permanent interest of the Mexican nation. In Mexico we lack a body of public opinion capable of pointing out the fact that a political failure may bear within it the seeds of brilliant success for the eventual destiny of the nation; and, inversely, apparently great political successes may turn out to be nothing but stumbling blocks on the highroad of history. Lacking an awareness of the basic values of nationality, and its lasting interests, we let ourselves be dragged along, almost beyond the point of no return, by the partial awareness of different political groups who identify their momentary successes with those of the nation. This explains why for a hundred years we have been launching attacks at the *gachupines*, and why in an entire century of political disaster we have not yet learned, once and for all, the great lesson of history which Lucas Alamán gave us in his stubborn determination to revive a past that was hopelessly dead. But, on the other hand, we glorify as inspirations or transcendental successes the miserable political intrigues, the chicanery, the jockeying for power, better or worse concealed.

If during my brief activity as a rebel there were things of which I should have sincerely repented, none of them lay so heavily on my conscience at the moment as my determination two months earlier that Eulalio should make Don Valentín Gama minister. The ephemeral days of his ministry had been little less than spiritual torture for my wise teacher, and now they were probably going to cause him complications of a practical nature. And all this without the slightest benefit for the country, or for him, or for us. It was easy to imagine the harm done the spirit of this great mathematician, trained in the rigors of the purest of disciplines, by the absurd confusion of the revolutionary machinery, whose jerks and spasms, like those caused by hysteria or epilepsy, could not be foretold from one hour to the next. Could there have been a greater absurdity, for example, than for the government of the Convention to have so arranged it that the troops of Carranza (our principal enemy) should defeat those of Zapata (one of our allies)? And like this, everything else.

In performing his ministerial duties, this scholar daily encountered enough asperities to disconcert and disillusion the most enthusiastic person of intellectual formation suddenly thrown into the political arena. Not even the fact that there were men in Gutiérrez's cabinet of the caliber of Rodríguez Cabo, Vasconcelos, Alessio, could prevent this.

Of that harsh climate, with its back turned on culture, which is light and gentleness, nothing is perhaps so typical as what took place at a meeting of ministers held in the National Palace, with Gutiérrez presiding. The question under discussion was the intolerable behavior of the Zapatistas, presumably instigated or encouraged by their mentor, Antonio Díaz Soto y Gama. Díaz Soto, more turbulent in those days than during any other phase of his career (and that is saying a lot), was driving the government out of its mind with the artful resources of his slippery shenanigans. Eulalio laid at his door much of the harm which, according to him, Zapata was doing the cause of the Convention. That morning, forgetting for the moment that Díaz Soto was a close

relative of Don Valentín, he felt the need to speak his mind
with revolutionary forthrightness before his council of ministers—at which, naturally, Don Valentín Gama was present
—on the subject of the offenses of Zapata's intellectual adviser. But as this did not wholly assuage his wrath, he let
himself be carried away by the urge to sum up his setting
forth, which had been abundantly vigorous and expressive, in
a phrase which synthesized the opinion he felt Antonio Díaz
Soto y Gama deserved and in which he should be held. And
so he concluded his remarks, before his cabinet solemnly assembled in plenary session, with a few words, extraordinary
in that company though common enough in the street; words
which ricocheted from the table where weighty decisions were
taken, from the bronze-trimmed ministerial writing desks;
words which shook the velvet curtains and fell upon the soft
carpet with a louder crash than if all the windows of the
palace had been shattered.

"To sum it up, gentlemen," said the President of the Republic in his gentle voice, gentle despite his wrath, "Díaz
Soto is a son of a bitch, yes, a son of a bitch."

The ministers sat aghast, not knowing what to do or which
way to look, even though Eulalio's words were fundamentally
unimportant. To those who knew him well, those picturesque
sallies of his served as a contrast which threw into relief his
many exceptional gifts. But in view of the relationship between Don Valentín Gama and Antonio Díaz Soto, on this
occasion the impact of the presidential words was tremendous. Fortunately, Don Valentín, understanding even in this,
fully grasped the political reality; possibly he even perceived
the humorous side of the matter. All he did was to bow cere-
moniously from his place at the other end of the table, and
ask, in keeping with the best tradition and forms of protocol:

"Do you think so, Mr. President?"

And Eulalio answered, without altering his words by a single letter:

"I do, Mr. Minister. Díaz Soto is a son of a bitch, don't
you doubt it for a minute."

BOOK VII

In the Lion's Mouth

---

1 A REVOLUTIONARY ASSAULT

I was afraid the Zapatistas might lay a trap for me, so I used to change my sleeping quarters frequently. During the day, one way or another, we civilian officers of the Convention government managed to defend ourselves from the enemies that surrounded us; but at night we were exposed to the most brutal assaults. Finally things got so that I never slept two nights in the same place after those dark days in which Vasconcelos, Secretary of Education, had to flee to Pachuca to keep from being ambushed.

Nobody, naturally, ever knew where I was going to sleep. At the last minute I would decide to leave my car almost anywhere; I would take out the pistols, rifles, and cartridge cases I carried under the seat, and then spend the night, in the company of my military aide and chauffeur, in whatever hotel or boardinghouse I decided on at the moment. Nor did my precautions stop with this: my two companions and I used to barricade ourselves in the room or suite we occupied together, with our arms loaded and within easy reach.

This was the state of affairs when one morning, the moment I stepped out into the street flooded with light, I felt something unusual in the air. I seemed to sense the approach or the wake of something new. Was it perhaps that I was politically hypersensitive, what with our departure from Mexico City so close at hand? Then I decided not to pay any attention to my uneasiness and put it down to imagination. But as the auto rolled along, trifles, things you could not put your finger on, seemed to multiply and took such a hold on me that I ordered the chauffeur to drive faster. And as we approached the War Office, I began to feel a touch of panic.

When we came out of Rosales Street into the Plaza de la Reforma, I could not stand it any longer. The Trojan Horse was bathed in sunlight, but if I saw it, I did not take it in, because my eyes traveled past it to a policeman standing motionless on the corner of Bucareli on the other side of the square. I ordered the chauffeur to stop.

"You see that policeman over there?" I asked my aide, who always accompanied me at this hour.

"Yes, sir."

"Well, get out and ask him what is going on."

The man looked at me blankly. And really, to judge from appearances, nothing was happening. Vehicles and people were coming and going as usual. The policeman was leaning lazily against the corner of a building, basking in the sun.

My aide said: "Would you mind repeating what you said?"

"Ask the policeman what is happening."

"Happening, sir? Where?"

"Here, in the city!"

He jumped out of the car with military agility, crossed the street, and, after exchanging a few words with the policeman, hurried back to the car.

"He says," he informed me, "that this morning the Convention government and its troops evacuated the city."

"What!"

"Yes, sir!"

"That's impossible!"

"Well, that's what he says they say, sir!"

We found the doors of the War Office bolted and locked and without the customary sentinels. We knocked loudly; nobody answered. But at the sight of the car or the noise two officers of José Isabel Robles's staff came over to me from the opposite side of the street.

"What are you doing here?" I asked.

"We're not doing anything, Chief. You could have knocked us over with a feather. We were out on a tear last night, and when we got here this morning, if you please, the troops were gone. We'll do whatever you order."

I thought for a moment. Then I asked: "Have you got your guns?"

"The pistols."

"And where are your rifles?"

"God only knows. Last night, about ten, they were in the general's house; that is, we left them there. But who knows where they are now?"

I understood from all this that something unforeseen and imperative had obliged Eulalio Gutiérrez to leave for San Luis sooner than he had intended. I felt sure that he had left word for me at my house as to where I should join them.

"All of you get in the car," I said to the officers, though the order created difficulties. It was a struggle to get more than three people into that small auto. One of the officers had to sit on my aide's lap, and the other on the floor, so as not to attract attention.

When I got to my house, I found that my suppositions were correct. There had been several telephone calls for me during the night, and Gutiérrez had sent for me at twelve and at two. At about four that morning General Robles, accompanied by Colonel Domínguez, had come to the house and had made them open the doors to assure himself that I was not there. Finally he had left a message for me. It read: "I am sorry not to have found you, and that you have to be left behind, but we have been looking everywhere for you since midnight. Things have taken a very serious turn and we have to evacuate the city immediately. I'll explain it all when I see you. We're leaving by the Pachuca road, where I hope you will join us as quickly as possible. Please God you receive this in time, because I know that by morning the city will be in the hands of Zapata's troops. I'm taking your horse along so it won't be lost in the disorder that's coming in a few hours. Unless some better way occurs to you, or something special comes up, the best thing for you to do will be to leave by automobile. Watch out for Madinabeitia as well as Zapata. Hope to see you soon.—*Robles*."

The dining-room clock was just striking half past eight as I finished the letter.

My difficulties in escaping began with the automobile. Mine was a ridiculous little coupé, which in Huerta's days had been used by Chucho Rábago, the private secretary of Urrutia, while the latter had been Minister of the Interior. It would not run two miles on an unpaved road. Besides, it was very small, and, to make matters worse, as I passed the park of San Fernando, I had picked up two more of Robles's officers who had been left behind. The first and most urgent thing to do, then, was to get hold of a seven-passenger touring car, and I set out to look for one.

At first, I wanted to hire one, but two or three attempts in this direction convinced me that I would never get one that way. The chauffeurs would take in at a glance our revolutionary stamp, hear us say we wanted to go out of the city, and flatly refuse. Besides, these cars that were for hire were in a lamentable state. Of the four tires probably not a single one was any good.

And it was getting late. The clocks had struck nine, and in the streets one could see signs of the military change occasioned by the withdrawal of the Convention troops.

I stood on the corner of Balderas and Juárez avenues, hesitating as to which of various courses to take. Up and down the street, cars of every size, make, and description went hurrying by, of American and foreign manufacture, old and new. And although, no doubt, each was serving its master's desire, nobody had such pressing need of a car at that moment as I. I looked at my watch; it was ten minutes past nine. Every minute that went by sent twenty, thirty, fifty cars whirling past me and at the same time made my possibilities of salvation more remote. Then I made up my mind: why should there be laws to guarantee the property rights of two thousand automobiles and none to guarantee my life? Law, like everything else in the world, is mutual, reciprocal, and correlative. I got into my car with my aide and the two officers and said to the chauffeur:

"Drive ahead slowly, and the first Hudson Super-six you see, turn around in the street and block its way."

We had not gone three hundred feet when, coming behind us, we saw exactly the car we were looking for, brand-new and shining with paint and sun. Holding out his hand, my chauffeur turned quickly, so quickly and so short that the Hudson had to jam on its brakes and stalled. The other chauffeur began to protest furiously, but he stopped as two of my officers jumped onto either side of the running board, and the third addressed himself to the owner, who was in the car.

The officer's words were brief and to the point: "This car is needed for the service. Kindly get out at once."

The owner of the car probably wondered if he was dreaming. His first reaction was astonishment, and his second righteous indignation, accompanied by unsuccessful attempts at resistance. But at this juncture my other two officers, who were armed with rifles, approached him, and I myself went over to try to convince him.

The attempts at persuasion were not, if the truth be told, very successful. The owner insisted that he was being the victim of a holdup in the middle of Juárez Avenue, and on this ground resisted giving up his car, and I tried to persuade him that although it did look that way, it only went to show how we all had to submit to the stern exigencies of war.

In a frenzy of indignation he shouted: "Your reasoning sounds like that of a highwayman."

To which I replied, unruffled: "Sounds and is."

Finally the threat of taking him along with us brought him

to terms, and I promised to return his car to him that same afternoon.

In a rage, for which I don't blame him, he gave me his card and I handed him mine, on which I wrote out a sort of receipt, binding myself both officially and privately.

He and his chauffeur got out of the Hudson. My officers and I got in, and my chauffeur took the wheel.

"What's the good of this?" the owner of the car asked contemptuously as he read my card.

"Not much, probably," I answered. "But keep it anyway, just on the off-chance."

And as the motor started, I said:

"One last favor: take my little car and use it until yours is returned this afternoon."

"What if I don't want to?"

"Then leave it. I meant it for your own good. A bad car is better than none. So long!"

And we drove off.

2 González Garza, President

Had anybody noticed the means we had employed to secure our Hudson? Not many, at any rate, for we did not seem to attract more than an occasional glance of curiosity or surprise as we drove two blocks farther down the avenue and then turned towards Humboldt. There we stopped.

"Look the car over," I said to the chauffeur, who with the help of the five officers gave it a quick examination. Everything seemed to be in good shape except the supply of gasoline. There was not more than enough for twenty kilometers in the tank.

And then our troubles began again, for gasoline was not to be found in Mexico City in those days at any price. After we had asked for it at a number of places and begged for it at others, finally, pistol in hand, we persuaded a garage in Atenas Street to part with the four cans they said they kept on hand for emergencies. There could be no greater emergency than mine. We emptied two of them into the tank and fastened the other two as best we could on the running board.

At last we were ready to start! But just then I happened to remember that I had two more rifles in my house and a supply of bullets for them, and we went back there again. I got the guns and some food, and when everything and everybody was settled, I gave the order:

"To Pachuca!"

It was a little past nine-thirty.

As we drove down Hombres Ilustres Avenue, I noticed a great crowd of what looked like revolutionists in front of the Hotel Lascuráin. There seemed to be a meeting going on, and undoubtedly at that meeting the departure of Eulalio and his forces was being discussed. Should I stop to find out about things? Prudence counseled me to lose no more time; but my instinct said: "Find out all you can. . . ." We stopped. I jumped out of the car, joined the crowd, and made my way into the hotel.

On the first floor the mass of people was tremendous; civilians and soldiers, supporters of Zapata, Villa, the Convention. In the main parlor, as I entered, all attention seemed focused on the dais. There, standing up on something that raised him above the crowd so he could be seen and heard, Roque González Garza was eloquently and excitedly haranguing the multitude. "It is in moments of anxiety and perplexity like these that the true patriots . . ." As he reached this point he spied me (I had just come into the room), and, breaking off his speech, he shouted to me over the hundreds of heads:

"Have you heard the news?"

"No, that's what I came to find out. What's happened?"

"A mere trifle: they've just betrayed us, that's all. Gutiérrez, Robles, Blanco, and the rest of their bunch ran away this morning with the troops. They've left the Convention flat, and they've broken with Villa and Zapata. They've deserted us to go over to Carranza."

As he talked, I had been moving toward him, in the midst of a general silence. But he had lowered his voice as I drew nearer, and when we were only a few steps apart private conversations and dialogues started up all over the room.

Then I said: "Well, now what do you think we ought to do?"

"First of all, keep our heads. Then make the best of whatever comes along. For the present I'm going to take charge of things. I have taken over the executive power. I haven't a doubt that General Villa will approve of what I do, and I'm going to have the Convention ratify the functions I am taking over as an emergency measure, this very afternoon if possible. And, since you are familiar with the work in the War Department, would you take charge of it right away?"

"I don't quite understand. You want to make me your Minister of War and the Navy?"

"Minister or whatever you want to call it. The important thing is for us to hang together and keep on functioning as the legitimate government."

In all Roque was saying to me, which was in contrast to his gestures and his childish lisp, there was nothing pedantic, but rather the awareness, though he did not overstress it, of the responsibilities he was assuming. Roque had really grown in stature as a politician in the last few months, even though he had not changed outwardly. Years later his enemies who scoffed at him did so because of their own inability to distinguish the good from the inept, the candid from the obtuse. But the fact remains that the decision with which he inaugurated his ephemeral presidency could be considered a preview of the many manly traits, stalwart, upright, strong, of which he was to give proof in the stormy weeks ahead.

I did not want to deceive him, nor did I want to give myself away, either. So I replied ambiguously:

"Very good, very good."

And after talking a little while longer with him and with some of the others that were there, I went out. Fortunately, judging from Roque's invitation, my presence in Mexico City was not ascribed to its real cause, but to the supposition that I was more loyal to Villa than to the ideas Eulalio Gutié-rrez represented. The thing to do was to take advantage of this mistake.

We drove as fast as we could through Santa María la Re-donda. We left the little plaza of Santiago behind us and made for Peralvillo. The Hudson behaved like an angel. Along the Guadalupe road we began to meet officers and soldiers, singly or in groups. Some were going, others coming. Some looked tired, bewildered, or frightened and had sat down along the edge of the road or were stretched out under the trees.

La Villa, dirty and restless, busy with its insignificant trade and in a state of expectation, revealed at a glance the recent passing of a considerable army. We drove through without stopping. A group of officers waved to us. We did not know them and pretended not to see them. We passed the Pocito Chapel and were just coming into the wide street that leads out on the road. Five hundred meters more and we would have been out on the highway. But just as I was thinking this, a group of soldiers on horseback trotted out to meet us. They were from Zapata's forces. We had to stop.

The leader of the troop came over and asked, ironically and maliciously:

"Where you heading for, partner?"

"You can see for yourself," I answered. "That way."

"Well, you can't get through that way. Them's orders."

"Nobody is allowed through?"

"Nobody."

"All right, if we can't get through, we can't. Thanks. We'll go back."

And I said to the chauffeur: "Turn around."

But the officer interposed:

"No, sir. You can't do that either. Orders are to arrest any-body heading that way."

There was no chance to argue with him. The soldiers

crowded around us while the officer directed the chauffeur
toward a wide gate near by, which might have been that of
an inn or a barnyard. They made him drive through and then
took us, car and all, into a big yard that looked like a barn
lot. There was a crowd of prisoners in there of the most varied
classes and categories.

Just as we were about to get out, an idea came to me so
clear, so obvious in its life-saving possibilities that, in spite of
our situation, I smiled to myself.

Assuming an air of great assurance, I said to the officer:
"By the way, do you know who it is you have just put in
here?"

His attitude was one of humble contempt. "We'll find out
in good time."

"No," I answered, "you'll find out right now. Do you know
who I am?"

"But what's the hurry, chief?"

I became more emphatic. "Who are you?"

"Major Margarito Sifuentes, at your orders, sir."

"Very well, Major. I am the Minister of War in the Cabinet
of the new Convention government. The President is General
Roque González Garza."

Major Sifuentes's eyes opened as wide as saucers, and,
pushing back the brim of his palm-leaf hat with one hand,
he exclaimed, half incredulous and half impressed:

"You don't say so, General!"

"Exactly as I've told you, Major. And these gentlemen who
are with me are members of my staff. Now you can use your
own judgment about what you do."

For several seconds the Zapata officer sat motionless. Then
he got down from his horse and, coming toward me, said:

"General, will you excuse me if I go and get some advice
on the matter? What did you say your name was?"

I told him. He repeated it twice and then walked over to
the group of houses that closed the lot on one side. There he
disappeared, swallowed up in one of the splotches of shadow
that covered the crumbling, blackened walls. In a little while

he was back, accompanied by another Zapata officer, wearing tighter pants, a broader hat and a fiercer expression.

The new conversation with them was in keeping with the earlier one. The second officer began: "I'm the colonel of the regiment stationed here to cut off the escape of traitors on this side. Is it true that you are the Minister of War in the new government?"

"It is."

"You won't be offended, will you, General, if I ask you for some identification?"

"How shall I identify myself?"

"Haven't you got some papers?"

"None suitable for this purpose. I was appointed only an hour ago."

"Then if you don't mind (and it isn't that I doubt your word; it's that I have to do my duty), we'll go together to see the new President of the Republic, so he can back up what you say. That is, if you wouldn't rather we did something else that fits in with my orders."

"I think that's an excellent idea," I answered. "Get into the car."

The officers who were with me got up to give him their place. But the Zapata colonel went on, without moving from where he stood:

"And I hope you won't take offense, but if you don't mind, I'd rather we left your aides here. That way we won't need to take along an escort, and just you and I and one of my captains will be enough."

Perhaps if I had raised my voice to him at that moment and had blustered a little, there would have been no need for trips and identifications. But at the same time I might ruin everything by violence, so I decided to choose the part of meekness. I lauded the colonel's military procedure and accepted all the conditions he laid down.

Half an hour later I was back again in the Hotel Lascuráin. There were more people than before. Roque was filled with the spirit of his office and was perorating and giving orders at a great rate. His new functions seemed to have communicated to him a new and unwonted importance; he seemed taller, more capable, more intelligent; the lisp that characterized him was less noticeable, and he was as active as a canary in a cage.

I walked over to him, followed by the Zapata colonel, who was so overwhelmed at the sight of so many mirrors and so many people that he hardly knew where he was going, in spite of his rigorous sense of duty.

Then in a loud voice, so the colonel could hear, I said to Roque: "I have come to get my appointment as Minister of War in writing, so I can accredit my position. Otherwise I'll have more trouble than I am looking for. I just had a lot over in Guadalupe Hidalgo."

"Of course, man. Right away. Here, you write it out yourself."

I sat down at the table Roque indicated, and, putting a sheet of paper in the typewriter, I began to compose, as modestly as I could, the wording of my appointment as Minister of War and the Navy in the new government. After reading it through, Roque signed it, folded it, and handed it over to me. Then with sudden curiosity (an inkling of suspicion) he asked:

"What were you doing over in Guadalupe?"

Bending over until my face almost brushed his, I whispered to him:

"I was looking for Robles. They say he's over that way."

"Do you think it's possible?"

"I don't know, but I was looking for him on the chance. Well, so long!"

As soon as we were outside, I said to the colonel:

"Are you satisfied?"

"General, I'm at your orders!"

Beyond a doubt, in the mind of that Zapata colonel, I was a general.

We got into the car again to go back to La Villa for my officers. But when I had picked them up and we were at liberty, I gave up the idea of risking escape via Pachuca, and turned back to Mexico City. I had learned from the colonel in the course of our conversation that troops were stationed all along the road to Pachuca, and I realized that it would be folly to try to get away by that route. Two hours earlier it might have been possible, but not now.

At the Zócalo the five officers and I separated. "It is impossible for us to get away together," I said. "Let each save himself as best he can. It won't be hard for you. Leave your arms or hide them, put on civilian clothes, and go by train as far as you can. I'll see what I had better do."

The first thing I did was to drive to the address our reluctant savior had given me that morning. I was going to keep my promise and return his Hudson Super-six that very afternoon.

3   FROM FRYING PAN TO FIRE

González Garza did not in the least like my resigning without any satisfactory explanation the post he had assigned me in his new Cabinet. Our interview the day after what took place in Guadalupe was long and stormy. He brought it to an end with these words:

"Well, I've said all I have to say. Now you either change your mind within twelve hours or you go to the penitentiary."

It was not easy to change my ideas or even pretend that I had changed. I did not want to be locked up, either. So when the period he had set was up, I decided to take refuge with Vito Alessio Robles, who was still governor of the Federal District.

Then, as always, Vito placed above every other consideration his civic responsibilities and his honor as man and soldier. At every turn he displayed that fundamental rebelliousness characteristic of the Alessio family. He hated a coward and a flatterer and despised a fool and felt himself irresistibly drawn to the non-conformists. He had been born to the opposition, to act as the scourge and accuser of false, lying politicians. His keen and biting sarcasm had left many a rancorous memory among the unprincipled and self-seeking of the Revolution. But toward the men whom he admired and who shared his convictions and aims his kindness and devotion knew no bounds, and he stood by them in defeat as in victory. And if the hour was of defeat, he gave the cowards who fled or deserted their leader and companions a lesson by going himself in search of the dead or vanquished friend. From any angle at which one approached him, one found a man.

"But are you afraid of González Garza?" he asked me.

"No, not of him, but of the penitentiary, which has been turned into a Zapata stronghold. Roque, at heart, is a good fellow."

"And now what are your plans?"

"I need three or four days so I can join Eulalio some way."

"But if I tell Roque that, he'll have you shot."

"Don't tell him that. Tell him something else. You tell him that he ought to let me alone, because the proof that I'm not against Villa is that I didn't go with Gutiérrez. And tell him that I am talking about going to Aguascalientes as soon as there's a train, which is the truth. He doesn't need to know that I'm going there on my way to San Luis, but will think I'm on my way to have a talk with Villa."

Vito looked at me in astonishment. "But would you risk going to Aguascalientes?"

"Why not?"

"It's dangerous. Villa is not a man to fool with, you know."

"I don't see any other way."

"Stay here."

"Here? That's worse yet. At least in Aguascalientes there's only one danger, though it's a big one: Villa. But here there are at least three: Villa, Zapata, and Carranza. Besides, from there I may be able to escape and rejoin Gutiérrez; but from

Mexico City, never. . . . Villa is a big risk, that's true; but I
know him well, and I'll try to avoid the danger."

"You won't be able to avoid it, because Villa is not a man
to fool with. But, anyway, I'll at least talk with Roque."

The news that I wanted to join Villa pleased Roque beyond expression. He promised Vito that in this case he would
make no trouble for me. And when we met again, he said to
me with a certain ironical note in his voice, which was unusual
in him, who, as a rule, was ingenuous and frank:

"Yes, do go there, as soon as you can. I know you'll be well
received, as well as you deserve."

But this did not add to my uneasiness. I felt pretty sure
that since Roque had first wanted to make me a member of
his Cabinet, he would take care not to paint me too black
to Villa. Besides, it was not my intention to convince Villa
of my innocence, but to avoid conversation with him. There
was just one serious danger, and that was that while I was
waiting for a train to leave, bad reports of me might reach
Villa at his headquarters, in Aguascalientes.

At the last minute I found, to my surprise, I was not to
make the trip alone, but with Luis G. Malváez, who had been
bottled up like me in Mexico City since Gutiérrez's departure. Then we found out that Luis Zamora Plowes and Fernando Galván, whom I had made managing editor and treas-
urer respectively of *El Monitor*, the short-lived daily of the
Convention administration, were coming with us. Dr. Atl,
too, was on the point of joining us, but in the end he desisted because of an automobile to which he had completely
lost his heart. Original in this as in all other matters, Atl
converted his automobile into a transcendent and very amusing problem. It was an automobile he had come by in a
highly revolutionary fashion, and which, after brief possession by him, became his master. Atl was no longer the
owner of the car, but the car was the owner of Atl, like some
slave girl seized by a conqueror as a prize of war and who,

by making herself loved, in the end becomes the sole conqueror. What that picturesque revolutionist did not do to keep his treasure from falling into the clutches of the enemy! When Gutiérrez fled, Atl hid the automobile. Then, still uneasy, he cemented over the doors leading to its hiding place; even so he did not feel that it was safe, so he gave up the trip with us to keep watch over the object of his thoughts. When they told me he was not coming, I said to myself, "Now here is a man of real talent, almost genius, who is going to make a political career out of owning an automobile! How fortunate to be like that, to have the divine gift which sees the infinite in the finite, the ideal in the performance of the most limited and specific act; the gift, in a word, of the artist, the artist capable of attempting, for the sake of one beautiful line—on canvas, in marble, in a machine—what others would not undertake for the world itself."

The trip was long and tiresome. The train was a peculiar mixture of a military and freight train, on which anybody could travel who wanted to, without the formality of a ticket. Galván had brought along among his luggage several rolls of the paper used to print *El Monitor*, and they had become public property. The passengers—everybody traveled third-class—soon got in the habit of putting the paper to the most varied uses. At night they improvised paper curtains, paper sheets, paper blankets, mufflers, shawls, capes of paper. In the darkness the multitude of white spots gave the car the appearance of a camp of lost souls, or of whole communities at prayer or in an ecstasy. The January cold slid over the white surfaces. The bundles, with their baroque curves and edges, rustled with every jerk the train gave, at every stop and every start. It was a gentle froufrou, in strange contrast to the grinding of the wheels and the screeching of the springs and axles. Every now and then the cigarette butts, carelessly tossed away, put us in danger of fire.

At the station in Irapuato we had to lay over for more than twelve hours. The troops of Calixto Contreras and Rodolfo Fierro were returning from Guadalajara, where they had been defeated by Diéguez and Murguía. Every half hour a train went by. The endless cordon of convoys of men, horses, and cannon closed the road for us, and as the telegraph line to the north had been cut, travel was further delayed.

At midnight, when we were about ready to start, Malváez returned from the town in a state of great excitement and uneasiness.

"Bad news," he said to me. "The telegrams from Mexico City to the north are being held here till the line is fixed, and I have just found out in the telegraph office that one of the messages is from Roque to Villa and it's about you."

"What does Roque say?"

"It's serious. He tells Villa that we're going through Aguascalientes and advises him to have you shot."

"Do you think Roque would do that?"

"That's what they've just told me."

"I can hardly believe it."

"Well, I haven't a doubt of it."

There is no denying that this news upset me and gave me a shock. I recalled Vito Alessio Robles and his prudent counsel. Malváez was of the opinion that we ought to change our route or else disappear and hide for a while.

"It is foolish to hide," I answered, "because we should have to stay hidden indefinitely so they would not find us. We can't change our route either, for all roads are the same for five hundred kilometers around. If it's not Villa, it's Zapata or Carranza; to take flight is the surest way to fall into the clutches of one of them. The safest thing is for us to beard the lion in his den, in the hope that our anomalous situation may save us."

Anybody but Malváez would never have listened to me, much less followed me. Because, no question about it, I was committing an act of folly. But Malváez was always brave, and he accepted the situation and decided to risk his life with me. This was really heroic on his part, for he was not familiar with Villa's psychology, as I was, nor had he reason to cherish the hope that buoyed me up a little in spite of Roque's terrible message: the hope that Villa, when he saw me come to him, would ascribe Roque's attitude to personal animosity.

It took us two and a half days to get from Irapuato to Aguascalientes, held back all the way by the military convoys. The last of these was Rodolfo Fierro's. Sometimes we caught up with him, and Villa's general would often come to keep me company as we spent long hours seated on the embankment waiting. Those were difficult hours for me, for I was torn between two feelings. His first words in that mellifluous voice of his brought to my mind the memory of the infamous assassination of David Berlanga which filled me with indignation and sorrow. Fierro, who must have suspected or felt what I was thinking, exaggerated his air of a repentant sinner, which he had assumed with me ever since that day in the War Office when he confessed what had happened, and this touched me to the point of pitying him.

At the stop before Aguascalientes the engine of Fierro's train got out of order and pulled onto a siding to let us pass. Two hours later ours arrived and stopped about a kilometer and a half from the cradle of the Convention. We got out. Engines and coaches crowded the tracks, still filled with the troops from Jalisco and their equipment, and began to make of the surrounding country a noisy, incoherent primitive little world, like all encampments of Mexican soldiers.

Making our way through the soldiers and their women, we walked toward the city. Zamora Plowes was delighted to have an opportunity at last to meet Villa personally and offer him his services as journalist. What dreams he conjured up! Galván was determined to take the first train for Chihuahua and the United States, and Malváez and I, with the words of Roque's telegram ringing in our ears, were so tense we could hardly breathe. The thing that worried me most of all was the necessity of an interview with Villa, which was now in- evitable as my one defense against Roque's supposed intrigues. This was staking everything on one card; I was risking not only my life, but, supposing I should get off alive, my future part in the Revolution. The one was as important from the material standpoint as the other from the moral.

4 AT THE MERCY OF PANCHO VILLA

When we got into Aguascalientes Galván and Zamora Plowes went off to look for a hotel, and Malváez and I made our way down the railroad tracks. Under the train shed there was an even greater conglomeration of trains and troops; but not far away we soon made out the unmistakable figures of Villa's *dorados*. As we proceeded, the soldier crowd grew thinner until it finally disappeared altogether from the railway landscape, leaving no trace of itself except a few dogs and Villa's guard.

My heart began to pound at the sight of the *dorados*, a quick, noisy thumping in contrast with my feet, which, through some suddenly mechanical or biological force alien to my will, were moving in perfect time. I do not ever recall walking with such precision and lack of effort. The ground seemed to slip away under my rhythmic feet as though responding to an impulse in which I had no share. At that moment mine was the delight of witnessing, at once a spectator and a disembodied will, an exercise of the muscles, feeling and appreciating it to the fullest. Through my memory there floated like dim remote pictures the scenes of the executions in Tacuba two months before: those five condemned men walking toward the cemetery. Against the evocative background of these images, the cadence of my walk became smoother and my pleasure in it grew.

At the steps of Villa's car I said mechanically to the soldier who was standing guard on the step:

"Tell the general I'm here and I want to talk to him."

I listened to my own words as to a doom that destiny had planned for me since the beginning of time. The soldier looked at me with a smile. He made no movement. His smile prolonged itself; likewise his immobility. This unforeseen obstacle in the smooth unfurling of my fate gave me a sudden and strange sick feeling.

"Did you hear me?" I insisted.

The soldier went on smiling and staring at me. Slowly, as though from a different world than the dizzily moving one in which I was living, he answered:

"The general ain't here. He's out riding."

His voice sounded unreal. Inside myself existed the only reality.

Leaning up against the car, I prepared to wait. Without a word Malváez ranged himself alongside me.

Time went by. The gray light of the afternoon had been taking on a translucent blue and silver tone. The dust in the air was made luminous by the last rays of the setting sun. From time to time a dark bird plowed a furrow across the sky. Little by little, like a convalescent, my soul grew calmer at that placid sight, and my inward rhythm began to slow down until it was in time with the exterior.

Perhaps half an hour had elapsed.

Malváez said: "The most sensible thing would be for us to leave."

"No."

"I'm not thinking about myself, but about you."

"I know it, Malváez. But I won't go."

"We've still got time. Make up your mind."

"It would only be losing time if we went. I know everything is against us; but our one chance lies in the impression we make when we first meet Villa. If he thinks we are running away, he'll pursue us and shoot us; but if he thinks we have come to him, he's even capable of rewarding us."

Another quarter of an hour went by. It was beginning to get dark.

A little while later I began again: "What I do think is unnecessary is for you to stay here with me, Malváez. I think it would be better for us both if you went away. If your presence adds anything, it adds danger."

Malváez stubbornly refused to go, but I finally persuaded him. He left; his figure was lost to view between the rectangular masses of two boxcars. I was alone. The sky grew dimmer; the *dorados*' indifferent voices came from far off. One of them, gazing into space, was humming:

> *I told you not to go down for water. . . .*

The melancholy sound rose toward the sky and seemed to hang there:

> *And if you went, not to go so late. . . .*

The melancholy of the song, repeated again and again, wiped out all sense of time:

> *Someone may be waiting there, loved one,*
> *Who will make you forget about me. . . .*

Song and twilight seemed blended into one, both distant, both all-enveloping. As I listened, I forgot where I was. A group of riders was coming up the street which the rows of cars formed. I hardly noticed their approach, so carried away I was by the song and the evening. The soldier softly hummed:

> *Someone may be waiting there, loved one. . . .*

But suddenly, out of the group, a familiar figure, a silhouette I knew, swam into my consciousness. There, cantering along on his splendid sorrel, came Villa. He was wearing a brown sweater that revealed every movement of the muscles of his breast and arms. His broad-brimmed hat was pushed back from his forehead by his thatch of curly hair. I could not analyze any more. His torso grew and grew, as his horse ambled toward me until its expanse flooded my eyes. Again I felt the beating of my heart filling my whole breast, my throat, and throbbing in my temples.

I saw Villa pull up two paces from where I stood. I saw him look at me, throw down his reins, and jump off his horse at one bound.

"He's going to kill me on the spot," I thought to myself, and involuntarily the fingers of the hand behind my back closed on the butt of my pistol.

He reached me in two steps. Then I felt myself lifted a foot off the ground in his arms, and his breath and mine were intermingled.

"Roque González Garza . . . ," I began, forming the words so clearly that it surprised me. (These three words were floating about in my inward agitation like three drops of oil on water.)

"Don't talk about Roque now," Villa replied. "Tell me about yourself. Well, well, partner, I knew you wouldn't desert me. You wouldn't do a thing like that, would you?" and he put me down on the ground again.

Slowly I was coming to myself.

"But from now on," he continued, holding me by the lapels of my coat, and fixing his restless eyes on mine, "you're going to stay here with me. I don't want you running around with dirty sons of bitches. When did you get here?"

"About an hour ago, General."

He did not let go of me.

"Come on and tell me all about things. You're the first one that's got here since that son of a bitch Ulalio double-crossed me. Oh, the sons of bitches, if I get hold of them, God help them. They're going to pay for everything."

With his arm around my shoulders he was gently pushing me toward the steps of his car.

"Come in, come in. You know nobody but men come in here. I want to hear all the details. What do you think of Eugenio Aguirre Benavides? Who would have believed it! The cross-eyed traitor! And Isabel Robles? But no, he's not to blame, they just got round him some way. Robles is good. If he'd come back, I'd forgive him."

He opened the door of his sitting room and made me walk in first. I was surprised to find Rodolfo Fierro there, for I thought he was still on the road. Villa exclaimed as he caught sight of him:

"So you're here at last, are you?"

Fierro got up from his chair and replied with an arrogance that showed even through the wary respect with which he spoke:

"I just got in, General!"

"And a nice story you've got to tell, friend. The more I think about it, the less I understand how you were defeated. . . ."

Fierro prepared to enter upon explanations. "You see, this is what happened: the day after—"

But Villa cut him short. "No, friend. I don't want to hear about your defeats."

And leaving him with the phrase on his lips, and putting his arm around my neck again, he led me toward the little corridor that opened into his private office.

We sat down opposite each other, across a little table fastened to the window ledge.

Still obsessed by the possible consequences of González Garza's telegram, I began: "You know, Roque . . . well . . ."

But Villa did not let me go on. "Don't talk about Roque, I told you. I don't give a damn about your little fusses. I want to hear about the other thing: why did Ulalio finally decide to play me false? Why did Robles and Aguirre Benavides follow him? You understand?"

"Perfectly, General."

And then I told him everything that had happened, not, however, from the inside, as I knew the facts, but as it would have seemed to a mere spectator. We talked on like this for over an hour. I was on tenterhooks all the time, for he was alert for my every word and gesture, even the most insignificant. Every now and then he would interrupt me with ingenuous comments:

"Don't tell me that. Is it possible? What a pity I didn't trust you more! We'd have fixed their clock."

The anger he displayed was that they should have taken him in and betrayed him, not because he felt any weaker on account of their defection.

"Those dirty sons of bitches, they'll see who they're up against. Not one of them is going to get away."

Halfway through our talk he ordered his supper and invited me to join him. With great difficulty I managed to excuse myself. That night his supper was more frugal than usual: two glasses of milk and a piece of baked sweet potato. I talked on while he ate. Between swallow and swallow, and with his eyes always fixed on me, the names of my friends elicited wrathful remarks and judgments:

"I knew that Vasconcelos was nothing but a traitor with book learning. . . .

"General Blanco? That's no general. Nothing but a show-off full of airs. . . .

"I told you Eugenio was the worst of the lot, the most treacherous. He's the one that spoiled the others. And do you know what Luisito did, too? I can't believe my own eyes. Now you just tell me, in all his miserable existence who ever treated him better than I did? . . .

"Ulalio is the one I blame least of all. He was no friend of mine. He told me he'd do it the first chance he got, and he did. He acted like a man. But those others, the ones that double-crossed me . . ."

When he had finished eating, he got up and listened to the remainder of what I had to say. Then he walked two or three times up and down the narrow room and changed the hat he was wearing for another that was hanging on a hook. As he reached up, the folds of his sweater revealed the cartridge belt full of bullets and the butt of his pistol; his vigorous hip revealed its strength.

Going over to him, I said: "Well, General . . ."

"Yes, friend," he answered, "you're tired and you better get some rest. From tonight on you're to stay here with me.

Right now I'm going to have them fix up Luisito's room for you because from now on you're to be my secretary. Or don't you want to? Talk to me like a man."

I felt my life hanging once more by a hair. But I had to see the thing through.

"There's just one thing I want to ask of you, General."

"What is it?"

"My family left Mexico City on the last passenger train. I don't know if they got to Chihuahua or not. Maybe they're in El Paso. I should like—if it is possible—you to let me—go and find them. . . ."

Villa bent over me and looked steadily into my eyes; he was holding me by the lapels of my coat. After several seconds' silence, he said:

"You want to desert me, too?"

I seemed to see death in his pupils.

"I, General . . ."

"Don't desert me, friend; don't do it, for, honestly, I'm your friend. You're not going to desert me, are you?"

"General . . ."

"And go find your family. You have my permission. Do you need money? Do you want a special train?"

I drew a long breath for the first time that evening.

At ten that same night a train left for El Paso. Villa had accompanied me to the Pullman. He came up on the platform and said to the conductor:

"Now, friend, this gentleman here is one of my men. Understand? One of my men. You take good care of him; otherwise, you know me. Remember how I shoot. . . ."

"Oh, General," the conductor answered with a nervous laugh.

Villa embraced me again before he jumped off.

The train began to speed away through the shadows of the night. Mexico is so big! Fourteen hundred kilometers to the border!